INSTRUCTOR'S GUIDE AND TEST BANK

MICROBIOLOGY

AN INTRODUCTION

TENTH EDITION

Christine L. Case

SKYLINE COLLEGE

D1211035

Benjamin Cummings

San Francisco   Boston   New York
Cape Town   Hong Kong   London   Madrid   Mexico City
Montreal   Munich   Paris   Singapore   Sydney   Tokyo   Toronto

Executive Editor: Leslie Berriman
Assistant Editor: Katie Heimsoth
Managing Editor: Wendy Earl
Production Editor: Leslie Austin
Copyeditor: Sally Peyrefitte
Compositor: Cecelia G. Morales
Interior Designer: Cecelia G. Morales
Cover Design: Riezebos Holzbaur Design Group
Senior Manufacturing Buyer: Stacey Weinberger
Senior Marketing Manager: Neena Bali

Cover Photo Credit: Science Photo Library/Eric Graves

Benjamin Cummings
is an imprint of

www.pearsonhighered.com

ISBN 10: **0-321-58187-3**; ISBN 13: **978-0-321-58187-7**

1 2 3 4 5 6 7 8 9 10—**B&B**—13 12 11 10 09
Manufactured in the United States of America.

Instructor's Guide Contents

Preface

There is no substitute for an instructor's interaction with students, and your presence stimulates a student's enthusiasm for learning. This *Instructor's Guide for Microbiology: An Introduction,* Tenth Edition, provides some new ideas and reinforcement for teaching your course. If you are just beginning to teach microbiology, this guide can provide a framework for developing your course.

This guide is divided into three sections. The first section, Introduction, includes several alternative course outlines for use with *Microbiology: An Introduction,* Tenth Edition. This section lists sequences of topics and pertinent pages in the text for presenting microbial diseases by etiology (taxonomic group), portal of entry, or method of transmission.

The second section contains chapter notes, for each chapter, that include six subsections: Learning Objectives, New in This Edition, Chapter Summary, The Loop, Answers, and Case Study. The Learning Objectives section provides an overview of the chapter contents. They are the same as the objectives in the text, and they are correlated to the Check Your Understanding questions in the text. The scope of each chapter is highlighted in Chapter Summary. Cross-references to other chapters are listed in The Loop.

For many users of the Ninth Edition, changes and additions new to this Tenth Edition are highlighted in the section New in This Edition. Answers to the study questions in the text follow the Chapter Summary. These answers are brief but should be sufficient to provide you with insight regarding the intent in asking particular questions. Answers to the Critical Thinking and Clinical Applications questions are not included in the Answers section of the main text and will not be posted on The Microbiology Place (www.microbiologyplace.com) website, so you can use these as homework or test questions if you wish. Answers to the case histories discussed in the Disease in Focus boxes in Chapters 21 through 26 are also provided. The Case Studies require analysis and application of new information; additionally, many require quantitative analysis. In Microbiology for Allied Health at Skyline College, we make selected case studies available for extra credit. The students can choose one or two to turn in. Many are suitable for use as essay questions on tests; however, keep in mind that students will need time to think through the problem. The Microtriviology exercise (Chapter 11) can be used to encourage students to use reference materials such as *Bergey's Manual.* The answers to the multiple-choice questions for all 28 chapters close out this section.

The third section, Test Bank, contains objective test questions with answers provided. You can reproduce the tests and use them directly from the guide to test students' recall and understanding of material presented in the text. The Test Bank also provides essay questions or analytical problems for each chapter.

v

Introduction

The First Day

The first day of a semester is hectic. Introductory remarks on regulations, requirements, and grading are needed; roll must be taken; and students are adding and dropping classes. Generally, the first day is not a good day to present material on which students will be tested.

I begin my class by distributing the course syllabus and explaining it. Then I show (PowerPoint®) slides for the remainder of the period. Because students are usually unfamiliar with microbiology, slides can introduce the subject with pictures of representative organisms, laboratory cultures, and environmental and industrial applications. A discussion of food and agriculture generates an awareness of the importance of microbiology.

Course content can emphasize general microbiology with examples and specific details from medical microbiology and biotechnology. First-day slides focus on ecology and applied microbiology. I sometimes give the students study questions that can be answered from the slide narration and Chapter 1.

Educational Technology

Instructor Resource DVD/CD-ROM

The Instructor Resource DVD/CD-ROM organizes instructor media resources by chapter for easy reference and classroom presentation. It includes all figures from the book, with and without labels, in both JPEG and PowerPoint® formats; all figures from the book with the Label Edit feature in PowerPoint® format; select "process" figures from the book with the Step Edit feature in PowerPoint® format; and all tables from the book. It also offers multimedia features, including Microbiology Animations, Microbiology Videos, and BioFlix™ Animations; PRS-enabled Active Lecture Clicker Questions; PRS-enabled Quiz Show Clicker Questions; the Instructor's Guide and Test Bank as editable Microsoft® Word files; and a CD-ROM of the Test Bank in TestGen format.

Additionally, the Instructor Resource DVD/CD-ROM contains PowerPoint® lecture slides written by Christine L. Case. These lecture outlines concisely present the content of each chapter alongside images and tables from the text. Instructors can adapt the PowerPoint® slides to their specific course without the need to assemble presentations from scratch.

Instructor's Visual Guide

The Instructor's Visual Guide is a black-and-white print supplement showing thumbnails of all images available on the Instructor Resource DVD/CD-ROM. This allows you to plan lectures even when you are away from a computer.

Transparencies

Acetate overhead transparencies of 450 full-color figures from the text are available free to instructors who adopt *Microbiology: An Introduction,* Tenth Edition.

Transparencies are a useful teaching tool because they accurately illustrate structures or events and eliminate the need to spend time carefully drawing on the chalkboard during a lecture. Moreover, transparencies can be used in a fully lighted room so that the students can take notes.

The use of transparencies copied directly from the text will stimulate the students to use their text as a reference. Additionally, the students will not have to copy the entire transparency but can make notes in their text or take notes that refer to a specific figure in the text.

Slides

Biological Agents of Disease/HIV Slide Set for Microbiology offers 80 clinical photos of microbes and pathologies not seen in the text, covering a broad range of diseases and infections.

Microbiology Place Companion Website (www.microbiologyplace.com)

The Microbiology Place website features simply organized and easy-to-use study and assessment materials. This newly organized website features a simple three-step approach for self-study, allowing students to take a pre-test (step 1); to learn and practice by using a variety of tools and resources, such as interactive tutorials, activities, case studies, microbiology animations and videos, flashcards, glossary, and pronunciation guides (step 2); and then to test themselves (step 3) using the website's gradable chapter quizzes and chapter post-tests, as well as gradable quizzes on the animations and foundation figures.

Suggested Uses for Special Features in *Microbiology: An Introduction*, Tenth Edition

Learning Objectives

The objectives at the beginning of each major heading focus the student's attention on major concepts presented in the text. You may wish to modify the objectives into mastery objectives. To do this, identify the performance and conditions necessary for the student to show the desired competence.

For example, an additional sentence to Learning Objective 1-7 ("Identify the contributions . . . ") would define the test conditions. You can tell the students whether they will be expected to identify contributions from a list or to write an essay on the historical background of microbiology including contributions made by four of these people.

Objective 1-6 ("Compare spontaneous generation and biogenesis.") should tell the student what test conditions to expect. The student might anticipate writing an essay or making a list to show differences between these theories. Should the student expect to differentiate these concepts by providing supporting evidence for each concept? Sample questions are sometimes useful to clarify an objective.

You can make additions and deletions to the lists of Learning Objectives to suit your needs.

Check Your Understanding

Check Your Understanding questions, a new feature for the tenth edition, appear at key points throughout the chapters, and highlight important principles and concepts. This feature encourages students to engage interactively with the text and self-assess their understanding of the corresponding Learning Objectives. Instructors can ask these questions in class to reinforce important information.

Study Questions

Four levels of study questions are provided at the end of each chapter. The Review level allows students to test their recall of information. The Multiple Choice section includes questions that require recall and questions that require analysis. The Critical Thinking level provides problems that require knowledge and reasoning. Actual case histories are included in the Clinical Applications questions. Only the main answers to the Review and Multiple Choice questions appear in the Answers section of the text. Answers to all the study questions are provided in this guide.

Study questions can be a basis for class discussion.

Clinical Focus

These case studies are descriptions of current events reported in *MMWR*. Each case study features an area in epidemiology, laboratory identification, or diagnosis. They are written in a question-answer format to help students learn how to solve clinical problems.

Title	Pathogen	Page
Human Tuberculosis—New York City	*Mycobacterium tuberculosis*	p. 144
Delayed Bloodstream Infection Following Catheterization	*Pseudomonas fluorescens*	p. 134
Infection Following Steroid Injection	Mycobacteria, rapidly growing	p. 201
Tracking West Nile Virus	West Nile Virus	p. 223
The Most Frequent Cause of Recreational Waterborne Diarrhea	*Cryptosporidium*	p. 355
Influenza: Crossing the Species Barrier	Influenza virus	p. 370
Nosocomial Infections	MRSA	p. 422
Inflammation of the Eye	*Pseudomonas*	p. 444
A World Health Problem	Measles virus	p. 501
A Delayed Rash	Penicillin allergy	p. 531
Antibiotics in Animal Feed Linked to Human Disease	*Campylobacter, Enterococcus*	p. 577
Infections in the Gym	MRSA	p. 593
A Neurological Disease	Rabies virus	p. 625
A Sick Child	*Francisella tularensis*	p. 644
Outbreak	*Legionella pneumophila*	p. 691
A Foodborne Infection	*Salmonella enterica*	p. 715
Survival of the Fittest	*Neisseria gonorrhoeae*	p. 751

Mycology and Parasitology

In addition to bacteriology and virology, Chapter 12 provides an overview of mycology and parasitology, and Chapters 21 through 26 include representative diseases. A few examples from mycology and parasitology can provide students with an introduction to general biological principles as well as broaden their concept of disease-causing organisms.

The content of your course is determined by you and the other faculty involved in allied health programs. Most health personnel must have some familiarity with a wide range of disease-causing organisms. Your state public health department publishes reference material on diseases that occur in your geographic area. When discussing mycology and parasitology, I find it useful to refer to organisms that local clinicians have encountered.

Scheduling Topics

The following outline is suggested for a one-semester course. It is based on 45 fifty-minute lectures.

Topic	Number of Lectures
Welcome and First-Day Business	1
The Microbial World and You	1
Chemical Principles	3
Observing Microorganisms Through a Microscope	1
Functional Anatomy of Prokaryotic and Eukaryotic Cells	3
Microbial Metabolism	3
Microbial Growth	1
The Control of Microbial Growth	2
Microbial Genetics	3
Biotechnology and Recombinant DNA	1
Classification of Microorganisms	0.5

Topic	Number of Lectures
Bacteria and Archaea	1
Fungi	1
Protozoa and Algae	1
Multicellular Parasites	1
Viruses	2
Principles of Disease and Epidemiology	0.5
Microbial Mechanisms of Pathogenicity	0.5
Innate Immunity: Nonspecific Defenses of the Host	1
Adaptive Immunity: Specific Defenses of the Host	3
Disorders Associated with the Immune System	2
Practical Applications of Immunology	0.5
Antimicrobial Drugs	1
Microbial Diseases of the Skin and Eyes	1
Nosocomial Infections	1
Microbial Diseases of the Nervous System	1
Microbial Diseases of the Cardiovascular and Lymphatic Systems	1
Microbial Diseases of the Respiratory System	2
Microbial Diseases of the Digestive System	2
Microbial Diseases of the Urinary and Reproductive Systems	1
Environmental Microbiology	1.5
Applied and Industrial Microbiology	0.5

Flexibility

The text is flexible and can be adapted to suit the schedule you prefer. On the following pages, selected topics are grouped to assist you in preparing your course outline.

Biotechnology

Introduction	pp. 17–18
Bioremediation—Bacteria Clean Up Pollution	p. 33, 775
What Is Fermentation?	p. 135
Designer Jeans	p. 3
From Plant Disease to Shampoo and Salad Dressing	p. 801
Biosensors: Bacteria That Detect Toxic Pollutants and Pathogens	p. 780
Protection from Bioterrorism	p. 649
Food Production	pp. 797–800
Genetic Engineering	Chapter 9
Industrial Products from Microbes	pp. 800–806
Alternative Energy Sources	pp. 806–808
Fermentation Technology	pp. 801–804
Vaccines	pp. 501–506
Diagnostics	pp. 507–518
Immunotherapy	p. 538
Monoclonal Antibodies	pp. 507–509
Stem Cells	p. 535

Biochemistry

Many instructors do not cover basic chemistry (Chapter 2) as a lecture topic because chemistry is a prerequisite to their microbiology courses. Some instructors feel that they can incorporate the necessary basic concepts of chemistry into metabolism and genetics. In either case, Chapter 2 can provide a review for the students.

The following sections deal with the biochemical process in living cells.

Organic Compounds	pp. 37–49
Microbial Metabolism	Chapter 5
Microbial Genetics	Chapter 8

Alternative Course Outlines

Specific diseases and etiologies can be covered by systems, taxa, or methods of transmission. It is up to you to decide which diseases need to be covered for each group of students. For example, you may wish to emphasize bacterial diseases but include a representative disease caused by a virus, fungus, protozoan, and helminth for comparison and breadth. Some nonbacterial agents are important causes of diseases worldwide. In a class in which all the students are in an allied health program, you might present all the microbial diseases relevant to those students. For example, respiratory therapy students need to learn about diseases of the respiratory and circulatory systems. Although bacterial and viral diseases are the most common, protozoan and multicellular parasites will be encountered in clinical work. Additionally, liberal arts students often find examples from parasitology interesting.

Taxonomic Approach

Bacteria and the Diseases They Cause

Proteobacteria

Alphaproteobacteria

Cat-scratch disease, *Bartonella henselae*	p. 654
Anaphasmosis, *Anaplasma phagocytophilum*	p. 654
Ehrlichiosis, *Ehrlichia* spp.	p. 654
Endemic murine typhus, *Rickettsia typhi*	p. 655
Epidemic typhus, *R. prowazekii*	p. 654
Rocky Mountain spotted fever, *R. rickettsii*	p. 655
Brucellosis, *Brucella* spp.	pp. 643–645

Betaproteobacteria

Gonorrhea, *Neisseria gonorrhoeae*	pp. 747–750
Ophthalmia neonatorum, *N. gonorrhoeae*	pp. 613–614
Pelvic inflammatory disease, *N. gonorrhoeae*	pp. 751–752
Meningitis, *N. meningitidis*	pp. 613–614
Nosocomial infections, *Burkholderia* spp.	p. 440
Melioidosis, *B. pseudomallei*	pp. 690–691
Whooping cough, *Bordetella pertussis*	pp. 680–682
Rat-bite fever, *Spirillum minor*	p. 647

Gammaproteobacteria

Animal bites, *Pasteurella multocida*	pp. 647–648
Bacillary dysentery, *Shigella* spp.	p. 712
Epiglottitis, *Haemophilus influenzae*	pp. 676–677
Meningitis, *H. influenzae*	p. 613
Otitis media, *H. influenzae*	p. 679
Pneumonia, *H. influenzae*	p. 688
Conjunctivitis, *H. influenzae*	p. 603
Chancroid, *H. ducreyi*	p. 756
Cholera, *Vibrio cholerae*	pp. 713–717
Gastroenteritis, *V. parahaemolyticus*	p. 717
Gastroenteritis, *V. vulnificus*	p. 717
Cystitis, *Escherichia coli*	p. 746
Gastroenteritis, *E. coli*	pp. 717–718
Pyelonephritis, *E. coli*	p. 746
Dermatitis, *Pseudomonas aeruginosa*	p. 591
Otitis externa, *P. aeruginosa*	p. 593
Septicemia, *P. flluorescens*	p. 164
Legionellosis, *Legionella pneumophila*	pp. 688–689, 691
Plague, *Yersinia pestis*	pp. 648–650
Gastroenteritis, *Y. enterocolitica*	p. 720
Otitis media, *Moraxella catarrhalis*	p. 679
Q-fever, *Coxiella burnetti*	pp. 689–690
Salmonellosis, *Salmonella enterica*	pp. 712–714, 715
Typhoid fever, *S. enterica* typhi	pp. 714–716
Tularemia, *Francisella tularensis*	pp. 642–643

Epsilonproteobacteria

Gastroenteritis, *Campylocabter jejuni*	p. 718
Gastritis, *Helicobacter pylori*	p. 718–720
Peptic ulcers, *H. pylori*	p. 718–720

For a listing of pathogens that enter through the skin/mucous membranes and parenteral route or by vectors, see the following section, Method of Transmission Approach.

Method of Transmission Approach

A discussion of the transmission of disease is on pages 409–413 of *Microbiology: An Introduction*. Diseases acquired through the respiratory tract are usually transmitted by direct contact including droplet infection. Diseases acquired through the gastrointestinal tract are most often transmitted by indirect contact in food and water. These diseases are listed in the Portal of Entry Approach section of this guide.

Pathogens that enter through the skin/mucous membranes and parenteral route have the most varied methods of transmission and are listed below.

Diseases Acquired by Direct Contact through the Skin/Mucous Membranes
Bacterial
Buruli ulcer p. 594

Viral
    Arthropod-borne encephalitis   pp. 624, 626
    Chikungunya fever   p. 658
    Dengue   p. 624
    Yellow fever   p. 659
Bacterial
    Endemic murine typhus   p. 655
    Epidemic typhus   p. 654
    Lyme disease   pp. 641–654
    Plague   pp. 648, 650
    Relapsing fever   pp. 650–651
    Rocky Mountain spotted fever   p. 655
    Tularemia   pp. 642–643
Protozoan
    Malaria   pp. 663–665
    African trypanosomiasis   pp. 627, 629
    Chagas' disease   p. 661
    Babesiosis   p. 666
    Leishmaniasis   pp. 665–666

Animal Reservoirs

This is a list of diseases acquired from animals by direct contact, indirect contact, or arthropod vectors.

Bacterial
    Anthrax   p. 645
    Bites and scratches   pp. 647–648
    Brucellosis   pp. 643–645
    Cat-scratch disease   p. 654
    Ehrlichiosis   p. 654
    Endemic murine typhus   p. 655
    Epidemic typhus   p. 654
    From marine mammals   p. 283
    Leptospirosis   pp. 746–747
    Listeriosis   pp. 614–615
    Lyme disease   pp. 651–654
    Plague   pp. 648–650
    Psittacosis   p. 689
    Q fever   pp. 689–690
    Rat-bite fever   p. 647
    Relapsing fever   pp. 650–651
    Rocky Mountain spotted fever   p. 655
    Tuberculosis   pp. 144, 682–685
    Tularemia   pp. 642–643

Viral
    Arthropod-borne encephalitis   pp. 624, 626
    Dengue   p. 624
    Monkeypox   p. 596
    Rabies   pp. 622–624
    Yellow fever   pp. 659

Protozoan
    African trypanosomiasis   p. 627, 629
    Chagas' disease   p. 661
    Babesiosis   p. 666

Bacteriophages	pp. 373, 377, 379–382
Plant viruses	pp. 393–394

Normal bacteria of the human body

Bacteria of the skin	pp. 585–586
Bacteria of the respiratory tract	pp. 675–676
Bacteria of the mouth	pp. 706–707
Bacteria of the gastrointestinal tract	pp. 706–707
Bacteria of the urogenital tract	p. 745

Unknowns

Enterotube	Fig. 10.9
Unknown identification	pp. 137–139, 282–294, Appendix F

Epidemiology

Epidemiology	pp. 418–420
Koch's postulates	pp. 404–406

Immunology

Innate immunity	pp. 449–453, 463–472
ABO and Rh blood groups	pp. 526–528
Agglutination reactions	pp. 287, 510–511
ELISA technique	pp. 514–518

Environmental and applied microbiology

MPN test	pp. 175, 779–781, Fig. 6.19
Membrane filtration	p. 175, Figs. 6.18, 7.4
Standard plate count	pp. 174–175, Fig. 6.17
Yogurt	p. 799
Nitrogen and sulfur cycles	pp. 770–772
Bioremediation	p. 775

ASM Curriculum Recommendations

ASM recommends the following core curriculum guidelines for all introductory microbiology courses. *Microbiology: An Introduction,* Tenth Edition and *Laboratory Experiments in Microbiology,* Ninth Edition, support all of the ASM's curriculum recommendations. These core curriculum guidelines are meant to support the development of learning objectives that can be met within the introductory microbiology courses. The asterisks in the list below denote those themes and concepts considered essential to the laboratory content.

	Chapter(s) in *Microbiology: An Introduction,* Tenth Edition	Exercise(s) in *Laboratory Experiments in Microbiology,* Ninth Edition
Theme 1: Microbial cell biology*		
1. Information flow within a cell	8	27–28
2. Regulation of cellular activities	8	27
3. Cellular structure and function*	4	5–10
4. Growth and division*	6, 28	20
5. Cell energy metabolism*	5	13–17

	Chapter(s) in *Microbiology: An Introduction*, Tenth Edition	Exercise(s) in *Laboratory Experiments in Microbiology*, Ninth Edition
Theme 2: Microbial genetics*		
1. Inheritance of genetic information	8	
2. Causes, consequences, and uses of mutations*	8–9	28, 32
3. Exchange and acquisition of genetic information	8	29
Theme 3: Interactions and impact of microorganisms and humans		
1. Host defense mechanisms	16–19	41–44
2. Microbial pathogenicity mechanisms*	15, 21–26	45–49
3. Disease transmission	14	39–40
4. Antibiotics and chemotherapy*	7, 20	24–25
5. Genetic engineering	9	31
6. Biotechnology	9, 28	29, 30, 55, 57
Theme 4: Interactions and impact of microorganisms in the environment*		
1. Adaptation and natural selection	9	
2. Symbiosis	27	56
3. Microbial recycling of resources	27	57
4. Microbes transforming the environment	6, 27–28	56
Theme 5: Integrating themes*		
1. Microbial evolution	10	
2. Microbial diversity*	11–13, 27	33–36

Menu à la Laboratoire

Soup

Miso (soybeans arranged by *Aspergillus* and *Saccharomyces*)

Salad

Olives prepared by *Leuconostoc*
Fleshy fungi (*Agaricus*) grown on thoroughbred
manure and seasoned by *Acetobacter* (vinegar)

Entrées

S. cerevisiae and (by request) *Lactobacillus* will
prepare rye, pumpernickel, and sourdough

Hawaiian Single-Cell Protein

A delightful casserole of sewage-fed cyanobacteria. Flavored
with poi (lactic-acid bacteria work their magic on taro root)

Thai Noodles

Noodles "proteinized" with *Candida utilis* yeast and flavored with fish sauce
made by a team of moderately halophilic *Bacillus* and coryneforms

Beef Bonanza

Tender slices of *Methylophilus*-fed beef marinated in soy sauce
(produced by a symphony of microbes)

Carne Macha

An assortment of sausages from *Pediococcus* and *Penicillium italicum*

Vegetable

Cabbage fermented to pH 3.5 by *L. plantarum*. Natto beans by *Bacillus subtilis*.

Desserts

Chocolate prepared by *Kluyveromyces* and lactic acid bacteria.
Chef *Leu CoNostoc* will smother it in dextran, an α-1,6-glucose polymer
Assorted cheeses
Streptococcus and *Lactobacillus*, assisted by *P. roquefortii* and *P. camembertii*

Drinks

Alcohol served by the sweet	Nonalcoholic beverages
fungus *Saccharomyces*	*Lactobacillus'* buttermilk
Beer	*Saccharomyces'* root beer
Wine	Coffee by *Erwinia dissolvens*

1 The Microbial World and You

LEARNING OBJECTIVES	CHECK YOUR UNDERSTANDING
1-1 List several ways in which microbes affect our lives.	Describe some of the destructive and beneficial actions of microbes.
1-2 Recognize the system of scientific nomenclature that uses two names: a genus and a specific epithet.	Distinguish a genus from a specific epithet.
1-3 Differentiate the major characteristics of each group of microorganisms.	Which groups of microbes are prokaryotes? Which are eukaryotes?
1-4 List the three domains.	What are the three domains?
1-5 Explain the importance of observations made by Hooke and van Leeuwenhoek.	What is the cell theory?
1-6 Compare spontaneous generation and biogenesis.	What evidence supported spontaneous generation?
1-7 Identify the contributions to microbiology made by Needham, Spallanzani, Virchow, and Pasteur.	How was spontaneous generation disproved?
1-8 Explain how Pasteur's work influenced Lister and Koch.	Summarize in your own words the germ theory of disease.
1-9 Identify the importance of Koch's postulates.	What is the importance of Koch's postulates?
1-10 Identify the importance of Jenner's work.	What is the significance of Jenner's discovery?
1-11 Identify the contributions to microbiology made by Ehrlich and Fleming.	What was Ehrlich's "magic bullet"?
1-12 Define *bacteriology, mycology, parasitology, immunology,* and *virology.*	Define *bacteriology, mycology, parasitology, immunology,* and *virology.*
1-13 Explain the importance of molecular genetics and molecular biology.	Differentiate microbial genetics from molecular biology.
1-14 List at least four beneficial activities of micro-organisms.	Name two beneficial uses of bacteria.
1-15 Name two examples of biotechnology that use recombinant DNA technology and two examples that do not.	Differentiate biotechnology from recombinant DNA technology.
1-16 Define *normal microbiota* and *resistance.*	Differentiate normal microbiota and infectious disease.
1-17 Define *biofilm.*	Why are biofilms important?
1-18 Define *emerging infectious disease.*	What factors contribute to the emergence of an infectious disease?

NEW IN THIS EDITION

- New information on biofilms, including a photo.
- Updated coverage of emerging infectious diseases.
- New section on antibiotic-resistant bacteria.

CHAPTER SUMMARY

Microbes in Our Lives (p. 2)

1. Living things too small to be seen with the unaided eye are called microorganisms.
2. Microorganisms are important in maintaining Earth's ecological balance.
3. Some microorganisms live in humans and other animals and are needed to maintain good health.
4. Some microorganisms are used to produce foods and chemicals.
5. Some microorganisms cause disease.

Naming and Classifying Microorganisms (pp. 2–6)

Nomenclature (p. 2)

1. In a nomenclature system designed by Carolus Linnaeus (1735), each living organism is assigned two names.
2. The two names consist of a genus and a specific epithet, both of which are underlined or italicized.

Types of Microorganisms (pp. 3–6)

Bacteria (pp. 3–4)

3. Bacteria are unicellular organisms. Because they have no nucleus, the cells are described as prokaryotic.
4. The three major basic shapes of bacteria are bacillus, coccus, and spiral.
5. Most bacteria have a peptidoglycan cell wall; they divide by binary fission, and they may possess flagella.
6. Bacteria can use a wide range of chemical substances for their nutrition.

Archaea (p. 4)

7. Archaea consist of prokaryotic cells; they lack peptidoglycan in their cell walls.
8. Archaea include methanogens, extreme halophiles, and extreme thermophiles.

Fungi (p. 4)

9. Fungi (mushrooms, molds, and yeasts) have eukaryotic cells (cells with a true nucleus). Most fungi are multicellular.
10. Fungi obtain nutrients by absorbing organic material from their environment.

Protozoa (pp. 4, 6)

11. Protozoa are unicellular eukaryotes.
12. Protozoa obtain nourishment by absorption or ingestion through specialized structures.

Algae (p. 6)

13. Algae are unicellular or multicellular eukaryotes that obtain nourishment by photosynthesis.
14. Algae produce oxygen and carbohydrates that are used by other organisms.

Viruses (p. 6)

15. Viruses are noncellular entities that are parasites of cells.
16. Viruses consist of a nucleic acid core (DNA or RNA) surrounded by a protein coat. An envelope may surround the coat.

Multicellular Animal Parasites (p. 6)

17. The principal groups of multicellular animal parasites are flatworms and roundworms, collectively called helminths.
18. The microscopic stages in the life cycle of helminths are identified by traditional microbiological procedures.

Classification of Microorganisms (p. 6)

19. All organisms are classified into Bacteria, Archaea, and Eukarya. Eukarya include protists, fungi, plants, and animals.

A Brief History of Microbiology (pp. 6–16)

The First Observations (p. 7)

1. Robert Hooke observed that cork was composed of "little boxes"; he introduced the term *cell* (1665).
2. Hooke's observations laid the groundwork for development of the cell theory, the concept that all living things are composed of cells.
3. Anton van Leeuwenhoek, using a simple microscope, was the first to observe microorganisms (1673).

The Debate over Spontaneous Generation (p. 8)

4. Until the mid-1880s, many people believed in spontaneous generation, the idea that living organisms could arise from nonliving matter.
5. Francesco Redi demonstrated that maggots appear on decaying meat only when flies are able to lay eggs on the meat (1668).
6. John Needham claimed that microorganisms could arise spontaneously from heated nutrient broth (1745).
7. Lazzaro Spallanzani repeated Needham's experiments and suggested that Needham's results were due to microorganisms in the air entering his broth (1765).
8. Rudolf Virchow introduced the concept of biogenesis: living cells can arise only from preexisting cells (1858).
9. Louis Pasteur demonstrated that microorganisms are in the air everywhere and offered proof of biogenesis (1861).
10. Pasteur's discoveries led to the development of aseptic techniques used in laboratory and medical procedures to prevent contamination by microorganisms.

The Golden Age of Microbiology (pp. 9–11)

11. The science of microbiology advanced rapidly between 1857 and 1914.

Fermentation and Pasteurization (p. 9)

12. Pasteur found that yeast ferment sugars to alcohol and that bacteria can oxidize the alcohol to acetic acid.
13. A heating process called pasteurization is used to kill bacteria in some alcoholic beverages and milk.

The Germ Theory of Disease (pp. 9, 11)

14. Agostino Bassi (1835) and Pasteur (1865) showed a causal relationship between microorganisms and disease.

15. Joseph Lister introduced the use of a disinfectant to clean surgical wounds in order to control infections in humans (1860s).

16. Robert Koch proved that microorganisms cause disease. He used a sequence of procedures, now called Koch's postulates (1876), that are used today to prove that a particular microorganism causes a particular disease.

Vaccination (p. 11)

17. In a vaccination, immunity (resistance to a particular disease) is conferred by inoculation with a vaccine.

18. In 1798, Edward Jenner demonstrated that inoculation with cowpox material provides humans with immunity to smallpox.

19. About 1880, Pasteur discovered that avirulent bacteria could be used as a vaccine for fowl cholera; he coined the word *vaccine*.

20. Modern vaccines are prepared from living avirulent microorganisms or killed pathogens, from isolated components of pathogens, and by recombinant DNA techniques.

The Birth of Modern Chemotherapy: Dreams of a "Magic Bullet" (pp. 12–13)

21. Chemotherapy is the chemical treatment of a disease.

22. Two types of chemotherapeutic agents are synthetic drugs (chemically prepared in the laboratory) and antibiotics (substances produced naturally by bacteria and fungi to inhibit the growth of other microorganisms).

23. Paul Ehrlich introduced an arsenic-containing chemical called salvarsan to treat syphilis (1910).

24. Alexander Fleming observed that the *Penicillium* fungus inhibited the growth of a bacterial culture. He named the active ingredient penicillin (1928).

25. Penicillin has been used clinically as an antibiotic since the 1940s.

26. Researchers are tackling the problem of drug-resistant microbes.

Modern Developments in Microbiology (pp. 13–16)

27. Bacteriology is the study of bacteria, mycology is the study of fungi, and parasitology is the study of parasitic protozoa and worms.

28. Microbiologists are using genomics, the study of all of an organism's genes, to classify bacteria, fungi, and protozoa.

29. The study of AIDS, analysis of the action of interferons, and the development of new vaccines are among the current research interests in immunology.

30. New techniques in molecular biology and electron microscopy have provided tools for advancing our knowledge of virology.

31. The development of recombinant DNA technology has helped advance all areas of microbiology.

Microbes and Human Welfare (pp. 16–18)

1. Microorganisms degrade dead plants and animals and recycle chemical elements to be used by living plants and animals.

2. Bacteria are used to decompose organic matter in sewage.

3. Bioremediation processes use bacteria to clean up toxic wastes.

4. Bacteria that cause diseases in insects are being used as biological controls of insect pests. Biological controls are specific for the pest and do not harm the environment.

5. Using microbes to make products such as foods and chemicals is called biotechnology.

6. Using recombinant DNA, bacteria can produce important substances such as proteins, vaccines, and enzymes.

7. In gene therapy, viruses are used to carry replacements for defective or missing genes into human cells.

8. Genetically modified bacteria are used in agriculture to protect plants from frost and insects and to improve the shelf life of produce.

Microbes and Human Disease (pp. 18–21)

1. Everyone has microorganisms in and on the body; these make up the normal microbiota, or flora.

2. The disease-producing properties of a species of microbe and the host's resistance are important factors in determining whether a person will contract a disease.

3. Bacterial communities that form slimy layers on surfaces are called biofilms.

4. An infectious disease is one in which pathogens invade a susceptible host.

5. An emerging infectious disease (EID) is a new or changing disease showing an increase in incidence in the recent past or a potential to increase in the near future.

Contributions to the field of microbiology by the following individuals are noted in this chapter.

Oswald Avery	Rebecca Lancefield	Ignaz Semmelweis
Agostino Bassi	Laurent Lavoisier	Lazzaro Spallanzani
George Beadle	Joshua Lederberg	Wendell Stanley
Martinus Beijerink	Antoni van Leeuwenhoek	Edward Tatum
Francis Crick	Carolus Linnaeus	Rudolf Virchow
Paul Ehrlich	Joseph Lister	James Watson
Alexander Fleming	Colin MacLeod	Chaim Weizmann
Robert Hooke	Maclyn McCarty	Sergei Winogradsky
Dmitri Iwanowsky	Jacques Monod	Carl Woese
François Jacob	John Needham	
Edward Jenner	Louis Pasteur	
Robert Koch	Francesco Redi	

THE LOOP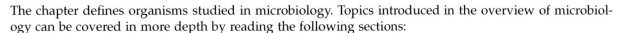

The chapter defines organisms studied in microbiology. Topics introduced in the overview of microbiology can be covered in more depth by reading the following sections:

Bioremediation	pp. 33, 775
Classification	Chapter 10
Emerging infectious diseases	pp. 416–418
Industrial microbiology/biotechnology	Chapters 9 and 28
Koch's postulates	pp. 404–406
Vaccines	pp. 501–506
Biofilms	pp. 162–163

ANSWERS

Review

1. People came to believe that living organisms arose from nonliving matter because they would see flies coming out of manure and maggots coming out of dead animals, and see microorganisms appear in liquids after a day or two.

2. a.   Certain microorganisms cause diseases in insects. Microorganisms that kill insects can be effective biological control agents because they are specific for the pest and do not persist in the environment.

   b.   Carbon, oxygen, nitrogen, sulfur, and phosphorus are required for all living organisms. Microorganisms convert these elements into forms that are useful for other organisms. Many bacteria decompose material and release carbon dioxide into the atmosphere that plants use. Some bacteria can take nitrogen from the atmosphere and convert it into a form that can be used by plants and other microorganisms.

   c.   Normal microbiota are microorganisms that are found in and on the human body. They do not usually cause disease and can be beneficial.

   d.   Organic matter in sewage is decomposed by bacteria into carbon dioxide, nitrates, phosphates, sulfate, and other inorganic compounds in a wastewater treatment plant.

   e.   Recombinant DNA techniques have resulted in insertion of the gene for insulin production into bacteria. These bacteria can produce human insulin inexpensively.

   f.   Microorganisms can be used as vaccines. Some microbes can be genetically engineered to produce components of vaccines.

   g.   Biofilms are aggregated bacteria adhering to each other and to a s solid surface.

3. a.   1, 3   d.   2   g.   4
    b.   8   e.   5   h.   7
    c.   1, 4, 5   f.   3

4. a.   7   d.   2   g.   1
    b.   4   e.   6
    c.   3   f.   5

5. a.   11   g.   10   m.   7
    b.   14   h.   2   n.   5
    c.   15   i.   1   o.   6
    d.   17   j.   12   p.   8
    e.   3   k.   18   q.   13
    f.   9   l.   4   r.   16

6.   *Erwinia amylovora* is the correct way to write this scientific name. Scientific names can be derived from the names of scientists. In this case, *Erwinia* is derived from Erwin F. Smith, an American plant pathologist. Scientific names also can describe the organism, its habitat, or its niche. *E. amylovora* is a pathogen of plants (*amylo* = starch, *vora* = eat).

7. a.   *B. thuringiensis* is sold as a biological insecticide.
    b.   *Saccharomyces* is the yeast sold for making bread, wine, and beer.

8.

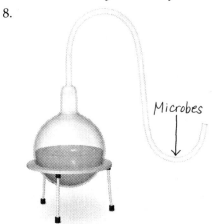

Microbes

Critical Thinking

1. Pasteur showed that life comes from preexisting life. The microorganisms that produced chemical and physical changes in beef broth and wine came from a few cells that entered the liquids from dust, containers, or the air. After showing that microorganisms could both grow on and change organic matter, Pasteur and others began to suspect that diseases were the result of microorganisms growing on living organic matter.

2. Semmelweis had observed an increased incidence of fever when medical students worked in obstetrics, as compared to the incidence during the students' summer break. The medical students were carrying bacteria from the autopsy room. Lister observed that compound bone fractures could result in death, whereas recovery from simple fractures occurred without incident.

3. There are many! Check the dairy section for fermented products, such as sour cream, yogurt, and cheese. Protein supplements often are yeasts. Bread, wine, and beer are products of yeasts and some bacteria. Sauerkraut is cabbage that has been fermented by lactobacilli. Vinegar is produced by bacterial growth on ethyl alcohol (wine). Xanthan, a thickener in many foods, is made by *Xanthomonas* bacteria.

4. Factors contributing to infectious disease include mutations in existing organisms, spread of diseases to new areas, ecological disturbances such as deforestation, lack of immunization, pesticide resistance, and antibiotic resistance.

Clinical Applications

1. a. Treatment with penicillin suggests a bacterial cause, because only bacterial diseases are treatable with this drug. The summer onset also suggested an infectious disease, perhaps related to an outdoor activity such as swimming or contact with mosquitoes or ticks.
   b. Lyme disease.
   c. The tick vector is more active during these months. Additionally, people spend more time outdoors and potentially in contact with ticks during these months.

2. Pasteur showed that microbes were omnipresent and were responsible for "diseases" (i.e., spoilage) of food; Lister reasoned that these microbes might be responsible for diseases of people. Neither Lister nor Pasteur proved that microbes caused diseases. Koch provided a repeatable proof to demonstrate that a microbe causes a disease.

CASE STUDY: ARE ULCERS AN INFECTIOUS DISEASE?

Background

In 1981, the following information came to the attention of Barry Marshall, a gastroenterologist at the Royal Perth Hospital in Australia. Household members of ulcer patients do not develop antibodies against *Helicobacter*. However, clinical staff involved in obtaining biopsy samples from ulcer patients develop antibodies against *Helicobacter*. If acid-suppressive therapy is combined with antibiotics, ulcers usually do not recur. Marshall concluded that ulcers are an infectious disease.

Questions

What caused Marshall to reach his conclusion? What additional proof would be needed?

The Solution

The presence of antibodies against *Helicobacter* is evidence of current or prior infection by the organism. Exchange of bacteria of the intestinal and skin microbiota, which is normal among household members, does not transmit *Helicobacter*, but direct contact with stomach contents does. Marshall collected the additional proof by demonstrating Koch's postulates. Healthy volunteers were inoculated with *Helicobacter*; they developed symptoms of the disease; and the *Helicobacter* was recovered from them.

2 Chemical Principles

LEARNING OBJECTIVES	CHECK YOUR UNDERSTANDING
2-1 Describe the structure of an atom and its relation to the physical properties of elements.	How does $^{14}_{6}C$ differ from $^{12}_{6}C$? What is the atomic number of each carbon atom? The atomic weight?
2-2 Define *ionic bond, covalent bond, hydrogen bond, molecular weight,* and *mole*.	Differentiate an ionic bond from a covalent bond.
2-3 Diagram three basic types of chemical reactions.	The chemical reaction below is used to remove chlorine from water. What type of reaction is it? $$HClO + Na_2SO_3 \rightarrow Na_2SO_4 + HCl$$
2-4 List several properties of water that are important to living systems.	Why is the polarity of a water molecular important?
2-5 Define *acid, base, salt,* and *pH*.	Antacids neutralize acid by the following reaction. $$Mg(OH)_2 + HCl \rightarrow MgCl_2 + H_2O$$ Identify the acid, base, and salt.
2-6 Distinguish organic and inorganic compounds.	Define *organic*.
2-7 Define *functional group*.	Add the appropriate functional group(s) to this ethyl group to produce each of the following compounds: ethanol, acetic acid, acetaldehyde, ethanolamine, diethyl ether.
2-8 Identify the building blocks of carbohydrates.	Give an example of a monosaccharide, a disaccharide, and a polysaccharide.
2-9 Differentiate simple lipids, complex lipids, and steroids.	How do simple lipids differ from complex lipids?
2-10 Identify the building blocks and structure of proteins.	What two functional groups are in all amino acids?
2-11 Identify the building blocks of nucleic acids.	What is the structure of DNA? Of RNA?
2-12 Describe the role of ATP in cellular activities.	Which can provide more energy for a cell and why: ATP or ADP?

NEW IN THIS EDITION

- Expanded definitions of *atoms, charges,* and *cis* and *trans fatty acids*.

CHAPTER SUMMARY

Introduction (p. 26)

1. The science of the interaction between atoms and molecules is called chemistry.
2. The metabolic activities of microorganisms involve complex chemical reactions.
3. Microbes break down nutrients to obtain energy and to make new cells.

The Structure of Atoms (pp. 27–28)

1. An atom is the smallest unit of a chemical element that exhibits the properties of that element.
2. Atoms consist of a nucleus, which contains protons and neutrons, and electrons, which move around the nucleus.
3. The atomic number is the number of protons in the nucleus; the total number of protons and neutrons is the atomic weight.

Chemical Elements (pp. 27–28)

4. Atoms with the same number of protons and the same chemical behavior are classified as the same chemical element.
5. Chemical elements are designated by abbreviations called chemical symbols.
6. About 26 elements are commonly found in living cells.
7. Atoms that have the same atomic number (are of the same element) but different atomic weights are called isotopes.

Electronic Configurations (p. 28)

8. In an atom, electrons are arranged around the nucleus in electron shells.
9. Each shell can hold a characteristic maximum number of electrons.
10. The chemical properties of an atom are due largely to the number of electrons in its outermost shell.

How Atoms Form Molecules: Chemical Bonds (pp. 28–32)

1. Molecules are made up of two or more atoms; molecules consisting of at least two different kinds of atoms are called compounds.
2. Atoms form molecules in order to fill their outermost electron shells.
3. Attractive forces that bind the atomic nuclei of two atoms together are called chemical bonds.
4. The combining capacity of an atom—the number of chemical bonds the atom can form with other atoms—is its valence.

Ionic Bonds (pp. 28, 30)

5. A positively or negatively charged atom or group of atoms is called an ion.
6. A chemical attraction between ions of opposite charge is called an ionic bond.
7. To form an ionic bond, one ion is an electron donor, and the other ion is an electron acceptor.

Covalent Bonds (pp. 30–31)

8. In a covalent bond, atoms share pairs of electrons.
9. Covalent bonds are stronger than ionic bonds and are far more common in organisms.

Hydrogen Bonds (pp. 31–32)

10. A hydrogen bond exists when a hydrogen atom covalently bonded to one oxygen or nitrogen atom is attracted to another oxygen or nitrogen atom.
11. Hydrogen bonds form weak links between different molecules or between parts of the same large molecule.

Molecular Weight and Moles (p. 32)

12. The molecular weight is the sum of the atomic weights of all the atoms in a molecule.
13. A mole of an atom, ion, or molecule is equal to its atomic or molecular weight expressed in grams.

Chemical Reactions (pp. 32–34)

1. Chemical reactions are the making or breaking of chemical bonds between atoms.
2. A change of energy occurs during chemical reactions.
3. Endergonic reactions require more energy than they release; exergonic reactions release more energy.
4. In a synthesis reaction, atoms, ions, or molecules are combined to form a larger molecule.
5. In a decomposition reaction, a larger molecule is broken down into its component molecules, ions, or atoms.
6. In an exchange reaction, two molecules are decomposed, and their subunits are used to synthesize two new molecules.
7. The products of reversible reactions can readily revert to form the original reactants.

IMPORTANT BIOLOGICAL MOLECULES (pp. 34–49)

Inorganic Compounds (pp. 34–37)

1. Inorganic compounds are usually small, ionically bonded molecules.
2. Water and many common acids, bases, and salts are examples of inorganic compounds.

Water (pp. 34–35)

3. Water is the most abundant substance in cells.
4. Because water is a polar molecule, it is an excellent solvent.
5. Water is a reactant in many of the decomposition reactions of digestion.
6. Water is an excellent temperature buffer.

Acids, Bases, and Salts (p. 35)

7. An acid dissociates into H^+ and anions.
8. A base dissociates into OH^- and cations.
9. A salt dissociates into negative and positive ions, neither of which is H^+ or OH^-.

Acid–Base Balance: The Concept of pH (pp. 35–37)

10. The term *pH* refers to the concentration of H^+ in a solution.
11. A solution of pH 7 is neutral; a pH value below 7 indicates acidity; pH above 7 indicates alkalinity.
12. The pH inside a cell and in culture media is stabilized with pH buffers.

Organic Compounds (pp. 37–49)

1. Organic compounds always contain carbon and hydrogen.
2. Carbon atoms form up to four bonds with other atoms.
3. Organic compounds are mostly or entirely covalently bonded, and many of them are large molecules.

Structure and Chemistry (pp. 37–38)

4. A chain of carbon atoms forms a carbon skeleton.
5. Functional groups of atoms are responsible for most of the properties of organic molecules.
6. The letter *R* may be used to denote the remainder of an organic molecule.
7. Frequently encountered classes of molecules are R—OH (alcohols) and R—COOH (organic acids).
8. Small organic molecules may combine into very large molecules called macromolecules.
9. Monomers usually bond together by dehydration synthesis, or condensation reactions, that form water and a polymer.
10. Organic molecules may be broken down by hydrolysis, a reaction involving the splitting of water molecules.

Carbohydrates (pp. 39–40)

11. Carbohydrates are compounds consisting of atoms of carbon, hydrogen, and oxygen, with hydrogen and oxygen in a 2:1 ratio.
12. Carbohydrates include sugars and starches.
13. Carbohydrates can be classified as monosaccharides, disaccharides, and polysaccharides.
14. Monosaccharides contain from three to seven carbon atoms.
15. Isomers are two molecules with the same chemical formula but different structures and properties—for example, glucose ($C_6H_{12}O_6$) and fructose ($C_6H_{12}O_6$).
16. Monosaccharides may form disaccharides and polysaccharides by dehydration synthesis.

Lipids (pp. 40–41)

17. Lipids are a diverse group of compounds distinguished by their insolubility in water.
18. Simple lipids (fats) consist of a molecule of glycerol and three molecules of fatty acids.
19. A saturated lipid has no double bonds between carbon atoms in the fatty acids; an unsaturated lipid has one or more double bonds. Saturated lipids have higher melting points than unsaturated lipids.
20. Phospholipids are complex lipids consisting of glycerol, two fatty acids, and a phosphate group.
21. Steroids have carbon ring structures; sterols have a functional hydroxyl group.

Proteins (pp. 42–46)

22. Amino acids are the building blocks of proteins.
23. Amino acids consist of carbon, hydrogen, oxygen, nitrogen, and sometimes sulfur.
24. Twenty amino acids occur naturally in proteins.
25. By linking amino acids, peptide bonds (formed by dehydration synthesis) allow the formation of polypeptide chains.
26. Proteins have four levels of structure: primary (sequence of amino acids), secondary (helices or pleats), tertiary (overall three-dimensional structure of a polypeptide), and quaternary (two or more polypeptide chains).
27. Conjugated proteins consist of amino acids combined with other organic or inorganic compounds.

Nucleic Acids (p. 47)

28. Nucleic acids—DNA and RNA—are macromolecules consisting of repeating nucleotides.

29. A nucleotide is composed of a pentose, a phosphate group, and a nitrogen-containing base. A nucleoside is composed of a pentose and a nitrogen-containing base.

30. A DNA nucleotide consists of deoxyribose (a pentose) and one of the following nitrogen-containing bases: thymine or cytosine (pyrimidines) or adenine or guanine (purines).

31. DNA consists of two strands of nucleotides wound in a double helix. The strands are held together by hydrogen bonds between purine and pyrimidine nucleotides: AT and GC.

32. Genes consist of sequences of nucleotides.

33. An RNA nucleotide consists of ribose (a pentose) and one of the following nitrogen-containing bases: cytosine, guanine, adenine, or uracil.

Adenosine Triphosphate (ATP) (pp. 47–49)

34. ATP stores chemical energy for various cellular activities.

35. When the bond to ATP's terminal phosphate group is hydrolyzed, energy is released.

36. The energy from oxidation reactions is used to regenerate ATP from ADP and inorganic phosphate.

THE LOOP

1. Have students study Chapter 2 and use the Study Questions as a self-test.

2. Have students study Chapter 2 and take a pretest for Chapter 5. Pretests can be administered individually during office hours, open laboratories, or study sessions. Students who score at least 9 points out of 15 questions from the Chapter 2 Test Bank show mastery. A student who does not achieve mastery can study and take a second chapter test.

3. Students with some chemistry but less than one year of college chemistry may find it useful to have the last half of this chapter, "Important Biological Molecules" (pp. 34–49), used as an introduction to Chapter 5, "Microbial Metabolism."

ANSWERS

Review

1. Atoms with the same atomic number and chemical behavior are classified as chemical elements.

2.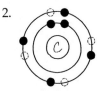

3. a. Ionic
   b. Single covalent bond
   c. Double covalent bonds
   d. Hydrogen bond

4. a. Synthesis reaction, condensation, or dehydration
   b. Decomposition reaction, digestion, or hydrolysis
   c. Exchange reaction
   d. Reversible reaction

5. The enzyme lowers the activation energy required for the reaction and therefore speeds up this decomposition reaction.

6. a. Lipid
   b. Protein
   c. Carbohydrate
   d. Nucleic acid

7. a. Amino acids
   b. Right to left
   c. Left to right

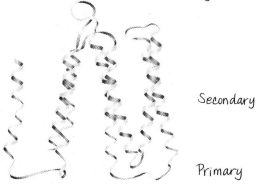

8. The entire protein shows tertiary structure, held by disulfide bonds. No quaternary structure.

   Secondary

   Primary

9.

   Removal of a fatty acid and addition of a phosphate →

Critical Thinking

1. a.   Synthesis reaction.

   b. H_2CO_3 is an acid.

2. ATP and DNA have 5-carbon sugars. ATP has ribose, and DNA has deoxyribose; ATP and DNA contain the purine, adenine.

3. To maintain the proper fluidity, the percentage of unsaturated lipids decreases at the higher temperature.

4. These animals have cellulose-degrading bacteria in specialized structures in their digestive tracts.

Clinical Applications

1. PHB is a fatty acid used as an energy storage molecule by *Ralstonia*.

2. *T. ferrooxidans* can oxidize sulfur ("thio") as well as iron ("ferro"). The oxidation of sulfide in pyrite produces sulfuric acid, which dissolves the limestone. Gypsum forms in a subsequent exchange reaction.

$$2S^{2-} + 3O_2 + 2H_2O \longrightarrow 2SO_4^{2-} + 4H^+$$

$$2CaCO_3 + 4H^+ + 2SO_4^{2-} \longrightarrow 2CaSO_4 + 2H^+ + 2HCO_3{-}$$

3. Because L-isomers are more common in nature, most cells, such as phagocytes, will be able to degrade the L-isomers. D-isomers will be resistant to metabolism by most cells.

4. Amphotericin B would not work against most bacteria because they lack sterols. Fungi have sterols and are generally susceptible to amphotericin B. Human cells have sterols.

5. Methionine and cysteine.

CASE STUDY: KESTERSON NATIONAL WILDLIFE REFUGE

Background

Kesterson National Wildlife Refuge, California: In the San Joaquin Valley, irrigation water wasn't draining properly, and crops were dying in the water-logged soil. In 1981, a drainage system was built to channel irrigation runoff into shallow ponds called Kesterson Reservoir. In addition to receiving field runoff, the new reservoir was to be a waterfowl habitat. In 1983, an unusually large number of dead birds was found, indicating that something was wrong with the water.

Selenium from the soil (in the form of selenate, SeO_4^{2-}) was dissolving in the irrigation water and being carried to Kesterson Reservoir, where it stayed. The concentration of selenium in Kesterson rose to 29 times higher than that which was considered safe.

Kesterson Reservoir has been drained and filled with soil to prevent the killing of more birds, but the selenium remains. Further study has revealed 14 other locations experiencing this so-called "Kesterson Effect."

A number of bacteria, including *Bacillus, Acinetobacter,* and *Pseudomonas,* can convert selenate (SeO_4^{2-}) to nontoxic elemental selenium. The bacteria do this for their own survival—to prevent the accumulation of toxic levels in their cells.

Question

What is the chemical reaction that shows how the bacteria make Se^0, using hydrogen sulfide (H_2S) and selenate?

The Solution

$$SeO_4^{2-} + 4H_2S \longrightarrow Se^0 + 4H_2O + 4S^0$$

3

Observing Microorganisms Through a Microscope

LEARNING OBJECTIVES

3-1 List the metric units of measurement that are used for microorganisms.

3-2 Diagram the path of light through a compound microscope.

3-3 Define *total magnification* and *resolution*.

3-4 Identify a use for darkfield, phase-contrast, differential interference contrast, fluorescence, confocal, two-photon, and scanning acoustic microscopy, and compare each with brightfield illumination.

3-5 Explain how electron microscopy differs from light microscopy.

3-6 Identify one use for the TEM, SEM, and scanned-probe microscopes.

3-7 Differentiate an acidic dye from a basic dye.

3-8 Explain the purpose of simple staining.

3-9 List the steps in preparing a Gram stain, and describe the appearance of gram-positive and gram-negative cells after each step.

3-10 Compare and contrast the Gram stain and the acid-fast stain.

3-11 Explain why each of the following is used: capsule stain, endospore stain, flagella stain.

CHECK YOUR UNDERSTANDING

If a microbe measures 10 μm in length, how long is it in nanometers?

Through what lenses does light pass in a compound microscope?

What does it mean when a microscope has a resolution of 0.2 nm?

How are brightfield, darkfield, phase-contrast, and fluorescence microscopy similar?

Why do electron microscopes have greater resolution than light microscopes?

For what is TEM used? SEM? Scanned-probe microscopy?

Why doesn't a negative stain color a cell?

Why is fixing necessary for most staining procedures?

Why is the Gram stain so useful?

Which stain would be used to identify microbes in the genera *Mycobacterium* and *Nocardia*?

How do unstained endospores appear? Stained endospores?

NEW IN THIS EDITION

- Coverage of two-photon microscopy.
- Addition of several new photos.

CHAPTER SUMMARY

Units of Measurement (p. 55)

1. The standard unit of length is the meter (m).
2. Microorganisms are measured in micrometers, μm (10^{-6} m), and in nanometers, nm (10^{-9} m).

Microscopy: The Instruments (p. 55)

1. A simple microscope consists of one lens; a compound microscope has multiple lenses.

Light Microscopy (pp. 56, 58–62)

Compound Light Microscopy (pp. 56, 58–59)

2. The most common microscope used in microbiology is the compound light microscope (LM).
3. The total magnification of an object is calculated by multiplying the magnification of the objective lens by the magnification of the ocular lens.
4. The compound light microscope uses visible light.
5. The maximum resolution, or resolving power (the ability to distinguish two points) of a compound light microscope is 0.2 μm; maximum magnification is 2000×.
6. Specimens are stained to increase the difference between the refractive indexes of the specimen and the medium.
7. Immersion oil is used with the oil immersion lens to reduce light loss between the slide and the lens.
8. Brightfield illumination is used for stained smears.
9. Unstained cells are more productively observed using darkfield, phase-contrast, or DIC microscopy.

Darkfield Microscopy (p. 59)

10. The darkfield microscope shows a light silhouette of an organism against a dark background.
11. It is most useful for detecting the presence of extremely small organisms.

Phase-Contrast Microscopy (pp. 59–60)

12. A phase-contrast microscope brings direct and reflected or diffracted light rays together (in phase) to form an image of the specimen on the ocular lens.
13. It allows the detailed observation of living organisms.

Differential Interference Contrast (DIC) Microscopy (p. 60)

14. The DIC microscope provides a colored, three-dimensional image of the object being observed.
15. It allows detailed observations of living cells.

Fluorescence Microscopy (pp. 61–62)

16. In fluorescence microscopy, specimens are first stained with fluorochromes and then viewed through a compound microscope by using an ultraviolet light source.
17. The microorganisms appear as bright objects against a dark background.
18. Fluorescence microscopy is used primarily in a diagnostic procedure called fluorescent-antibody (FA) technique, or immunofluorescence.

Confocal Microscopy (p. 62)

19. In confocal microscopy, a specimen is stained with a fluorescent dye and illuminated with short-wavelength light.
20. Using a computer to process the images, two-dimensional and three-dimensional images of cells can be produced.

Two-Photon Microscopy (p. 62)

21. In TPM, a live specimen is stained with a fluorescent dye and illuminated with long-wavelength light.

Scanning Acoustic Microscopy (p. 63)

22. Scanning acoustic microscopy (SAM) is based on the interpretation of sound waves through a specimen.

23. It is used to study living cells attached to surfaces such as cancer cells, artery plaque, and biofilms.

Electron Microscopy (pp. 63–65)

24. Instead of light, a beam of electrons is used with an electron microscope.

25. Instead of glass lenses, electromagnets control focus, illumination, and magnification.

26. Thin sections of organisms can be seen in an electron micrograph produced using a transmission electron microscope (TEM). Magnification: 10,000–100,000×. Resolving power: 2.5 nm.

27. Three-dimensional views of the surfaces of whole microorganisms can be obtained with a scanning electron microscope (SEM). Magnification: 1000–10,000×. Resolving power: 20 nm.

Scanned-Probe Microscopy (p. 65)

28. Scanning tunneling microscopy (STM) and atomic force microscopy (AFM) produce three-dimensional images of the surface of a molecule.

Preparation of Specimens for Light Microscopy (pp. 68–72)

Preparing Smears for Staining (pp. 68–69)

1. Staining means coloring a microorganism with a dye to make some structures more visible.

2. Fixing uses heat or alcohol to kill and attach microorganisms to a slide.

3. A smear is a thin film of material used for microscopic examination.

4. Bacteria are negatively charged, and the colored positive ion of a basic dye will stain bacterial cells.

5. The colored negative ion of an acidic dye will stain the background of a bacterial smear; a negative stain is produced.

Simple Stains (p. 69)

6. A simple stain is an aqueous or alcohol solution of a single basic dye.

7. It is used to make cellular shapes and arrangements visible.

8. A mordant may be used to improve bonding between the stain and the specimen.

Differential Stains (pp. 69–71)

9. Differential stains, such as the Gram stain and acid-fast stain, differentiate bacteria according to their reactions to the stains.

10. The Gram stain procedure uses a purple stain (crystal violet), iodine as a mordant, an alcohol decolorizer, and a red counterstain.

11. Gram-positive bacteria retain the purple stain after the decolorization step; gram-negative bacteria do not and thus appear pink from the counterstain.

12. Acid-fast microbes, such as members of the genera *Mycobacterium* and *Nocardia*, retain carbolfuchsin after acid-alcohol decolorization and appear red; non–acid-fast microbes take up the methylene blue counterstain and appear blue.

Special Stains (pp. 71–72)

13. Negative staining is used to make microbial capsules visible.

14. The endospore stain and flagella stain are special stains that color only certain parts of bacteria.

THE LOOP

Chapter 3 should provide a good reference for laboratory exercises on microscopy and staining. The test questions can be used as laboratory quizzes.

ANSWERS

Review

1. a. 10^{-6} m
    b. nm
    c. 10^3 nm

2. a. Compound light microscope
    b. Darkfield microscope
    c. Phase-contrast microscope
    d. Fluorescence microscope
    e. Electron microscope
    f. Differential interference contrast microscope

3.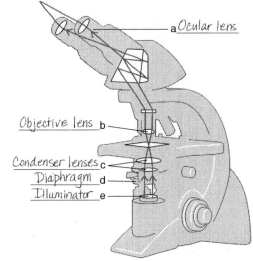

4. Ocular lens magnification $\times$ oil immersion lens magnification $=$ total magnification of specimen

    $\qquad\qquad$ 10$\times$ $\qquad\qquad\times\qquad\qquad$ 100$\times$ $\qquad\qquad=\qquad\qquad$ 1000$\times$

5. a. 2,000$\times$ $\qquad\qquad$ c. 0.2 µm $\qquad\qquad$ e. Seeing three-dimensional detail
    b. 100,000$\times$ $\qquad\qquad$ d. 0.0025 µm

6. In a Gram stain, the mordant combines with the basic dye to form a complex that will not wash out of gram-positive cells. In a flagella stain, the mordant accumulates on the flagella so that they can be seen with a light microscope.

7. A counterstain stains the colorless non–acid-fast cells so that they are easily seen through a microscope.

8. In the Gram stain, the decolorizer removes the color from gram-negative cells. In the acid-fast stain, the decolorizer removes the color from non–acid-fast cells.

9. a. Purple $\qquad\qquad$ d. Purple $\qquad\qquad$ g. Colorless
    b. Purple $\qquad\qquad$ e. Purple $\qquad\qquad$ h. Red
    c. Purple $\qquad\qquad$ f. Purple

Critical Thinking

1. The counterstain safranin can be omitted. Gram-positive bacteria will appear purple, and gram-negative bacteria will be colorless.

2. You would be able to discern two objects separated by the four distances given because each is equal to or greater than the resolving power of the microscope.

3. The high lipid content of acid-fast cell walls makes them impermeable to most stains. If the primary stain penetrates, the Gram stain decolorizer will not decolorize the cell. Therefore, acid-fast bacteria would be gram-positive if they could be Gram stained.

4. Inclusions as well as endospores may not stain in a Gram stain. The endospore stain will identify the unstained structure as an endospore.

Clinical Applications

1. Ehrlich observed that mycobacteria could not be decolorized with acid-alcohol, so he reasoned that an acidic disinfectant would not be able to penetrate the cell wall.

2. *N. gonorrhoeae* bacteria are gram-negative (red) diplococci, often found in the large human cells (phagocytes).

3. These are called clue cells. The large red cells are human mucosal cells; gram-positive bacteria on the surface of the human cells.

4. The presence of acid-fast rods suggests the elephant had a mycobacterial infection. Subsequent cultures verified that the elephant had tuberculosis.

CASE STUDY: ELECTRON MICROSCOPY

Background

Samples prepared for transmission electron microscopy are embedded in an epoxy resin and sliced into ultrathin (100-nm) sections. The sections are usually stained with a heavy metal such as lead to enhance contrast. The sections are then examined with a transmission electron microscope. The photographs of these thin sections are put in order according to their position in the living cell and used to determine the shape of the original sample.

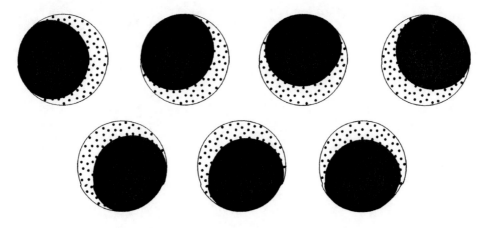

Question

Determine the appearance of the original, intact cell.

The Solution

A spirochete; see Figure 4.10. The solid area is the cross section of the cell body, and the "dots" are cross sections of axial filaments. The changing positions of the cell and axial filaments are due to the spiraling of the axial filaments around the cell.

4 Functional Anatomy of Prokaryotic and Eukaryotic Cells

LEARNING OBJECTIVES	CHECK YOUR UNDERSTANDING
4-1 Compare and contrast the overall cell structure of prokaryotes and eukaryotes.	What is the main feature that distinguishes prokaryotes from eukaryotes?
4-2 Identify the three basic shapes of bacteria.	How would you be able to identify streptococci through a microscope?
4-3 Describe the structure and function of the glycocalyx.	Why are bacterial capsules medically important?
4-4 Differentiate flagella, axial filaments, fimbriae, and pili.	How do bacteria move?
4-5 Compare and contrast the cell walls of gram-positive bacteria, gram-negative bacteria, acid-fast bacteria, archaea, and mycoplasmas.	Why are drugs that target cell wall synthesis useful?
4-6 Compare and contrast archaea and mycoplasmas.	Why are mycoplasmas resistant to antibiotics that interfere with cell wall synthesis?
4-7 Differentiate between protoplast, spheroplast, and L form.	How do protoplasts differ from L forms?
4-8 Describe the structure, chemistry, and functions of the prokaryotic plasma membrane.	Which agents can cause injury to the bacterial plasma membrane?
4-9 Define *simple diffusion, facilitated diffusion, osmosis, active transport,* and *group translocation.*	How are simple diffusion and facilitated diffusion similar? How are they different?
4-10 Identify the functions of the nucleoid and ribosomes.	Where is DNA located in a prokaryotic cell?
4-11 Identify the functions of four inclusions.	What is the general function of inclusions?
4-12 Describe the functions of endospores, sporulation, and endospore germination.	Under what conditions do endospores form?
4-13 Differentiate prokaryotic and eukaryotic flagella.	
4-14 Compare and contrast prokaryotic and eukaryotic cell walls and glycocalyxes.	
4-15 Compare and contrast prokaryotic and eukaryotic plasma membranes.	Identify at least one significant difference between eukaryotic and prokaryotic flagella and cilia, cell walls, plasma membrane, and cytoplasm.
4-16 Compare and contrast prokaryotic and eukaryotic cytoplasms.	
4-17 Compare the structure and function of eukaryotic and prokaryotic ribosomes.	The antibiotic erythromycin binds with the 50S portion of a ribosome. What effect does this have on a prokaryotic cell? On a eukaryotic cell?

4-18 Define *organelle.*	Compare the structure of the nucleus of a eukaryote and the nucleoid of a prokaryote.
4-19 Describe the functions of the nucleus, endoplasmic reticulum, Golgi complex, lysosomes, vacuoles, mitochondria, chloroplasts, peroxisomes, and centrosomes.	How do rough and smooth ER compare structurally and functionally?
4-20 Discuss evidence that supports the endosymbiotic theory of eukaryotic evolution.	Which three organelles are not associated with the Golgi complex? What does this suggest about their origin?

NEW IN THIS EDITION

- Revised discussion of classification of flagella, fimbriae, pili, motility, LPS, facilitated diffusion, aquaporins, and active transport.

CHAPTER SUMMARY

Comparing Prokaryotic and Eukaryotic Cells: An Overview (p. 77)

1. Prokaryotic and eukaryotic cells are similar in their chemical composition and chemical reactions.
2. Prokaryotic cells lack membrane-enclosed organelles (including a nucleus).
3. Peptidoglycan is found in prokaryotic cell walls but not in eukaryotic cell walls.
4. Eukaryotic cells have a membrane-bound nucleus and other organelles.

THE PROKARYOTIC CELL (pp. 77–98)

1. Bacteria are unicellular, and most of them multiply by binary fission.
2. Bacterial species are differentiated by morphology, chemical composition, nutritional requirements, biochemical activities, and source of energy.

The Size, Shape, and Arrangement of Bacterial Cells (pp. 77–79)

1. Most bacteria are 0.2 to 2.0 µm in diameter and 2 to 8 µm in length.
2. The three basic bacterial shapes are coccus (spherical), bacillus (rod-shaped), and spiral (twisted).
3. Pleomorphic bacteria can assume several shapes.

Structures External to the Cell Wall (pp. 79–84)

Glycocalyx (pp. 79–81)

1. The glycocalyx (capsule, slime layer, or extracellular polysaccharide) is a gelatinous polysaccharide and/or polypeptide covering.
2. Capsules may protect pathogens from phagocytosis.
3. Capsules enable adherence to surfaces, prevent desiccation, and may provide nutrients.

Flagella (pp. 81–82)

4. Flagella are relatively long filamentous appendages consisting of a filament, hook, and basal body.
5. Prokaryotic flagella rotate to push the cell.

6. Motile bacteria exhibit taxis; positive taxis is movement toward an attractant, and negative taxis is movement away from a repellent.

7. Flagellar (H) protein is an antigen.

Axial Filaments (pp. 82–83)

8. Spiral cells that move by means of an axial filament (endoflagellum) are called spirochetes.

9. Axial filaments are similar to flagella, except that they wrap around the cell.

Fimbriae and Pili (pp. 83–84)

10. Fimbriae help cells adhere to surfaces.

11. Pili are involved in twitching motility and DNA transfer.

The Cell Wall (pp. 84-89)

Composition and Characteristics (pp. 85-87)

1. The cell wall surrounds the plasma membrane and protects the cell from changes in water pressure.

2. The bacterial cell wall consists of peptidoglycan, a polymer consisting of NAG and NAM and short chains of amino acids.

3. Penicillin interferes with peptidoglycan synthesis.

4. Gram-positive cell walls consist of many layers of peptidoglycan and also contain teichoic acids.

5. Gram-negative bacteria have a lipopolysaccharide-lipoprotein-phospholipid outer membrane surrounding a thin peptidoglycan layer.

6. The outer membrane protects the cell from phagocytosis and from penicillin, lysozyme, and other chemicals.

7. Porins are proteins that permit small molecules to pass through the outer membrane; specific channel proteins allow other molecules to move through the outer membrane.

8. The lipopolysaccharide component of the outer membrane consists of sugars (O polysaccharides), which function as antigens, and lipid A, which is an endotoxin.

Cell Walls and the Gram Stain Mechanism (p. 87)

9. The crystal violet–iodine complex combines with peptidoglycan.

10. The decolorizer removes the lipid outer membrane of gram-negative bacteria and washes out the crystal violet.

Atypical Cell Walls (pp. 87–88)

11. *Mycoplasma* is a bacterial genus that naturally lacks cell walls.

12. Archaea have pseudomurein; they lack peptidoglycan.

13. Acid-fast cell walls have a layer of mycolic acid outside a thin peptidoglycan layer.

Damage to the Cell Wall (pp. 88–89)

14. In the presence of lysozyme, gram-positive cell walls are destroyed, and the remaining cellular contents are referred to as a protoplast.

15. In the presence of lysozyme, gram-negative cell walls are not completely destroyed, and the remaining cellular contents are referred to as a spheroplast.

16. L forms are gram-positive or gram-negative bacteria that do not make a cell wall.
17. Antibiotics such as penicillin interfere with cell wall synthesis.

Structures Internal to the Cell Wall (pp. 89–98)

The Plasma (Cytoplasmic) Membrane (pp. 89–91)

1. The plasma membrane encloses the cytoplasm and is a lipid bilayer with peripheral and integral proteins (the fluid mosaic model).
2. The plasma membrane is selectively permeable.
3. Plasma membranes contain enzymes for metabolic reactions, such as nutrient breakdown, energy production, and photosynthesis.
4. Mesosomes, irregular infoldings of the plasma membrane, are artifacts, not true cell structures.
5. Plasma membranes can be destroyed by alcohols and polymyxins.

The Movement of Materials across Membranes (pp. 91–94)

6. Movement across the membrane may be by passive processes, in which materials move from areas of higher to lower concentration and no energy is expended by the cell.
7. In simple diffusion, molecules and ions move until equilibrium is reached.
8. In facilitated diffusion, substances are transported by transporter proteins across membranes from areas of high to low concentration.
9. Osmosis is the movement of water from areas of high to low concentration across a selectively permeable membrane until equilibrium is reached.
10. In active transport, materials move from areas of low to high concentration by transporter proteins, and the cell must expend energy.
11. In group translocation, energy is expended to modify chemicals and transport them across the membrane.

Cytoplasm (p. 94)

12. Cytoplasm is the fluid component inside the plasma membrane.
13. The cytoplasm is mostly water, with inorganic and organic molecules, DNA, ribosomes, and inclusions.

The Nucleoid (pp. 94–95)

14. The nucleoid contains the DNA of the bacterial chromosome.
15. Bacteria can also contain plasmids, which are circular, extrachromosomal DNA molecules.

Ribosomes (p. 95)

16. The cytoplasm of a prokaryote contains numerous 70S ribosomes; ribosomes consist of rRNA and protein.
17. Protein synthesis occurs at ribosomes; it can be inhibited by certain antibiotics.

Inclusions (pp. 95–96)

18. Inclusions are reserve deposits found in prokaryotic and eukaryotic cells.
19. Among the inclusions found in bacteria are metachromatic granules (inorganic phosphate), polysaccharide granules (usually glycogen or starch), lipid inclusions, sulfur granules, carboxysomes (ribulose 1,5-diphosphate carboxylase), magnetosomes (Fe_3O_4), and gas vacuoles.

Endospores (pp. 96–98)

20. Endospores are resting structures formed by some bacteria; they allow survival during adverse environmental conditions.

21. The process of endospore formation is called sporulation; the return of an endospore to its vegetative state is called germination.

THE EUKARYOTIC CELL (pp. 98–106)

Flagella and Cilia (p. 98)

1. Flagella are few and long in relation to cell size; cilia are numerous and short.

2. Flagella and cilia are used for motility, and cilia also move substances along the surface of the cells.

3. Both flagella and cilia consist of an arrangement of nine pairs and two single microtubules.

The Cell Wall and Glycocalyx (p. 98)

1. The cell walls of many algae and some fungi contain cellulose.

2. The main material of fungal cell walls is chitin.

3. Yeast cell walls consist of glucan and mannan.

4. Animal cells are surrounded by a glycocalyx, which strengthens the cell and provides a means of attachment to other cells.

The Plasma (Cytoplasmic) Membrane (p. 100)

1. Like the prokaryotic plasma membrane, the eukaryotic plasma membrane is a phospholipid bilayer containing proteins.

2. Eukaryotic plasma membranes contain carbohydrates attached to the proteins and sterols not found in prokaryotic cells (except *Mycoplasma* bacteria).

3. Eukaryotic cells can move materials across the plasma membrane by the passive processes used by prokaryotes and by active transport and endocytosis (phagocytosis and pinocytosis).

Cytoplasm (pp. 100–101)

1. The cytoplasm of eukaryotic cells includes everything inside the plasma membrane and external to the nucleus.

2. The chemical characteristics of the cytoplasm of eukaryotic cells resemble those of the cytoplasm of prokaryotic cells.

3. Eukaryotic cytoplasm has a cytoskeleton and exhibits cytoplasmic streaming.

Ribosomes (pp. 101–102)

1. 80S ribosomes are found in the cytoplasm or attached to the rough endoplasmic reticulum.

Organelles (pp. 102–106)

1. Organelles are specialized membrane-enclosed structures in the cytoplasm of eukaryotic cells.

2. The nucleus, which contains DNA in the form of chromosomes, is the most characteristic eukaryotic organelle.

3. The nuclear envelope is connected to a system of membranes in the cytoplasm called the endoplasmic reticulum (ER).

4. The ER provides a surface for chemical reactions, serves as a transporting network, and stores synthesized molecules. Protein synthesis and transport occur on rough ER; lipid synthesis occurs on smooth ER.

5. The Golgi complex consists of flattened sacs called cisterns. It functions in membrane formation and protein secretion.

6. Lysosomes are formed from Golgi complexes. They store digestive enzymes.

7. Vacuoles are membrane-enclosed cavities derived from the Golgi complex or endocytosis. They are usually found in plant cells that store various substances, increase cell size, and provide rigidity to leaves and stems.

8. Mitochondria are the primary sites of ATP production. They contain 70S ribosomes and DNA, and they multiply by binary fission.

9. Chloroplasts contain chlorophyll and enzymes for photosynthesis. Like mitochondria, they contain 70S ribosomes and DNA and multiply by binary fission.

10. A variety of organic compounds are oxidized in peroxisomes. Catalase in peroxisomes destroys H_2O_2.

11. The centrosome consists of the pericentriolar material and centrioles. Centrioles are 9 triplet microtubules involved in formation of the mitotic spindle and microtubules.

The Evolution of Eukaryotes (p. 106)

1. According to the endosymbiotic theory, eukaryotic cells evolved from symbiotic prokaryotes living inside other prokaryotic cells.

THE LOOP

Methods of action of antibiotics, discussed in Chapter 20, can be included here to illustrate differences between prokaryotic and eukaryotic cells, as well as provide clinical applications to cell structure.

ANSWERS

Review

1.

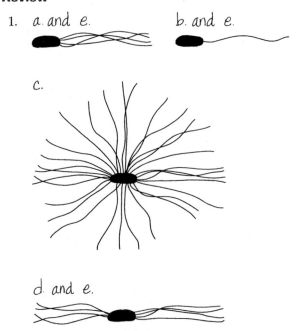

2. a. sporogenesis
   b. certain adverse environmental conditions
   c. germination
   d. favorable growth conditions

3.

4. a. 4   d. 3   g. 2, 8
   b. 6   e. 1, 5   h. 7
   c. 1   f. 3, 9

5. An endospore is called a resting structure because it is a method by which one cell "rests," or survives, as opposed to growing and reproducing. The protective endospore wall allows a bacterium to withstand adverse conditions in the environment.

6. a. Both allow materials to cross the plasma membrane from a high concentration to a low concentration without expending energy. Facilitated diffusion requires carrier proteins.
   b. Both require enzymes to move materials across the plasma membrane. In active transport, energy is expended.
   c. Both move materials across the plasma membrane with an expenditure of energy. In group translocation, the substrate is changed after it crosses the membrane.

7. a. Diagram (a) refers to a gram-positive bacterium because the lipopolysaccharide–phospholipids–lipoprotein layer is absent.
   b. The gram-negative bacterium initially retains the violet stain, but it is released when the outer membrane is dissolved by the decolorizing agent. After the dye–iodine complex enters, it becomes trapped by the peptidoglycan of gram-positive cells.
   c. The outer layer of the gram-negative cells prevents penicillin from entering the cells.
   d. Essential molecules diffuse through the gram-positive wall. Porins and specific channel proteins in the gram-negative outer membrane allow passage of small water-soluble molecules.
   e. Gram-negative.

8. An extracellular enzyme (amylase) hydrolyzes starch into disaccharides (maltose) and monosaccharides (glucose). A carrier enzyme (maltase) hydrolyzes maltose and moves one glucose into the cell. Glucose can be transported by group translocation as glucose-6-phosphate.

9. a. 3   d. 1   g. 5
   b. 4   e. 6
   c. 7   f. 2

Critical Thinking

1. Eukaryotic cells must be large enough to hold a nucleus and a mitochondrion (the minimum number of organelles). Prokaryotic cells contain molecules needed to carry on metabolic activities, but do not contain membrane-enclosed organelles, which require extra space.

2. *Micromonas* has a nucleus, one mitochondrion, one chloroplast, one Golgi complex, and one flagellum.

3. Like bacteria, archaea lack organelles. However, archaea also lack peptidoglycan cell walls. A more complete list of differences is in Table 10.1.

4. The large size of the organism caused the misidentification. Electron microscopy would reveal that this is a prokaryotic cell; chemical analysis of the cell wall would reveal peptidoglycan.

5. Water would passively leave the cell in a hypertonic environment. If a cell pumps K^+ in, water will follow, thus preventing plasmolysis.

Clinical Applications

1. Cell death released cell wall fragments. The gram-negative cell wall is responsible for the symptoms of septic shock.

2. The endospores allow survival in the presence of oxygen and during heating.

3. *Enterobacter, Pseudomonas,* and *Klebsiella* are gram-negative. Their cell walls contain lipid A endotoxin.

4. The bacteria were adhering to the inside of the pipes as a biofilm. Fimbriae and the glycocalyx allow the bacteria to adhere.

5. Bacterial endospores allow these bacteria to survive in products on store shelves. *B. thuringiensis* is sold as an insecticide, and *B. subtilis* as a fungicide.

CASE STUDY: *Coxiella burnetii*

Background

The life cycle of *Coxiella burnetii* wasn't described until 1981, although the bacterium had been recognized more than 40 years earlier. Observations made by many researchers were finally assembled to show that this bacterium has a more complex life cycle than most. See if you can propose a life cycle for this bacterium from the information provided.

Coccoid and bacillary forms of *Coxiella burnetii* were first described in 1938. Subsequently, other researchers described round particles that passed through bacteriological filters (0.45 μm) and were capable of infecting guinea pig cells.

In 1981, electron microscopy studies of *Coxiella* revealed a large cell variant (LCV) and a small cell variant (SCV). The LCV has inner and outer membranes separated by a periplasm containing little peptidoglycan. The SCV lacks a periplasm and has a large peptidoglycan layer. LCVs develop a dense area in the periplasm at one end of the cell when nutrients are depleted or the pH increases. This area contains DNA and ribosomes.

In one study, suspensions of *C. burnetii* were put in distilled water, exposed to sonication (high-frequency vibration used to disrupt cells), and incubated at 45°C for 3 hr. Only SCVs were present after this treatment. *Coxiella* undergo binary fission in a host cell phagolysozyme. LCVs metabolize and divide more rapidly than SCVs.

Questions

1. Propose a life cycle for *Coxiella*.

2. Why do *Coxiella* show variable Gram stain results—that is, they may stain gram-positive or gram-negative? Should they be classified as gram-positive or gram-negative?

3. What disease does *C. burnetii* cause? Why can this disease be transmitted by airborne routes while other (closely related) rickettsia require insects and ticks for transmission to humans?

The Solution

1.

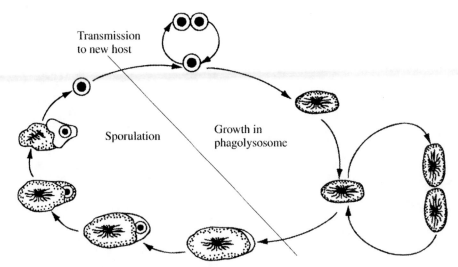

2. LCVs will stain gram-negative; SCVs, gram-positive. *Coxiella* is classified as gram-negative because the ultrastructure and chemical composition of the wall are gram-negative.

3. Q fever; SCVs (spores) allow this organism to survive outside a host.

5 Microbial Metabolism

LEARNING OBJECTIVES	CHECK YOUR UNDERSTANDING
5-1 Define *metabolism*, and describe the fundamental differences between anabolism and catabolism.	Distinguish catabolism from anabolism.
5-2 Identify the role of ATP as an intermediate between catabolism and anabolism.	How is ATP an intermediate between catabolism and anabolism?
5-3 Identify the components of an enzyme.	What is a coenzyme?
5-4 Describe the mechanism of enzymatic action.	Why is enzyme specificity important?
5-5 List the factors that influence enzymatic activity.	What happens to an enzyme below its optimal temperature? Above its optimal temperature?
5-6 Distinguish competitive and noncompetitive inhibition.	Why is feedback inhibition noncompetitive inhibition?
5-7 Define *ribozyme*.	What is a ribozyme?
5-8 Explain the term *oxidiation-reduction*.	Why is glucose such an important molecule for organisms?
5-9 List and provide examples of three phosphorylation reactions that generate ATP.	Outline the three ways that ATP is generated.
5-10 Explain the overall function of metabolic pathways.	What is the purpose of metabolic pathways?
5-11 Describe the chemical reactions of glycolysis.	What happens during the preparatory and energy-conserving stages of glycolysis?
5-12 Identify the functions of the pentose phosphate and Entner-Doudoroff pathways.	What is the value of the pentose phosphate and Entner-Doudoroff pathways if they produce only one ATP molecule?
5-13 Explain the products of the Krebs cycle.	What are the principal products of the Krebs cycle?
5-14 Describe the chemiosmotic model for ATP generation.	How do carrier molecules function in the electron transport chain?
5-15 Compare and contrast aerobic and anaerobic respiration.	Compare the energy yield (ATP) of aerobic and anaerobic respiration.
5-16 Describe the chemical reactions of, and list some products of, fermentation.	List four compounds that can be made from pyruvic acid by an organism that uses fermentation.
5-17 Describe how lipids and proteins undergo catabolism.	What are the end-products of lipid and protein catabolism?
5-18 Provide two examples of the use of biochemical tests to identify bacteria in the laboratory.	On what biochemical basis are *Pseudomonas* and *Escherichia* differentiated?

5-19 Compare and contrast cyclic photophosphorylation.	How is photosynthesis important to catabolism?
5-20 Compare and contrast the light-dependent and light-independent reactions of photosynthesis.	What is made during the light-dependent reactions?
5-21 Compare and contrast oxidative phosphorylation and photophosphorylation.	How are oxidative phosphorylation and photophosphorylation similar?
5-22 Write a sentence to summarize energy production in cells.	Summarize how oxidation enables organisms to get energy from glucose, sulfur, or sunlight.
5-23 Categorize the various nutritional patterns among organisms according to carbon source and mechanisms of carbohydrate catabolism and ATP generation.	Almost all medically important microbes belong to which of the four aforementioned groups?
5-24 Describe the major types of anabolism and their relationship to catabolism.	Where do amino acids required for protein synthesis come from?
5-25 Define *amphibolic pathways.*	Summarize the integration of metabolic pathways using peptidoglycan synthesis as an example.

NEW IN THIS EDITION

- Expanded discussion of biochemical testing to identify bacteria.
- A new Clinical Focus (*MMWR*) box illustrating the use of biochemical tests to identify slow-growing mycobacteria.

CHAPTER SUMMARY

Catabolic and Anabolic Reactions (p. 114)

1. The sum of all chemical reactions within a living organism is known as metabolism.
2. Catabolism refers to chemical reactions that result in the breakdown of more complex organic molecules into simpler substances. Catabolic reactions usually release energy.
3. Anabolism refers to chemical reactions in which simpler substances are combined to form more complex molecules. Anabolic reactions usually require energy.
4. The energy of catabolic reactions is used to drive anabolic reactions.
5. The energy for chemical reactions is stored in ATP.

Enzymes (pp. 115–121)

1. Enzymes are proteins, produced by living cells, that catalyze chemical reactions by lowering the activation energy.
2. Enzymes are generally globular proteins with characteristic three-dimensional shapes.
3. Enzymes are efficient, can operate at relatively low temperatures, and are subject to various cellular controls.

Naming Enzymes (p. 116)

4. Enzyme names usually end in *-ase.*
5. The six classes of enzymes are defined on the basis of the types of reactions they catalyze.

Enzyme Components (pp. 116–117)

6. Most enzymes are holoenzymes, consisting of a protein portion (apoenzyme) and a nonprotein portion (cofactor).

7. The cofactor can be a metal ion (iron, copper, magnesium, manganese, zinc, calcium, or cobalt) or a complex organic molecule known as a coenzyme (NAD^+, $NADP^+$, FMN, FAD, or coenzyme A).

The Mechanism of Enzymatic Action (pp. 117–118)

8. When an enzyme and substrate combine, the substrate is transformed, and the enzyme is recovered.

9. Enzymes are characterized by specificity, which is a function of their active sites.

Factors Influencing Enzymatic Activity (pp. 118–120)

10. At high temperatures, enzymes undergo denaturation and lose their catalytic properties; at low temperatures, the reaction rate decreases.

11. The pH at which enzymatic activity is maximal is known as the optimum pH.

12. Enzymatic activity increases as substrate concentration increases until the enzymes are saturated.

13. Competitive inhibitors compete with the normal substrate for the active site of the enzyme. Noncompetitive inhibitors act on other parts of the apoenzyme or on the cofactor and decrease the enzyme's ability to combine with the normal substrate.

Feedback Inhibition (pp. 120–121)

14. Feedback inhibition occurs when the end-product of a metabolic pathway inhibits an enzyme's activity near the start of the pathway.

Ribozymes (p. 121)

15. Ribozymes are enzymatic RNA molecules that cut and splice RNA in eukaryotic cells.

Energy Production (pp. 121–123)

Oxidation-Reduction Reactions (p. 122)

1. Oxidation is the removal of one or more electrons from a substrate. Protons (H^+) are often removed with the electrons.

2. Reduction of a substrate refers to its gain of one or more electrons.

3. Each time a substance is oxidized, another is simultaneously reduced.

4. NAD^+ is the oxidized form; NADH is the reduced form.

5. Glucose is a reduced molecule; energy is released during a cell's oxidation of glucose.

The Generation of ATP (pp. 122–123)

6. Energy released during certain metabolic reactions can be trapped to form ATP from ADP and Ⓟ (phosphate). Addition of a Ⓟ to a molecule is called phosphorylation.

7. During substrate-level phosphorylation, a high-energy Ⓟ from an intermediate in catabolism is added to ADP.

8. During oxidative phosphorylation, energy is released as electrons are passed to a series of electron acceptors (an electron transport chain) and finally to O_2 or another inorganic compound.

9. During photophosphorylation, energy from light is trapped by chlorophyll, and electrons are passed through a series of electron acceptors. The electron transfer releases energy used for the synthesis of ATP.

Metabolic Pathways of Energy Production (p. 123)

10. A series of enzymatically catalyzed chemical reactions called metabolic pathways store energy in and release energy from organic molecules.

Carbohydrate Catabolism (pp. 124–135)

1. Most of a cell's energy is produced from the oxidation of carbohydrates.
2. Glucose is the most commonly used carbohydrate.
3. The two major types of glucose catabolism are respiration, in which glucose is completely broken down, and fermentation, in which it is partially broken down.

Glycolysis (p. 124)

4. The most common pathway for the oxidation of glucose is glycolysis. Pyruvic acid is the end-product.
5. Two ATP and two NADH molecules are produced from one glucose molecule.

Alternatives to Glycolysis (pp. 125, 127)

6. The pentose phosphate pathway is used to metabolize five-carbon sugars; one ATP and 12 NADPH molecules are produced from one glucose molecule.
7. The Entner-Doudoroff pathway yields one ATP and two NADPH molecules from one glucose molecule.

Cellular Respiration (pp. 127–132)

8. During respiration, organic molecules are oxidized. Energy is generated from the electron transport chain.
9. In aerobic respiration, O_2 functions as the final electron acceptor.
10. In anaerobic respiration, the final electron acceptor is usually an inorganic molecule other than O_2.

Aerobic Respiration (pp. 127–132)
The Krebs Cycle (pp. 127–129)
11. Decarboxylation of pyruvic acid produces one CO_2 molecule and one acetyl group.
12. Two-carbon acetyl groups are oxidized in the Krebs cycle. Electrons are picked up by NAD^+ and FAD for the electron transport chain.
13. From one molecule of glucose, oxidation produces six molecules of NADH, two molecules of $FADH_2$, and two molecules of ATP.
14. Decarboxylation produces six molecules of CO_2.

The Electron Transport Chain (System) (pp. 129–130)
15. Electrons are brought to the electron transport chain by NADH.
16. The electron transport chain consists of carriers, including flavoproteins, cytochromes, and ubiquinones.

The Chemiosmotic Mechanism of ATP Generation (pp. 130–131)
17. Protons being pumped across the membrane generate a proton motive force as electrons move through a series of acceptors or carriers.
18. Energy produced from movement of the protons back across the membrane is used by ATP synthase to make ATP from ADP and Ⓟ.
19. In eukaryotes, electron carriers are located in the inner mitochondrial membrane; in prokaryotes, electron carriers are in the plasma membrane.

A Summary of Aerobic Respiration (pp. 131–132)

20. In aerobic prokaryotes, 38 ATP molecules can be produced from complete oxidation of a glucose molecule in glycolysis, the Krebs cycle, and the electron transport chain.
21. In eukaryotes, 36 ATP molecules are produced from complete oxidation of a glucose molecule.

Anaerobic Respiration (p. 132)

22. The final electron acceptors in anaerobic respiration include NO_3^-, SO_4^{2-}, and CO_3^{2-}.
23. The total ATP yield is less than in aerobic respiration because only part of the Krebs cycle operates under anaerobic conditions.

Fermentation (pp. 132–135)

24. Fermentation releases energy from sugars or other organic molecules by oxidation.
25. O_2 is not required in fermentation.
26. Two ATP molecules are produced by substrate-level phosphorylation.
27. Electrons removed from the substrate reduce NAD^+.
28. The final electron acceptor is an organic molecule.
29. In lactic acid fermentation, pyruvic acid is reduced by NADH to lactic acid.
30. In alcohol fermentation, acetaldehyde is reduced by NADH to produce ethanol.
31. Heterolactic fermenters can use the pentose phosphate pathway to produce lactic acid and ethanol.

Lipid and Protein Catabolism (pp. 136–137)

1. Lipases hydrolyze lipids into glycerol and fatty acids.
2. Fatty acids and other hydrocarbons are catabolized by beta-oxidation.
3. Catabolic products can be further broken down in glycolysis and the Krebs cycle.
4. Before amino acids can be catabolized, they must be converted to various substances that enter the Krebs cycle.
5. Transamination, decarboxylation, and dehydrogenation reactions convert the amino acids to be catabolized.

Biochemical Tests and Bacterial Identification (pp. 137–139)

1. Bacteria and yeast can be identified by detecting action of their enzymes.
2. Fermentation tests are used to determine whether an organism can ferment a carbohydrate to produce acid and gas.

Photosynthesis (p. 140)

1. Photosynthesis is the conversion of light energy from the sun into chemical energy; the chemical energy is used for carbon fixation.

The Light-Dependent Reactions: Photophosphorylation (p. 140)

2. Chlorophyll *a* is used by green plants, algae, and cyanobacteria; it is found in thylakoid membranes.
3. Electrons from chlorophyll pass through an electron transport chain, from which ATP is produced by chemiosmosis.

4. In cyclic photophosphorylation, the electrons return to the chlorophyll.

5. In noncyclic photophosphorylation, the electrons are used to reduce $NADP^+$. The electrons from H_2O or H_2S replace those lost from chlorophyll.

6. When H_2O is oxidized by green plants, algae, and cyanobacteria, O_2 is produced; when H_2S is oxidized by the sulfur bacteria, S granules are produced.

The Light-Independent Reactions: The Calvin-Benson Cycle (p. 140)

7. CO_2 is used to synthesize sugars in the Calvin-Benson cycle.

A Summary of Energy Production Mechanisms (p. 141)

1. Sunlight is converted to chemical energy in oxidation-reduction reactions carried on by phototrophs. Chemotrophs can use this chemical energy.

2. In oxidation-reduction reactions, energy is derived from the transfer of electrons.

3. To produce energy, a cell needs an electron donor (organic or inorganic), a system of electron carriers, and a final electron acceptor (organic or inorganic).

Metabolic Diversity among Organisms (pp. 142–145)

1. Photoautotrophs obtain energy by photophosphorylation and fix carbon from CO_2 via the Calvin-Benson cycle to synthesize organic compounds.

2. Cyanobacteria are oxygenic phototrophs. Green bacteria and purple bacteria are anoxygenic phototrophs.

3. Photoheterotrophs use light as an energy source and an organic compound for their carbon source and electron donor.

4. Chemoautotrophs use inorganic compounds as their energy source and carbon dioxide as their carbon source.

5. Chemoheterotrophs use complex organic molecules as their carbon and energy sources.

Metabolic Pathways of Energy Use (pp. 146–147)

Polysaccharide Biosynthesis (p. 146)

1. Glycogen is formed from ADPG.

2. UDPNAc is the starting material for the biosynthesis of peptidoglycan.

Lipid Biosynthesis (p. 146)

3. Lipids are synthesized from fatty acids and glycerol.

4. Glycerol is derived from dihydroxyacetone phosphate, and fatty acids are built from acetyl CoA.

Amino Acid and Protein Biosynthesis (pp. 146–147)

5. Amino acids are required for protein biosynthesis.

6. All amino acids can be synthesized either directly or indirectly from intermediates of carbohydrate metabolism, particularly from the Krebs cycle.

Purine and Pyrimidine Biosynthesis (p. 147)

7. The sugars composing nucleotides are derived from either the pentose phosphate pathway or the Entner-Doudoroff pathway.

8. Carbon and nitrogen atoms from certain amino acids form the backbones of the purines and pyrimidines.

The Integration of Metabolism (pp. 147, 149–150)

1. Anabolic and catabolic reactions are integrated through a group of common intermediates.

2. Such integrated metabolic pathways are referred to as amphibolic pathways

THE LOOP

Complete metabolic pathways are provided in Appendix A. The boxes in Chapter 1, Chapter 2, Chapter 11, Chapter 27, and Chapter 28 illustrate applications of microbial metabolism in bioremediation and industry. Chapters 27 and 28 can be included with the study of Chapter 5 to provide students with applications of metabolism.

ANSWERS

Review

1. (a) is the Calvin-Benson cycle, (b) is glycolysis, and (c) is the Krebs cycle.

   a. Glycerol is catabolized by pathway (b) as dihydroxyacetone phosphate. Fatty acids by pathway (c) as acetyl groups.

   b. In pathway (c) at α-ketoglutaric acid.

   c. Glyceraldehyde-3-phosphate from the Calvin-Benson cycle enters glycolysis. Pyruvic acid from glycolysis is decarboxylated to produce acetyl for the Krebs cycle.

   d. In (a), between glucose and glyceraldehyde-3-phosphate.

   e. The conversion of pyruvic acid to acetyl, isocitric acid to α-ketoglutaric acid, and α-ketoglutaric acid to succinyl~CoA.

   f. By pathway (c) as acetyl groups.

   g.

	Uses	Produces
Calvin-Benson cycle	6 NADPH	
Glycolysis		2 NADH
Pyruvic acid $\longrightarrow$ acetyl		1 NADH
Isocitric acid $\longrightarrow$ α-ketoglutaric acid		1 NADH
α-ketoglutaric acid $\longrightarrow$ Succinyl~CoA		1 NADH
Succinic acid $\longrightarrow$ Fumaric acid		1 FADH$_2$
Malic acid $\longrightarrow$ Oxaloacetic acid		1 NADH

   h. Dihydroxyacetone phosphate; acetyl; oxaloacetic acid; α-ketoglutaric acid.

2.

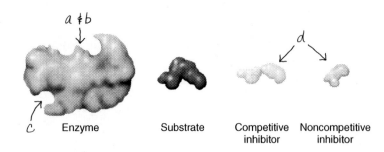

Enzyme   Substrate   Competitive   Noncompetitive
                             inhibitor   inhibitor

e. When the enzyme and substrate combine, the substrate molecule will be transformed.

When the competitive inhibitor binds to the enzyme, the enzyme will not be able to bind with the substrate.

When the noncompetitive inhibitor binds to the enzyme, the active site of the enzyme will be changed so the enzyme cannot bind with the substrate.

3.

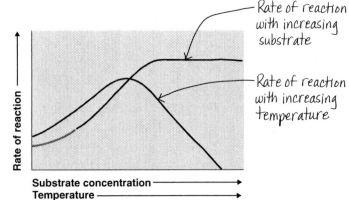

4. a. Oxidation-reduction: A coupled reaction in which one substance loses electrons and another gains electrons.

    b. The final electron acceptor in aerobic respiration is molecular oxygen; in anaerobic respiration, it is another inorganic molecule.

    c. In cyclic photophosphorylation, electrons are returned to chlorophyll. In noncyclic photophosphorylation, chlorophyll receives electrons from hydrogen atoms.

5. a. Photophosphorylation

    b. Oxidative phosphorylation

    c. Substrate-level phosphorylation

6. Oxidation

7. a. CO_2 d. Light   g. Organic molecules

    b. Light   e. CO_2 h. Organic molecules

    c. Organic molecules   f. Inorganic molecules

8. Protons are pumped from one side of the membrane to the others; transfer of protons back across the membrane generates ATP. (a) Outer portion is acidic and (b) has a positive electrical charge. (c) Energy-conserving sites are the three loci where protons are pumped out. (d) Kinetic energy is realized at ATP synthase.

9. NAD^+ is needed to pick up more electrons. NADH is usually reoxidized in respiration. NADH can be reoxidized in fermentation.

Critical Thinking

1. *Streptococcus* is only capable of fermentation, which yields two molecules of ATP for each molecule of glucose consumed. Most of the energy that cells obtain from catabolism is from respiration.

2. The rate at which an enzyme converts substrate to product is partly a function of initial concentration of substrate. The more substrate molecules available, the more frequently they access the active site of the enzyme. The reaction proceeds at a linear rate (black). When the concentration of substrate is high enough that all enzyme molecules have their active sites engaged, the reaction rate will remain constant. When the enzyme becomes saturated with competitive inhibitor, the reaction will completely stop (red).

3. Carbohydrate catabolism:

    a. Oxidation of glucose (glycolysis, Krebs, aerobic ETC).

    b. Following the Calvin-Benson cycle: Oxidation of glucose (glycolysis, Krebs, aerobic ETC).

    c. Following the Calvin-Benson cycle: Oxidation of glucose (glycolysis, Krebs, anaerobic ETC).

    Energy production. All three use chemiosmotic mechanisms. In addition to oxidative phosphorylation, *Spirulina* and *Ectothiorhodospira* use photophosphorylation.

4. Glucose = 38 ATP

    Butterfat = 88 ATP. Glycerol goes into glycolysis to produce 1 ATP and 1 NADH. Six acetyl groups are produced from each of the 12-carbon chains by beta-oxidation. Each acetyl can be used to produce 14 ATPs in the Krebs cycle and electron transport chain.

5. Two electrons removed from As^{3+} are picked up by NAD^+ for use in the electron transport chain. *Thiobacillus* could be used to remove arsenic from industrial wastewater and groundwater.

Clincial Applications

1. X factor is necessary to synthesize cytochromes. V factor is used as an electron acceptor in oxidation reactions.

2. The drug ddC is missing an O atom on C_3, so it cannot be joined to the phosphate group of another nucleotide.

3. Live bacteria or whole bacterial cells are not being injected. Enzymes are specific for their substrates, so streptokinase will react only with its substrate, fibrin.

CASE STUDY: THE PASTEUR EFFECT

Background

In 1861, Louis Pasteur observed that when yeasts grow in a sugar-and-protein medium completely free of air, they ferment vigorously, and for every gram of yeast that forms, 60 to 80 grams of sugar disappear. If the experiment is carried out in the presence of air, for 1 gram of yeast that forms, only 4 to 10 grams of sugar are removed. The yeasts again ferment if transferred to a sugar-containing medium absent air.

When the experiment is repeated with a protein medium, the yeasts grow only in the presence of oxygen. Pasteur concluded that the yeasts can take oxygen from air, and in the absence of air, the yeasts take oxygen from the sugar.

Pasteur applied quantitative methods to his studies of fermentation and was the first to report on organisms that could live and reproduce in the absence of oxygen. His conclusion was, however, incorrect. These different behaviors of yeasts are known today as the Pasteur effect.

Questions

1. Explain the three yeast behaviors based on modern concepts of microbial metabolism.
2. What was incorrect about Pasteur's conclusion?

The Solution

1. The yeasts are able to grow anaerobically if a fermentable sugar is available. Fermentation consumes more sugar than respiration to produce the same amount of energy.
2. Pasteur assumed yeasts were taking oxygen from the sugar.

6 Microbial Growth

LEARNING OBJECTIVES

6-1 Classify microbes into five groups on the basis of preferred temperature range.

6-2 Identify how and why the pH of culture media is controlled.

6-3 Explain the importance of osmotic pressure to microbial growth.

6-4 Name a use for each of the four elements (carbon, nitrogen, sulfur, and phosphorus) needed in large amounts for microbial growth.

6-5 Explain how microbes are classified on the basis of oxygen requirements.

6-6 Identify ways in which aerobes avoid damage by toxic forms of oxygen.

6-7 Describe the formation of biofilms and their potential for causing infection.

6-8 Distinguish chemically defined and complex media.

6-9 Justify the use of each of the following: anaerobic techniques, living host cells, candle jars, selective and differential media, enrichment medium.

6-10 Differentiate biosafety levels 1, 2, 3, and 4.

6-11 Define *colony*.

6-12 Describe how pure cultures can be isolated by using the streak plate method.

6-13 Explain how microorganisms are preserved by deep-freezing and lyophilization (freeze-drying).

CHECK YOUR UNDERSTANDING

Why are hyperthermophiles that grow at temperatures above 100°C seemingly limited to oceanic depths?

Other than controlling acidity, what is an advantage to using phosphate salt buffers in growth media?

Why might primitive civilizations have used food preservation techniques that rely on osmotic pressure?

If bacterial cells were given a sulfur source containing radioactive sulfur (^{35}S) in their culture media, in what molecules would the ^{35}S be found in the cells?

How would one determine whether a microbe is a strict anaerobe?

Oxygen is so pervasive in the environment that it would be very difficult for a microbe to always avoid physical contact. What, therefore, is the most obvious way for a microbe to avoid damage?

Identify a way in which pathogens find it advantageous to form biofilms.

Could humans exist on chemically defined media, at least under laboratory conditions?

Could Louis Pasteur, in the 1800s, have grown rabies viruses in cell culture instead of in living animals?

What BSL is your laboratory?

Can you think of any reason why a colony does not grow to an infinite size, or at least fill the confines of the Petri plate?

Could a pure culture of bacteria be obtained by the streak plate method if there were only one desired microbe in a bacterial suspension of billions?

If the Space Station in Earth orbit suddenly ruptured, the humans on board would die instantly from cold and the vacuum of space. Would all the bacteria in the capsule also be killed?

6-14 Define *bacterial growth*, including *binary fission*.	Can a complex organism, such as a beetle, divide by binary fission?
6-15 Compare the phases of microbial growth, and describe their relation to generation time.	If two mice started a family within a fixed enclosure, with a fixed food supply, would the population curve be the same as a bacterial growth curve?
6-16 Explain four direct methods of measuring cell growth.	Why is it difficult to measure realistically the growth of a filamentous mold isolate by the plate count method?
6-17 Differentiate direct and indirect methods of measuring cell growth.	Direct methods usually require an incubation time for a colony. Why is this not always feasible for analysis of foods?
6-18 Explain three indirect methods of measuring cell growth.	If there is no good method for analyzing a product for its vitamin content, what is a feasible method of determining the vitamin content?

NEW IN THIS EDITION

- A significantly updated and expanded discussion of biofilms (which previously appeared in Chapter 27).
- A discussion of biosafety levels with a figure illustrating Biosafety Level 4
- A new Clinical Focus (*MMWR*) box illustrating the role of biofilms in causing nosocomial infections

CHAPTER SUMMARY

The Requirements for Growth (pp. 157–163)

1. The growth of a population is an increase in the number of cells.
2. The requirements for microbial growth are both physical and chemical.

Physical Requirements (pp. 157–160)

3. On the basis of preferred temperature ranges, microbes are classified as psychrophiles (cold-loving), mesophiles (moderate-temperature–loving), and thermophiles (heat-loving).
4. The minimum growth temperature is the lowest temperature at which a species will grow, the optimum growth temperature is the temperature at which it grows best, and the maximum growth temperature is the highest temperature at which growth is possible.
5. Most bacteria grow best at a pH value between 6.5 and 7.5.
6. In a hypertonic solution, most microbes undergo plasmolysis; halophiles can tolerate high salt concentrations.

Chemical Requirements (pp. 160–162)

7. All organisms require a carbon source; chemoheterotrophs use an organic molecule, and autotrophs typically use carbon dioxide.
8. Nitrogen is needed for protein and nucleic acid synthesis. Nitrogen can be obtained from the decomposition of proteins or from NH_4^+ or NO_3^-; a few bacteria are capable of nitrogen (N_2) fixation.
9. On the basis of oxygen requirements, organisms are classified as obligate aerobes, facultative anaerobes, obligate anaerobes, aerotolerant anaerobes, and microaerophiles.
10. Aerobes, facultative anaerobes, and aerotolerant anaerobes must have the enzymes superoxide dismutase ($2\ O_2^- + 2\ H^+ \longrightarrow O_2 + H_2O_2$) and either catalase ($2\ H_2O_2 \longrightarrow 2\ H_2O + O_2$) or peroxidase ($H_2O_2 + 2\ H^+ \longrightarrow 2\ H_2O$).

11. Other chemicals required for microbial growth include sulfur, phosphorus, trace elements, and, for some microorganisms, organic growth factors.

Biofilms (pp. 162–163)

1. Microbes adhere to surfaces and accumulate as biofilms on solid surfaces in contact with water.
2. Biofilms form on teeth, contact lenses, and catheters.
3. Microbes in biofilms are more resistant to antibiotics than are free swimming microbes.

Culture Media (pp. 164–169)

1. A culture medium is any material prepared for the growth of bacteria in a laboratory.
2. Microbes that grow and multiply in or on a culture medium are known as a culture.
3. Agar is a common solidifying agent for a culture medium.

Chemically Defined Media (p. 165)

4. A chemically defined medium is one in which the exact chemical composition is known.

Complex Media (p. 165)

5. A complex medium is one in which the exact chemical composition varies slightly from batch to batch.

Anaerobic Growth Media and Methods (pp. 166–167)

6. Reducing media chemically remove molecular oxygen (O_2) that might interfere with the growth of anaerobes.
7. Petri plates can be incubated in an anaerobic jar, anaerobic chamber, or OxyPlate.

Special Culture Techniques (pp. 167–168)

8. Some parasitic and fastidious bacteria must be cultured in living animals or in cell cultures.
9. CO_2 incubators or candle jars are used to grow bacteria that require an increased CO_2 concentration.
10. Procedures and equipment to minimize exposure to pathogenic microorganisms are designated as biosafety levels 1 through 4.

Selective and Differential Media (pp. 168–169)

11. By inhibiting unwanted organisms with salts, dyes, or other chemicals, selective media allow growth of only the desired microbes.
12. Differential media are used to distinguish different organisms.

Enrichment Culture (p. 169)

13. An enrichment culture is used to encourage the growth of a particular microorganism in a mixed culture.

Obtaining Pure Cultures (pp. 169–170)

1. A colony is a visible mass of microbial cells that theoretically arose from one cell.
2. Pure cultures are usually obtained by the streak plate method.

Preserving Bacterial Cultures (p. 170)

1. Microbes can be preserved for long periods of time by deep-freezing or lyophilization (freeze-drying).

The Growth of Bacterial Cultures (pp. 171–179)

Bacterial Division (p. 171)

1. The normal reproductive method of bacteria is binary fission, in which a single cell divides into two identical cells.
2. Some bacteria reproduce by budding, aerial spore formation, or fragmentation.

Generation Time (p. 171)

3. The time required for a cell to divide or a population to double is known as the generation time.

Logarithmic Representation of Bacterial Populations (pp. 171–172)

4. Bacterial division occurs according to a logarithmic progression (two cells, four cells, eight cells, and so on).

Phases of Growth (pp. 172–174)

5. During the lag phase, there is little or no change in the number of cells, but metabolic activity is high.
6. During the log phase, the bacteria multiply at the fastest rate possible under the conditions provided.
7. During the stationary phase, there is an equilibrium between cell division and death.
8. During the death phase, the number of deaths exceeds the number of new cells formed.

Direct Measurement of Microbial Growth (pp. 174–178)

9. A standard plate count reflects the number of viable microbes and assumes that each bacterium grows into a single colony; plate counts are reported as number of colony-forming units (CFU).
10. A plate count may be done by either the pour plate method or the spread plate method.
11. In filtration, bacteria are retained on the surface of a membrane filter and then transferred to a culture medium to grow and subsequently be counted.
12. The most probable number (MPN) method can be used for microbes that will grow in a liquid medium; it is a statistical estimation.
13. In a direct microscopic count, the microbes in a measured volume of a bacterial suspension are counted with the use of a specially designed slide.

Estimating Bacterial Numbers by Indirect Methods (pp. 178–179)

14. A spectrophotometer is used to determine turbidity by measuring the amount of light that passes through a suspension of cells.
15. An indirect way of estimating bacterial numbers is measuring the metabolic activity of the population (for example, acid production or oxygen consumption).
16. For filamentous organisms such as fungi, measuring dry weight is a convenient method of growth measurement.

THE LOOP

Appendix B, "Exponents, Exponential Notation, Logarithms, and Generation Time," is useful here. Bioenhancement with N and P is described in the box in Chapter 2, p. 33. The use of MPN in water quality testing is discussed on p. 175 and Figure 6.19.

ANSWERS

Review

1. In binary fission, the cell elongates and the chromosome replicates. Next, the nuclear material is evenly divided. The plasma membrane invaginates toward the center of the cell. The cell wall thickens and grows inward between the membrane invaginations; two new cells result.

2. **Carbon:** Synthesis of molecules that make up a living cell. **Hydrogen:** Source of electrons and component of organic molecules. **Oxygen:** Component of organic molecules; electron acceptor in aerobes. **Nitrogen:** Component of amino acids. **Phosphorous:** In phospholipids and nucleic acids. **Sulfur:** In some amino acids.

3. a. Catalyzes the breakdown of H_2O_2 to O_2 and H_2O.

   b. H_2O_2; peroxide ion is O_2^{2-}.

   c. Catalyzes the breakdown of H_2O_2;

   $$NADH + H^+ + H_2O_2 \xrightarrow{\text{Peroxidase}} NAD^+ + 2H_2O$$

   d. O_2^-; this anion has one unpaired electron.

   e. Converts superoxide to O_2 and H_2O_2;

   $$2O_2^- + 2H^+ \xrightarrow{\text{Superoxide dismutase}} O_2 + H_2O_2$$

   The enzymes are important in protecting the cell from the strong oxidizing agents, peroxide and superoxide, that form during respiration.

4. Direct methods are those in which the microorganisms are seen and counted. Direct methods are direct microscopic count, plate count, filtration, and most probable number. Growth is inferred by indirect methods: turbidity, metabolic activity, and dry weight.

5. The growth rate of bacteria slows down with decreasing temperatures. Mesophilic bacteria will grow slowly at refrigeration temperatures and will remain dormant in a freezer. Bacteria will not spoil food quickly in a refrigerator.

6.

Number of cells	$\times$	$2^{n \text{ generations}}$	$=$	Total number of cells
6	$\times$	2^7	$=$	768

7. Petroleum can meet the carbon and energy requirements for an oil-degrading bacterium; however, nitrogen and phosphate are usually not available in large quantities. Nitrogen and phosphate are essential for making proteins, phospholipids, nucleic acids, and ATP.

8. A chemically defined medium is one in which the exact chemical composition is known. A complex medium is one in which the exact chemical composition is not known.

9.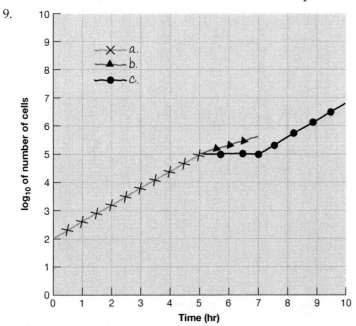

Critical Thinking

1. a. At x, the bacteria began a second lag phase during which they synthesized enzymes required to use the second carbon source.

    b. The first substrate provided the better growth conditions. The slope of the line is steeper, indicating that the bacteria grew faster.

2. In the presence of oxygen, H_2O_2 forms in *Clostridium*. The H_2O_2 accumulates in these catalase-negative cells and kills them. H_2O_2 does not form in *Streptococcus*.

3. Glucose provides a fermentable carbohydrate for chemoheterotrophs. Glucose is the carbon and energy source. Other macronutrients including nitrogen are provided in inorganic compounds in the "minimal salts."

4. a. A
    b. B
    c. A
    d. A
    e. A

Clinical Applications

1. 1.68×10^8. They are the progeny of the original 10.

2. At least 53°C; 60°C was recommended after this study. The bacteria get in the food during preparation and those buried inside do not get hot enough to be killed.

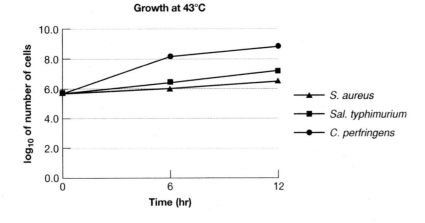

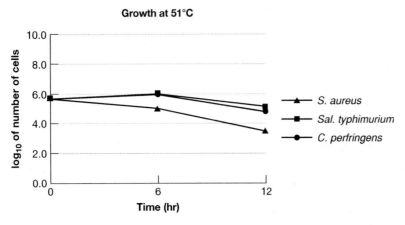

Growth at 53°C

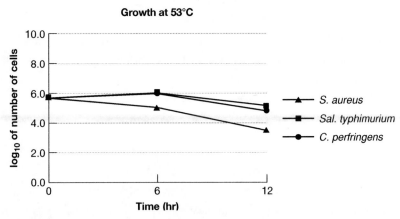

3. Mouthwash 2 decreased bacterial numbers by 89% compared to a 17% decrease for both Mouthwash 1 and 3. All the bacteria probably did not grow. Only those that could grow aerobically on nutrient agar were counted in the experiment.

CASE STUDY: DETERMINING THE EFFECTIVENESS OF A FOOD PRESERVATIVE

Background

To determine whether a newly synthesized chemical might be a useful food preservative, the chemical was tested for its ability to inhibit bacterial growth.

Control

500 ml of cottage cheese was inoculated with 2 ml of a 24-hr culture of *Pseudomonas aeruginosa* and incubated at 25°C. Five hours after inoculation, a standard plate count showed there were 200 bacterial cells/ml in the cottage cheese. After 29 hours at 25°C, there were 1,000,000 cells/ml in the cottage cheese.

Experiment

500 ml of cottage cheese containing the preservative was inoculated with 2 ml of a 24-hr culture of *P. aeruginosa*. After 6 hours of incubation at 25°C, a standard plate count was performed. There were 700 bacterial cells/ml in the cottage cheese. After 38 hours, there were 61,000,000 bacterial cells/ml in the cottage cheese.

Number	Log
1	0.00
2	0.30
5	0.70
6	0.78
24	1.38
32	1.51
200	2.30
700	2.85
1.00×10^6	6.00
6.10×10^6	6.79
6.10×10^7	7.79

Questions

1. Why were plate counts used instead of direct microscopic counts or turbidity measurements?
2. How did the control cottage cheese and the experiment cottage cheese differ? Was this a fair test?
3. Determine the effectiveness of the new food preservative.
4. Does this type of test determine bacteriostatic or bactericidal activity?

The Solution

1. The particles in cottage cheese would interfere with direct counts and turbidity.
2. The new chemical was added to the experiment and was lacking in the control. Yes, this is a fair test.
3. The two tests had the same generation time, proving that the new food preservative was *not* effective.
4. Both. The answer is "bactericidal" when the number of bacteria declines, and "bacteriostatic" if the number of bacteria stays the same.

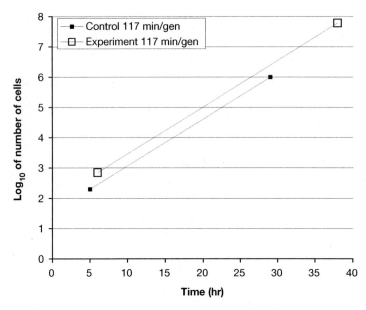

Determining the Effectiveness of a Food Preservative

7 The Control of Microbial Growth

LEARNING OBJECTIVES

CHECK YOUR UNDERSTANDING

7-1 Define the following key terms related to microbial control: *sterilization, disinfection, antisepsis, degerming, sanitization, biocide, germicide, bacteriostasis,* and *asepsis.*

The usual definition of *sterilization* is the removal or destruction of all forms of microbial life; how could there be practical exceptions to this simple definition?

7-2 Describe the patterns of microbial death caused by treatments with microbial control agents.

How is it possible that a solution containing a million bacteria would take longer to sterilize than one containing a half-million bacteria?

7-3 Describe the effects of microbial control agents on cellular structures.

Would a chemical microbial control agent that affected plasma membranes affect humans?

7-4 Compare the effectiveness of moist heat (boiling, autoclaving, pasteurization) and dry heat.

How is microbial growth in canned foods prevented?

7-5 Describe how filtration, low temperatures, high pressure, desiccation, and osmotic pressure suppress microbial growth.

Why would a can of pork take longer to sterilize at a given temperature than a can of soup that also contained pieces of pork?

7-6 Explain how radiation kills cells.

What is the connection between the killing effect of radiation and hydroxyl radical forms of oxygen?

7-7 List the factors related to effective disinfection.

If you wanted to disinfectant a surface contaminated by vomit and a surface contaminated by a sneeze, why would your choice of disinfectant make a difference?

7-8 Interpret the results of use-dilution tests and the disk-diffusion method.

Which is more likely to be used in a medical clinic laboratory, a use-dilution test or a disk-diffusion test?

7-9 Identify the methods of action and preferred uses of chemical disinfectants.

Why is alcohol effective against some viruses and not others?

7-10 Differentiate halogens used as antiseptics from halogens used as disinfectants.

Is Betadine an antiseptic or a disinfectant when it is used on skin?

7-11 Identify the appropriate uses for surface-active agents.

What characteristics make surface-active agents attractive to the dairy industry?

7-12 List the advantages of glutaraldehyde over other chemical disinfectants.

What chemical disinfectants can be considered sporicides?

7-13 Identify chemical sterilizers.

What chemicals are used to sterilize?

7-14 Explain how the type of microbe affects the control of microbial growth.

The presence or absence of endospores has an obvious effect on microbial control, but why are gram-negative bacteria more resistant to chemical biocides than gram-positive bacteria?

NEW IN THIS EDITION

- An updated definition of *sterilization,* qualified in consideration of the existence of prions, which have exceptional resistance to conventional sterilization
- New products and newly approved uses
- A new Clinical Focus (*MMWR*) box illustrating the relationship between improper disinfection and nosocomial infection

CHAPTER SUMMARY

The Terminology of Microbial Control (pp. 185–186)

1. The control of microbial growth can prevent infections and food spoilage.
2. Sterilization is the process of removing or destroying all microbial life on an object.
3. Commercial sterilization is heat treatment of canned foods to destroy *C. botulinum* endospores.
4. Disinfection is the process of reducing or inhibiting microbial growth on a nonliving surface.
5. Antisepsis is the process of reducing or inhibiting microorganisms on living tissue.
6. The suffix *-cide* means to kill; the suffix *-stat* means to inhibit.
7. Sepsis is bacterial contamination.

The Rate of Microbial Death (p. 186)

1. Bacterial populations subjected to heat or antimicrobial chemicals usually die at a constant rate.
2. Such a death curve, when plotted logarithmically, shows this constant death rate as a straight line.
3. The time it takes to kill a microbial population is proportional to the number of microbes.
4. Microbial species and life cycle phases (e.g., endospores) have different susceptibilities to physical and chemical controls.
5. Organic matter may interfere with heat treatments and chemical control agents.
6. Longer exposure to lower heat can produce the same effect as shorter time at higher heat.

Actions of Microbial Control Agents (pp. 186–187)

Alteration of Membrane Permeability (p. 186)

1. The susceptibility of the plasma membrane is due to its lipid and protein components.
2. Certain chemical control agents damage the plasma membrane by altering its permeability.

Damage to Proteins and Nucleic Acids (p. 187)

3. Some microbial control agents damage cellular proteins by breaking hydrogen bonds and covalent bonds.
4. Other agents interfere with DNA and RNA and protein synthesis.

Physical Methods of Microbial Control (pp. 187–194)

Heat (pp. 188–191)

1. Heat is frequently used to kill microorganisms.
2. Moist heat kills microbes by denaturing enzymes.
3. Thermal death point (TDP) is the lowest temperature at which all the microbes in a liquid culture will be killed in 10 minutes.
4. Thermal death time (TDT) is the length of time required to kill all bacteria in a liquid culture at a given temperature.

5. Decimal reduction time (DRT) is the length of time in which 90% of a bacterial population will be killed at a given temperature.

6. Boiling (100°C) kills many vegetative cells and viruses within 10 minutes.

7. Autoclaving (steam under pressure) is the most effective method of moist heat sterilization. The steam must directly contact the material to be sterilized.

8. In HTST pasteurization, a high temperature is used for a short time (72°C for 15 seconds) to destroy pathogens without altering the flavor of the food. Ultra-high-temperature (UHT) treatment (140°C for 4 seconds) is used to sterilize dairy products.

9. Methods of dry heat sterilization include direct flaming, incineration, and hot-air sterilization. Dry heat kills by oxidation.

10. Different methods that produce the same effect (reduction in microbial growth) are called equivalent treatments.

Filtration (p. 191)

11. Filtration is the passage of a liquid or gas through a filter with pores small enough to retain microbes.

12. Microbes can be removed from air by high-efficiency particulate air (HEPA) filters.

13. Membrane filters composed of cellulose esters are commonly used to filter out bacteria, viruses, and even large proteins.

Low Temperatures (pp. 191–192)

14. The effectiveness of low temperatures depends on the particular microorganism and the intensity of the application.

15. Most microorganisms do not reproduce at ordinary refrigerator temperatures (0–7°C).

16. Many microbes survive (but do not grow) at the subzero temperatures used to store foods.

High Pressure (p. 192)

17. High pressure denatures proteins in vegetative cells.

Desiccation (p. 192)

18. In the absence of water, microorganisms cannot grow but can remain viable.

19. Viruses and endospores can resist desiccation.

Osmotic Pressure (p. 192)

20. Microorganisms in high concentrations of salts and sugars undergo plasmolysis.

21. Molds and yeasts are more capable than bacteria of growing in materials with low moisture or high osmotic pressure.

Radiation (pp. 192–194)

22. The effects of radiation depend on its wavelength, intensity, and duration.

23. Ionizing radiation (gamma rays, X rays, and high-energy electron beams) has a high degree of penetration and exerts its effect primarily by ionizing water and forming highly reactive hydroxyl radicals.

24. Ultraviolet (UV) radiation, a form of nonionizing radiation, has a low degree of penetration and causes cell damage by making thymine dimers in DNA that interfere with DNA replication; the most effective germicidal wavelength is 260 nm.

25. Microwaves can kill microbes indirectly as materials get hot.

Chemical Methods of Microbial Control (pp. 195–202)

1. Chemical agents are used on living tissue (as antiseptics) and on inanimate objects (as disinfectants).
2. Few chemical agents achieve sterility.

Principles of Effective Disinfection (p. 195)

3. Careful attention should be paid to the properties and concentration of the disinfectant to be used.
4. The presence of organic matter, degree of contact with microorganisms, and temperature should also be considered.

Evaluating a Disinfectant (p. 195)

5. In the use-dilution test, bacterial survival in the manufacturer's recommended dilution of a disinfectant is determined.
6. Viruses, endospore-forming bacteria, mycobacteria, and fungi can also be used in the use-dilution test.
7. In the disk-diffusion method, a disk of filter paper is soaked with a chemical and placed on an inoculated agar plate; a zone of inhibition indicates effectiveness.

Types of Disinfectants (pp. 195–202)

Phenol and Phenolics (p. 195)

8. Phenolics exert their action by injuring plasma membranes.

Bisphenols (p. 196)

9. Bisphenols such as triclosan (over the counter) and hexachlorophene (prescription) are widely used in household products.

Biguanides (pp. 196–197)

10. Biguanides damage plasma membranes of vegetative cells.

Halogens (p. 197)

11. Some halogens (iodine and chlorine) are used alone or as components of inorganic or organic solutions.
12. Iodine may combine with certain amino acids to inactivate enzymes and other cellular proteins.
13. Iodine is available as a tincture (in solution with alcohol) or as an iodophor (combined with an organic molecule).
14. The germicidal action of chlorine is based on the formation of hypochlorous acid when chlorine is added to water.

Alcohols (pp. 197–198)

15. Alcohols exert their action by denaturing proteins and dissolving lipids.
16. In tinctures, they enhance the effectiveness of other antimicrobial chemicals.
17. Aqueous ethanol (60–95%) and isopropanol are used as disinfectants.

Heavy Metals and Their Compounds (pp. 198–199)

18. Silver, mercury, copper, and zinc are used as germicides.
19. They exert their antimicrobial action through oligodynamic action. When heavy metal ions combine with sulfhydryl (—SH) groups, proteins are denatured.

Surface-Active Agents (p. 199)

20. Surface-active agents decrease the surface tension among molecules of a liquid; soaps and detergents are examples.

21. Soaps have limited germicidal action but assist in removing microorganisms.

22. Acid-anionic detergents are used to clean dairy equipment.

23. Quats are cationic detergents attached to NH_4^+.

24. By disrupting plasma membranes, quats allow cytoplasmic constituents to leak out of the cell.

25. Quats are most effective against gram-positive bacteria.

Chemical Food Preservatives (pp. 199–200)

26. SO_2, sorbic acid, benzoic acid, and propionic acid inhibit fungal metabolism and are used as food preservatives.

27. Nitrate and nitrite salts prevent germination of *C. botulinum* endospores in meats.

Antibiotics (p. 200)

28. Nisin and natamycin are antibiotics used to preserve foods, especially cheese.

Aldehydes (p. 200)

29. Aldehydes such as formaldehyde and glutaraldehyde exert their antimicrobial effect by inactivating proteins.

30. They are among the most effective chemical disinfectants.

Chemical Sterilization (pp. 200–201)

31. Ethylene oxide is the gas most frequently used for sterilization.

32. It penetrates most materials and kills all microorganisms by protein denaturation.

Plasmas (p. 201)

33. Free radicals in plasma gases are used to sterilize plastic instruments.

Supercritical Fluids (pp. 201–202)

34. Supercritical fluids, which have properties of liquid and gas, can sterilize at low temperatures.

Peroxygens and Other Forms of Oxygen (p. 202)

35. Hydrogen peroxide, peracetic acid, benzoyl peroxide, and ozone exert their antimicrobial effect by oxidizing molecules inside cells.

Microbial Characteristics and Microbial Control (pp. 202–205)

1. Gram-negative bacteria are generally more resistant than gram-positive bacteria to disinfectants and antiseptics.

2. Mycobacteria, endospores, and protozoan cysts and oocysts are very resistant to disinfectants and antiseptics.

3. Nonenveloped viruses are generally more resistant than enveloped viruses to disinfectants and antiseptics.

4. Prions are resistant to disinfection and autoclaving.

THE LOOP   ○━━━▭━━

The chemical agents covered in this chapter are antiseptics and disinfectants. Antibiotics and other chemotherapeutic antimicrobials are discussed in Chapter 20.

ANSWERS

Review

1. Autoclave. Because of the high specific heat of water, moist heat is readily transferred to cells.

2. Pasteurization destroys most organisms that cause disease or rapid spoilage of food.

3. Variables that affect determination of the thermal death point:
   - The innate heat resistance of the strain of bacteria.
   - The past history of the culture, whether it was freeze-dried, wetted, etc.
   - The clumping of the cells during the test.
   - The amount of water present.
   - The organic matter present.
   - Media and incubation temperature used to determine viability of the culture after heating.

4. a. The ability of ionizing radiation to break DNA directly. However, because of the high water content of cells, the formation of free radicals (H· and OH·) that break DNA strands is likely to occur.

   b. Formation of thymine dimers.

5.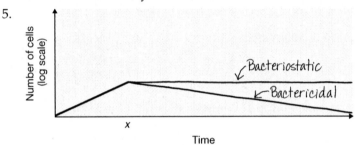

6. All three processes kill microorganisms; however, as moisture and/or temperatures are increased, less time is required to achieve the same result.

7. Salts and sugars create a hypertonic environment. Salts and sugars (as preservatives) do not directly affect cell structures or metabolism; instead, they alter the osmotic pressure. Jams and jellies are preserved with sugar; meats are usually preserved with salt. Molds are more capable of growth in high osmotic pressure than bacteria.

8. Disinfectant B is preferable because it can be diluted more and still be effective.

9. Quaternary ammonium compounds are most effective against gram-positive bacteria. Gram-negative bacteria that were stuck in cracks or around the drain of the tub would not have been washed away when the tub was cleaned. These gram-negative bacteria could survive the washing procedure. Some pseudomonads can grow on quats that have accumulated.

Critical Thinking

1. a. Z.
   b. No. A culture medium would have to be inoculated from the zone of inhibition to determine the presence of viable bacteria.

2. a. Acid-resistant cell wall.
   b. Metabolizes many organic molecules.
   c. Endospores.

3. a. Disinfectant B diluted with distilled water.
   b. Can't tell; the test was done on *Salmonella*.

4. Bactericidal effects of microwave radiation are due to heat.

Clinical Applications

1. a. Hot water does not achieve sterilization, and

   b. There were no check valves to prevent backflow. Also, adapters and other invasive items should be disposable whenever possible.

2. Iodophors are approved for antiseptic uses and not for disinfection.

3. *Serratia* from the environment entered the jar from the air, wash water, or hands. The effectiveness of the quat was reduced by the cotton, and quat-resistant *Serratia* were able to survive. The bacteria were introduced into the methylprednisolone by swabbing the top of the vial. The disinfectant needs to be changed.

CASE STUDY: THE EFFECT OF CLOSURE TYPE ON PREVENTING MICROBIAL CONTAMINATION OF COSMETICS

Bacteria were isolated and identified from containers of shampoo and skin lotion that were in normal use. The containers had different types of closures, and the products had low antimicrobial contents. The shampoos had been in use for 3 weeks and the lotions for 2 weeks.

Data

Organism	Contamination Incidence (%)				
	Shampoo		Skin Lotion		
	Screw	Slit	Screw	Flip	Pump
Citrobacter	2	0	0	0	0
Enterobacter	4	4	2	0	0
Klebsiella	1	1	2	0	0
Pseudomonas	1	1	2	0	0
Serratia	2	0	1	0	0
Gram-neg. rod, nonfermenter	0	0	1	1	0
Gram-neg. rod, fermenter	1	0	0	0	0

Questions

1. How did the bacteria get into the products?

2. Which type of closure is the best? Why do you suppose this closure works best?

3. Why did the researchers test for these bacteria?

The Solution

1. From the hands of the users.

2. The pump prevents the user from dropping bacteria into the opening. The slit/flip closures are also good because the openings are small and easily re-closed.

3. These are all gram-negative rods. Gram-negative bacteria are resistant to the antimicrobial action of detergents, a primary ingredient in the shampoos.

 **Microbial Genetics**

LEARNING OBJECTIVES	CHECK YOUR UNDERSTANDING
8-1 Define *genetics, genome, chromosome, gene, genetic code, genotype, phenotype,* and *genomics.*	Give a clinical application of genomics.
8-2 Describe how DNA serves as genetic information.	Why is the base pairing in DNA important?
8-3 Describe the process of DNA replication.	Describe DNA replication, including the functions of DNA gyrase, DNA ligase, and DNA polymerase.
8-4 Describe protein synthesis, including transcription, RNA processing, and translation.	What is the role of the promoter, terminator, and mRNA in transcription?
8-5 Compare protein synthesis in eukaryotes and prokaryotes.	How does mRNA production in eukaryotes differ from the process in prokaryotes?
8-6 Define *operon.*	What is an operon?
8-7 Explain the regulation of gene expression in bacteria by induction, repression, and catabolite repression.	What is the role of cAMP in catabolite represstion?
8-8 Classify mutations by type.	How can a mutation be beneficial?
8-9 Define *mutagen.*	How are mutations caused by chemicals? By radiation?
10 Describe two ways mutations can be repaired.	How can mutations be repaired?
8-11 Describe the effect of mutagens on the mutation rate.	How do mutagens affect the mutation rate?
8-12 Outline the methods of direct and indirect selection of mutants.	How would you isolate an antibiotic-resistant bacterium? An antibiotic-sensitive bacterium?
8-13 Identify the purpose of and outline the procedure for the Ames test.	What is the principle behind the Ames test?
8-14 Differentiate horizontal and vertical gene transfer.	Differentiate horizontal and vertical gene transfer.
8-15 Compare the mechanisms of genetic recombination in bacteria.	Compare conjugation between the following pairs: $F^+ \times F^-$, Hfr $\times$ F^-.
8-16 Describe the functions of plasmids and transposons.	What types of genes do plasmids carry?
8-17 Discuss how genetic mutation and recombination provide material for natural selection to act upon.	Natural selection means that the environment favors survival of some genotypes. From where does diversity in genotypes come?

NEW IN THIS EDITION

• A discussion of snRNPs

• Two figures explaining and comparing inducible and repressible operons

TRACKING WEST NILE VIRUS

A question in the Clinical Focus box on p. 223 asks students how similar the viruses are. One possible answer, based on % similarity of the viral envelope amino acids, is shown below.

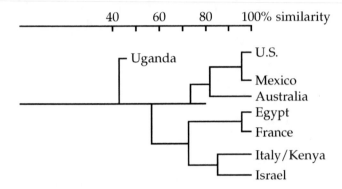

CHAPTER SUMMARY

Structure and Function of the Genetic Material (pp. 211–221)

1. Genetics is the study of what genes are, how they carry information, how their information is expressed, and how they are replicated and passed to subsequent generations or other organisms.

2. DNA in cells exists as a double-stranded helix; the two strands are held together by hydrogen bonds between specific nitrogenous base pairs: AT and CG.

3. A gene is a segment of DNA, a sequence of nucleotides, that codes for a functional product, usually a protein.

4. The DNA in a cell is duplicated before the cell divides, so each daughter cell receives the same genetic information.

Genotype and Phenotype (p. 211)

5. Genotype is the genetic composition of an organism, its entire complement of DNA.

6. Phenotype is the expression of the genes: the proteins of the cell and the properties they confer on the organism.

DNA and Chromosomes (pp. 211–212)

7. The DNA in a chromosome exists as one long double helix associated with various proteins that regulate genetic activity.

8. Bacterial DNA is circular; the chromosome of *E. coli*, for example, contains about 4 million base pairs and is approximately 1000 times longer than the cell.

9. Genomics is the molecular characterization of genomes.

The Flow of Genetic Information (p. 212)

10. Information contained in the DNA is transcribed into RNA and translated into proteins.

DNA Replication (pp. 212–215)

11. During DNA replication, the two strands of the double helix separate at the replication fork, and each strand is used as a template by DNA polymerases to synthesize two new strands of DNA according to the rules of nitrogenous base pairing.

12. The result of DNA replication is two new strands of DNA, each having a base sequence complementary to one of the original strands.

13. Because each double-stranded DNA molecule contains one original and one new strand, the replication process is called semiconservative.

14. DNA is synthesized in one direction designated $5' \rightarrow 3'$. At the replication fork, the leading strand is synthesized continuously and the lagging strand discontinuously.

15. DNA polymerase proofreads new molecules of DNA and removes mismatched bases before continuing DNA synthesis.

16. Each daughter bacterium receives a chromosome that is virtually identical to the parent's.

RNA and Protein Synthesis (pp. 216–221)

17. During transcription, the enzyme RNA polymerase synthesizes a strand of RNA from one strand of double-stranded DNA, which serves as a template.

18. RNA is synthesized from nucleotides containing the bases A, C, G, and U, which pair with the bases of the DNA strand being transcribed.

19. RNA polymerase binds the promoter; transcription begins at AUG; the region of DNA that is the end point of transcription is the terminator; RNA is synthesized in the $5' \rightarrow 3'$ direction.

20. Translation is the process in which the information in the nucleotide base sequence of mRNA is used to dictate the amino acid sequence of a protein.

21. The mRNA associates with ribosomes, which consist of rRNA and protein.

22. Three-base segments of mRNA that specify amino acids are called codons.

23. The genetic code refers to the relationship among the nucleotide base sequence of DNA, the corresponding codons of mRNA, and the amino acids for which the codons code.

24. The genetic code is degenerate; that is, most amino acids are coded for by more than one codon.

25. Of the 64 codons, 61 are sense codons (which code for amino acids), and 3 are nonsense codons (which do not code for amino acids and are stop signals for translation).

26. The start codon, AUG, codes for methionine.

27. Specific amino acids are attached to molecules of tRNA. Another portion of the tRNA has a base triplet called an anticodon.

28. The base pairing of codon and anticodon at the ribosome results in specific amino acids being brought to the site of protein synthesis.

29. The ribosome moves along the mRNA strand as amino acids are joined to form a growing polypeptide; mRNA is read in the $5' \rightarrow 3'$ direction.

30. Translation ends when the ribosome reaches a stop codon on the mRNA.

The Regulation of Bacterial Gene Expression (pp. 221–226)

1. Regulating protein synthesis at the gene level is energy-efficient because proteins are synthesized only as they are needed.

2. Constitutive enzymes produce products at a fixed rate. Examples are genes for the enzymes in glycolysis.

3. For these gene regulatory mechanisms, the control is aimed at mRNA synthesis.

Repression and Induction (p. 224)

4. Repression controls the synthesis of one or several (repressible) enzymes.

5. When cells are exposed to a particular end-product, the synthesis of enzymes related to that product decreases.

6. In the presence of certain chemicals (inducers), cells synthesize more enzymes. This process is called induction.

7. An example of induction is the production of β-galactosidase by *E. coli* in the presence of lactose; lactose can then be metabolized.

The Operon Model of Gene Expression (p. 224)

8. The formation of enzymes is determined by structural genes.

9. In bacteria, a group of coordinately regulated structural genes with related metabolic functions, plus the promoter and operator sites that control their transcription, are called an operon.

10. In the operon model for an inducible system, a regulatory gene codes for the repressor protein.

11. When the inducer is absent, the repressor binds to the operator, and no mRNA is synthesized.

12. When the inducer is present, it binds to the repressor so that it cannot bind to the operator; thus, mRNA is made, and enzyme synthesis is induced.

13. In repressible systems, the repressor requires a corepressor in order to bind to the operator site; thus, the corepressor controls enzyme synthesis.

Positive Regulation (pp. 224–226)

14. Transcription of structural genes for catabolic enzymes (such as β-galactosidase) is induced by the absence of glucose. Cyclic AMP and CRP must bind to a promoter in the presence of an alternative carbohydrate.

15. The presence of glucose inhibits the metabolism of alternative carbon sources by catabolite repression.

Mutation: Change in the Genetic Material (pp. 226–233)

1. A mutation is a change in the nitrogenous base sequence of DNA; that change causes a change in the product coded for by the mutated gene.

2. Many mutations are neutral, some are disadvantageous, and others are beneficial.

Types of Mutations (pp. 227–229)

3. A base substitution occurs when one base pair in DNA is replaced with a different base pair.

4. Alterations in DNA can result in missense mutations (which cause amino acid substitutions) or nonsense mutations (which create stop codons).

5. In a frameshift mutation, one or a few base pairs are deleted or added to DNA.

6. Mutagens are agents in the environment that cause permanent changes in DNA.

7. Spontaneous mutations occur without the presence of any mutagen.

Mutagens (pp. 229–231)

8. Chemical mutagens include base-pair mutagens, nucleoside analogs, and frameshift mutagens.

9. Ionizing radiation causes the formation of ions and free radicals that react with DNA; base substitutions or breakage of the sugar-phosphate backbone results.

10. Ultraviolet (UV) radiation is nonionizing; it causes bonding between adjacent thymines.

11. Damage to DNA caused by UV radiation can be repaired by enzymes that cut out and replace the damaged portion of DNA.

12. Light-repair enzymes repair thymine dimers in the presence of visible light.

The Frequency of Mutation (p. 231)

13. Mutation rate is the probability that a gene will mutate when a cell divides; the rate is expressed as 10 to a negative power.

14. Mutations usually occur randomly along a chromosome.

15. A low rate of spontaneous mutations is beneficial in providing the genetic diversity needed for evolution.

Identifying Mutants (pp. 231–232)

16. Mutants can be detected by selecting or testing for an altered phenotype.

17. Positive selection involves the selection of mutant cells and the rejection of nonmutated cells.

18. Replica plating is used for negative selection—to detect, for example, auxotrophs that have nutritional requirements not possessed by the parent (nonmutated) cell.

Identifying Chemical Carcinogens (pp. 232–233)

19. The Ames test is a relatively inexpensive and rapid test for identifying possible chemical carcinogens.

20. The test assumes that a mutant cell can revert to a normal cell in the presence of a mutagen and that many mutagens are carcinogens.

Genetic Transfer and Recombination (pp. 233–241)

1. Genetic recombination, the rearrangement of genes from separate groups of genes, usually involves DNA from different organisms; it contributes to genetic diversity.

2. In crossing over, genes from two chromosomes are recombined into one chromosome containing some genes from each original chromosome.

3. Vertical gene transfer occurs during reproduction when genes are passed from an organism to its offspring.

4. Horizontal gene transfer in bacteria involves a portion of the cell's DNA being transferred from donor to recipient.

5. When some of the donor's DNA has been integrated into the recipient's DNA, the resultant cell is called a recombinant.

Transformation in Bacteria (pp. 234–236)

6. During this process, genes are transferred from one bacterium to another as "naked" DNA in solution.

7. This process occurs naturally among a few genera of bacteria.

Conjugation in Bacteria (pp. 236–237)

8. This process requires contact between living cells.

9. One type of genetic donor cell is an F^+; recipient cells are F^-. F cells contain plasmids called F factors; these are transferred to the F^- cells during conjugation.

10. When the plasmid becomes incorporated into the chromosome, the cell is called an Hfr (high frequency of recombination) cell.

11. During conjugation, an Hfr cell can transfer chromosomal DNA to an F^- cell. Usually, the Hfr chromosome breaks before it is fully transferred.

Transduction in Bacteria (p. 237)

12. In this process, DNA is passed from one bacterium to another in a bacteriophage and is then incorporated into the recipient's DNA.

13. In generalized transduction, any bacterial genes can be transferred.

Plasmids and Transposons (pp. 237–241)

14. Plasmids are self-replicating circular molecules of DNA carrying genes that are not usually essential for the cell's survival.

15. There are several types of plasmids, including conjugative plasmids, dissimilation plasmids, plasmids carrying genes for toxins or bacteriocins, and resistance factors.

16. Transposons are small segments of DNA that can move from one region to another region of the same chromosome or to a different chromosome or a plasmid.

17. Transposons are found in chromosomes, in plasmids, and in the genetic material of viruses. They vary from simple (insertion sequences) to complex.

18. Complex transposons can carry any type of gene, including antibiotic-resistance genes, and are thus a natural mechanism for moving genes from one chromosome to another.

Genes and Evolution (p. 241)

1. Diversity is the precondition for evolution.

2. Genetic mutation and recombination provide a diversity of organisms, and the process of natural selection allows the growth of those best adapted to a given environment.

THE LOOP

Generalized transduction is covered in this chapter; specialized transduction is discussed in Chapter 13. Genetic engineering techniques (Chapter 9) and industrial microbiology (Chapter 28) can be covered with this chapter. Antibiotics that interfere with protein synthesis can be included (see Figure 20.4).

ANSWERS

Review

1. DNA consists of a strand of alternating sugars (deoxyribose) and phosphate groups with a nitrogenous base attached to each sugar. The bases are adenine, thymine, cytosine, and guanine. DNA exists in a cell as two strands twisted together to form a double helix. The two strands are held together by hydrogen bonds between their nitrogenous bases. The bases are paired in a specific, complementary way: A-T and C-G. The information held in the sequence of nucleotides in DNA is the basis for synthesis of RNA and proteins in a cell.

2.

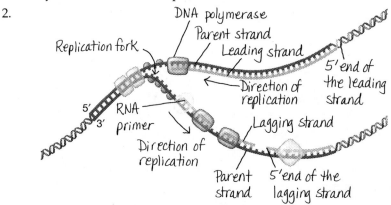

3. a. ATAT<u>TAC</u>TTT<u>GCATGGACT</u>.

    b. met-lys-arg-thr-(end).

    c. TATAATGAAACGTTCCTGA.

    d. No change.

    e. Cysteine substituted for arginine.

    f. Proline substituted for threonine (missense mutation).

    g. Frameshift mutation.

    h. Adjacent thymines might polymerize.

    i. ACT.

4. a. 2

    b. 4

    c. 3

    d. 1

    e. 5

5. a. (1) repressor

    (2) operator

    (3) repressor

    (4) transcription

    b. (1) corepressor

    (2) repressor

    (3) operator

    Derepression occurs when the corepressor is needed

    c. None; constitutive enzymes are produced at certain necessary levels regardless of the amount of substrate or end-product.

6. CTTTGA. Endospores and pigments offer protection against UV radiation. Additionally, repair mechanisms can remove and replace thymine polymers.

7. a. Culture 1 will remain the same. Culture 2 will convert to F$^+$ but will have its original genotype.

    b. The donor and recipient cells' DNA can recombine to form combinations of A$^+$B$^+$C$^+$ and A$^-$B$^-$C$^-$. If the F plasmid also is transferred, the recipient cell may become F$^+$.

8. Semiconservative replication ensures the offspring cell will have one correct strand of DNA. Any mutations that may have occurred during DNA replication have a greater chance of being correctly repaired.

9. Mutation and recombination provide genetic diversity. Environmental factors select for the survival of organisms through natural selection. Genetic diversity is necessary for the survival of some organisms through the processes of natural selection. Organisms that survive may undergo further genetic change, resulting in the evolution of the species.

Critical Thinking

1. Cancerous cells are growing faster than normal cells. Mutations have a greater effect when a cell is growing because it is synthesizing DNA and enzymes. The probability of a lethal mutation also is increased in rapidly growing cells.

2. The cell does not regulate the rate at which DNA is synthesized, but it regulates the rate at which replication forks on the chromosomes are initiated. The cell initiates multiple forks so that a daughter cell will inherit a complete chromosome plus additional portions from multiple replication forks. Chromosome replication begins during or immediately after division.

3. a. Mercuric ion.

    b. To detoxify it.

    c. Detoxifying mercuric ion will allow the cell to live where other organisms may not be able to.

Clinical Applications

1. a. Ciprofloxacin interferes with DNA replication; erythromycin interferes with translation; acyclovir interferes with DNA replication.

    b. Erythromycin is specific for bacterial ribosomes.

    c. Acyclovir will have the most effects on the host because it affects eukaryotic DNA. The effects of erythromycin on mitochondrial ribosomes are small for short-term use.

    d. Acyclovir is used against *Herpesvirus* infections. Erythromycin affects bacterial (70S) ribosomes, not viruses or eukaryotes.

2. Sequence B is the most dissimilar and, therefore, probably not closely related to the others. The amino acid sequence reflects the RNA (genome) of the virus.

3. 28% of the nucleotides are different; however, they differ in only one of the seven amino acids. Mutations account for the difference. HHV-8 causes Kaposi's sarcoma.

CASE STUDY: MAPPING A BACTERIAL CHROMOSOME

Background

Conjugation mapping can be used to locate genes on a bacterial chromosome. In this example, the F^+ strain is able to synthesize methionine, valine, leucine, and histidine. The F^- strain is unable to synthesize these amino acids; therefore, they must be supplied in the growth medium. Use the results from replica-plating to answer the questions.

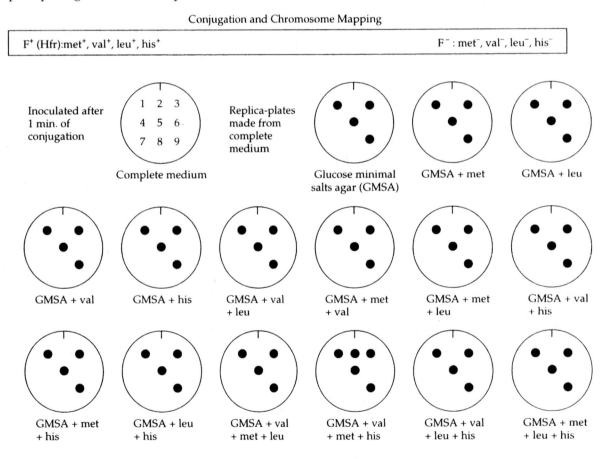

Conjugation and Chromosome Mapping

F^+ (Hfr):met$^+$, val$^+$, leu$^+$, his$^+$ F^- : met$^-$, val$^-$, leu$^-$, his$^-$

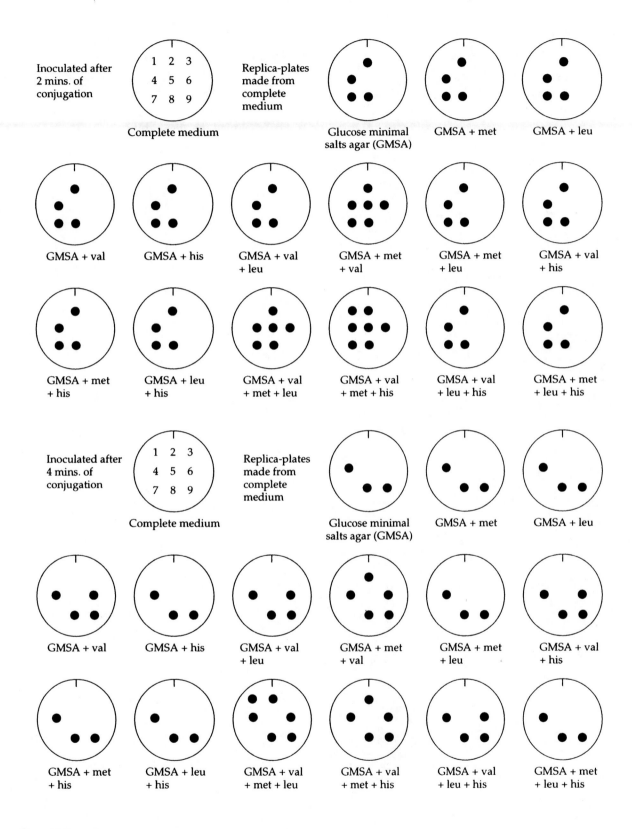

Questions

1. On which media, if any, should the F⁺ be able to grow? The F⁻?
2. Identify the prototrophs and auxotrophs. How can you tell?
3. Can you map the chromosome of this species? What further information do you need?

The Solution

1. F⁺ should be able to grow on all the media; F⁻ can only grow on the complete medium.

2. Colonies 1, 3, 5, and 9 are prototrophs. These are the F⁺ cells. Colonies 2, 4, 6, 7, and 8 are the auxotrophs. Auxotrophs have nutritional requirements that the original strain did not have.

3. The map order is *leu, his, met*. You need additional time-trials to find the location of *val*. Other genes must be tested to determine whether anything occurs between *leu, his, met,* and *val*.

9 Biotechnology and Recombinant DNA

LEARNING OBJECTIVES	CHECK YOUR UNDERSTANDING
9-1 Compare and contrast biotechnology, genetic modification, and recombinant DNA technology.	Differentiate biotechnology and recombinant DNA technology.
9-2 Identify the roles of a clone and a vector in making recombinant DNA.	In one sentence describe how a vector and clone are used.
9-3 Compare selection and mutation.	How are selection and mutation used in biotechnology?
9-4 Define *restriction enzymes*, and outline how they are used to make recombinant DNA.	What is the value of restriction enzymes in recombinant DNA technology?
9-5 List the four properties of vectors.	What criteria must a vector meet?
9-6 Describe the use of plasmid and viral vectors.	Why is a vector used in recombinant DNA technology?
9-7 Outline the steps in PCR, and provide an example of its use.	For what is each of the following used in PCR: primer, DNA polymerase, 94°C?
9-8 Describe five ways of getting DNA into a cell.	Contrast the five ways of putting DNA into a cell.
9-9 Describe how a genomic library is made.	What is the purpose of a genomic library?
9-10 Differentiate cDNA from synthetic DNA.	Why isn't cDNA synthetic?
9-11 Explain how each of the following is used to locate a clone: antibiotic-resistance genes, DNA probes, gene products.	How are recombinant clones identified?
9-12 List one advantage of modifying each of the following: *E. coli, Saccharomyces cerevisiae,* mammalian cells, plant cells.	What types of cells are used for cloning rDNA?
9-13 List at least five applications of rDNA technology.	Explain how rDNA technology can be used to treat disease and to prevent disease.
9-14 Define RNAi.	What is gene silencing?
9-15 Discuss the value of the Human Genome Project. 9-16 Define the following terms: *random shotgun sequencing, bioinformatics, proteomics.*	How are shotgun sequencing, bioinformatics, and proteomics related to the Human Genome Project?
9-17 Diagram the Southern blotting procedure, and provide an example of its use.	What is Southern blotting?
9-18 Diagram DNA fingerprinting, and provide an example of its use.	Why do RFLPs result in a DNA fingerprint?

9-19 Outline genetic engineering with *Agrobacterium*.	Of what value is the plant pathogen *Agrobacterium?*
9-20 List the advantages of, and problems associated with, the use of genetic modification techniques.	Identify two advantages and two problems associated with genetically modified organisms.

NEW IN THIS EDITION

- Discussion of gene silencing and real-time PCR
- Descriptions of proteomics and reverse genetics
- A new Clinical Focus (*MMWR*) box describing the use of reverse-transcription PCR to track a norovirus outbreak

CHAPTER SUMMARY
Introduction to Biotechnology (p. 247)

1. Biotechnology is the use of microorganisms, cells, or cell components to make a product.

Recombinant DNA Technology (p. 247)

2. Closely related organisms can exchange genes in natural recombination.
3. Genes can be transferred among unrelated species via laboratory manipulation, called recombinant DNA technology.
4. Recombinant DNA is DNA that has been artificially manipulated to combine genes from two different sources.

An Overview of Recombinant DNA Procedures (p. 247)

5. A desired gene is inserted into a DNA vector, such as a plasmid or a viral genome.
6. The vector inserts the DNA into a new cell, which is grown to form a clone.
7. Large quantities of the gene product can be harvested from the clone.

Tools of Biotechnology (pp. 247–252)
Selection (p. 249)

1. Microbes with desirable traits are selected for culturing by artificial selection.

Mutation (p. 249)

2. Mutagens are used to cause mutations that might result in a microbe with desirable traits.
3. Site-directed mutagenesis is used to change a specific codon in a gene.

Restriction Enzymes (pp. 249–250)

4. Prepackaged kits are available for rDNA techniques.
5. A restriction enzyme recognizes and cuts only one particular nucleotide sequence in DNA.
6. Some restriction enzymes produce sticky ends, short stretches of single-stranded DNA at the ends of the DNA fragments.

7. Fragments of DNA produced by the same restriction enzyme will spontaneously join by base pairing. DNA ligase can covalently link the DNA backbones.

Vectors (pp. 250–251)

8. Shuttle vectors are plasmids that can exist in several different species.
9. A plasmid containing a new gene can be inserted into a cell by transformation.
10. A virus containing a new gene can insert the gene into a cell.

Polymerase Chain Reaction (pp. 251–252)

11. The polymerase chain reaction (PCR) is used to make multiple copies of a desired piece of DNA enzymatically.
12. PCR can be used to increase the amounts of DNA in samples to detectable levels. This may allow sequencing of genes, the diagnosis of genetic diseases, or the detection of viruses.

Techniques of Genetic Modification (pp. 253–258)

Inserting Foreign DNA into Cells (pp. 253–254)

1. Cells can take up naked DNA by transformation. Chemical treatments are used to make cells that are not naturally competent take up DNA.
2. Pores made in protoplasts and animal cells by electric current in the process of electroporation can provide entrance for new pieces of DNA.
3. Protoplast fusion is the joining of cells whose cell walls have been removed.
4. Foreign DNA can be introduced into plant cells by shooting DNA-coated particles into the cells.
5. Foreign DNA can be injected into animal cells by using a fine glass micropipette.

Obtaining DNA (pp. 254–256)

6. Genomic libraries can be made by cutting up an entire genome with restriction enzymes and inserting the fragments into bacterial plasmids or phages.
7. Complementary DNA (cDNA) made from mRNA by reverse transcription can be cloned in genomic libraries.
8. Synthetic DNA can be made in vitro by a DNA synthesis machine.

Selecting a Clone (pp. 256–257)

9. Antibiotic-resistance markers on plasmid vectors are used to identify cells containing the engineered vector by direct selection.
10. In blue-white screening, the vector contains the genes for amp^R and β-galactosidase.
11. The desired gene is inserted into the β-galactosidase gene site, destroying the gene.
12. Clones containing the recombinant vector will be resistant to ampicillin and unable to hydrolyze X-gal (white colonies). Clones containing the vector without the new gene will be blue. Clones lacking the vector will not grow.
13. Clones containing foreign DNA can be tested for the desired gene product.
14. A short piece of labeled DNA called a DNA probe can be used to identify clones carrying the desired gene.

Making a Gene Product (pp. 257–258)

15. *E. coli* is used to produce proteins using rDNA because *E. coli* is easily grown and its genomics are well understood.

16. Efforts must be made to ensure that *E. coli*'s endotoxin does not contaminate a product intended for human use.

17. To recover the product, *E. coli* must be lysed, or the gene must be linked to a gene that produces a naturally secreted protein.

18. Yeasts can be genetically modified and are likely to secrete a gene product continuously.

19. Genetically modified mammalian cells can be grown to produce proteins such as hormones for medical use.

20. Genetically modified plant cells can be grown and used to produce plants with new properties.

Applications of rDNA (pp. 258–267)

1. Cloned DNA is used to produce products, study the cloned DNA, and alter the phenotype of an organism.

Therapeutic Applications (pp. 258–261)

2. Synthetic genes linked to the β-galactosidase gene (*lacZ*) in a plasmid vector were inserted into *E. coli*, allowing *E. coli* to produce and secrete the two polypeptides used to make human insulin.

3. Cells and viruses can be modified to produce a pathogen's surface protein, which can be used as a vaccine.

4. DNA vaccines consist of rDNA cloned in bacteria.

5. Gene therapy can be used to cure genetic diseases by replacing the defective or missing gene.

The Human Genome Project (p. 261)

6. Recombinant DNA techniques were used to map the human genome through the Human Genome Project.

7. This will provide tools for diagnosis and possibly the repair of genetic diseases.

Scientific Applications (pp. 261–264)

8. Recombinant DNA techniques can be used to increase understanding of DNA, for genetic fingerprinting, and for gene therapy.

9. DNA sequencing machines are used to determine the nucleotide base sequence of restriction fragments in random shotgun sequencing.

10. Bioinformatics is the use of computer applications to study genetic data; proteomics is the study of a cell's proteins.

11. Southern blotting can be used to locate a gene in a cell.

12. DNA probes can be used to quickly identify a pathogen in body tissue or food.

13. Forensic microbiologists use DNA fingerprinting to identify the source of bacterial or viral pathogens.

Agricultural Applications (pp. 264–267)

14. Cells from plants with desirable characteristics can be cloned to produce many identical cells. These cells can then be used to produce whole plants from which seeds can be harvested.

15. Plant cells can be modified by using the Ti plasmid vector. The tumor-producing T genes are replaced with desired genes, and the recombinant DNA is inserted into *Agrobacterium.* The bacterium naturally transforms its plant hosts.

16. Genes for glyphosate resistance, Bt toxin, and pectinase suppression have been engineered into crop plants.

17. Genetically modified *Rhizobium* has enhanced nitrogen fixation.

18. Genetically modified *Pseudomonas* is a biological insecticide that produces *Bacillus thuringiensis* toxin.

19. Bovine growth hormone is being produced by *E. coli.*

Safety Issues and the Ethics of Using rDNA (p. 268)

1. Strict safety standards are used to avoid the accidental release of genetically modified microorganisms.

2. Some microbes used in rDNA cloning have been altered so that they cannot survive outside the laboratory.

3. Microorganisms intended for use in the environment may be modified to contain suicide genes so that the organisms do not persist in the environment.

4. Genetic technology raises a number of ethical questions: Should employers and insurance companies have access to a person's genetic records? Will some people be targeted for either breeding or sterilization? Will genetic counseling be available to everyone?

5. Genetically modified crops must be safe for consumption and for release in the environment.

THE LOOP

This chapter can follow Chapter 8, "Microbial Genetics," and can be covered with Chapter 27. Chapter 28 includes industrial applications of microorganisms. The boxes on pp. 3, 33, 780, and 801 provide additional examples of biotechnology.

ANSWERS

Review

1. a. Both are DNA. cDNA is a segment of DNA made by RNA-dependent DNA polymerase. It is not necessarily a gene; a gene is a transcribable unit of DNA that codes for protein or RNA.
   b. Both are DNA. A restriction fragment is a segment of DNA produced when a restriction endonuclease hydrolyzes DNA. It is not usually a gene; a gene is a transcribable unit of DNA that codes for protein or RNA.
   c. Both are DNA. A DNA probe is a short, single-stranded piece of DNA. It is not a gene; a gene is a transcribable unit of DNA that codes for protein or RNA.
   d. Both are enzymes. DNA polymerase synthesizes DNA one nucleotide at a time using a DNA template; DNA ligase joins pieces (strands of nucleotides) together.
   e. Both are DNA. Recombinant DNA results from joining DNA from two different sources; cDNA results from copying a strand of RNA.
   f. The proteome is the expression of the genome. An organism's genome is one complete copy of its genetic information. The proteins encoded by this genetic material comprise the proteome.

2. In protoplast fusion, two wall-less cells fuse together to combine their DNA. A variety of genotypes can result from this process. In b, c, and d, specific genes are inserted directly into the cell.

3.

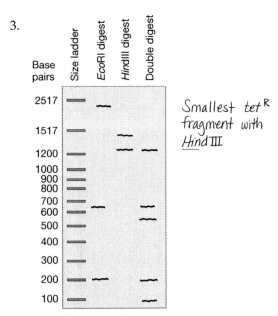

Smallest *tet*^R fragment with *Hind*III

4. a. *Bam*HI, *Eco*RI, and *Hind*III make sticky ends.

    b. Fragments of DNA produced with the same restriction enzyme will spontaneously anneal to each other at their sticky ends.

5. The gene can be spliced into a plasmid and inserted into a bacterial cell. As the cell grows, the number of plasmids will increase. The polymerase chain reaction can make copies of a gene using DNA polymerase in vitro.

6. In a eukaryotic cell, RNA polymerase copies DNA; RNA processing removes the introns, leaving the exons in the mRNA. cDNA can be made from the mRNA by reverse transcriptase.

7. See Tables 9.1 and 9.2.

8. You probably used a few plant cells in a Petri plate for your experiment. How will you select the plant cells that actually have the new Ti plasmid? You can grow these cells on plant-cell culture media with tetracycline. Only the cells with the new plasmid will grow.

9. In RNAi, siRNA binds mRNA creating double-stranded RNA which is enzymatically destroyed.

Critical Thinking

1. Isolate cDNA (or synthesize DNA) for the desired gene from HIV. Insert the HIV gene into vaccinia virus's DNA. Infect the host cells with vaccinia virus. As the virus reproduces, it will cause production of the HIV protein.

2. "Normal" DNA polymerase is denatured by the heating step, so a technician would have to add DNA polymerase to the reaction vessel every 2 minutes. DNA polymerase from *Thermus* is not denatured by 90°C, so fresh DNA polymerase does not have to be added every 2 minutes.

3. Large colonies are ampicillin-resistant because they are growing. Smaller ampicillin-sensitive colonies may appear later after the antibiotic has been degraded by the ampicillin-resistant bacteria. White colonies have the new gene.

Clinical Applications

1. Sample A was positive for *V. cholerae* because the probe paired with DNA in lane A. *V. cholerae* ingested by oysters is a source of disease for humans. The PCR doesn't require isolation and additional incubation for test results.

2. The vector and new gene fragments appear in the fifth lane; therefore, transformation did occur.

CASE STUDY: MAKING A PLASMID MODEL (SEE FIGURE ON P. 76)

Isolating a Plasmid Vector

Plasmids are self-replicating, extra-chromosomal molecules of DNA. Cut the three plasmid pieces on the solid lines, and paste together to form a circular molecule of DNA. In DNA synthesis, the 5' end of one sugar is attached to the 3' end of the preceding sugar. This plasmid carries the (shaded) genes for resistance to kanamycin (*Km*) and resistance to ampicillin (*Ap*).

Isolating a Gene

Genes can be isolated or, if small enough, synthesized. Cut out the gene on the solid lines.

Restriction Enzyme Digestion

Now, you must locate appropriate restriction sites. Can you find a restriction site for *Bam*HI? For *Hae*III? For *Eco*RI? Your scissors are the restriction enzyme *Eco*RI, which cuts between the G and A in the sequence GAATTC on both strands of double-stranded DNA. The enzyme reads from the 5' end of DNA. Note that the two strands of DNA are complementary, so you will have staggered (or *sticky*) ends after your cuts. Cut the plasmid and gene. Although enzymes work by trial and error to find their substrate, the carets (^) will help you locate the correct sequence.

Ligation

DNA ligase covalently joins pieces of DNA. Match the complementary bases of the staggered ends to paste the gene into the plasmid.

Voilà!

A recombinant plasmid.

Questions

1. Why were the *Bam*HI and *Hae*III sites not useful for this experiment?
2. How can you clone a plasmid by PCR? In a living cell?
3. How will you identify cells carrying the recombinant plasmid? Cells carrying the original plasmid? Cells without a plasmid?

Answers

1. Neither of these sites occurs in the plasmid and at the ends of the new gene. *Hae*III does not produce the sticky ends needed for splicing.
2. PCR can make copies of DNA using DNA polymerase and DNA primers. The plasmid can be inserted into a cell, so it will replicate itself in the cell.
3.

	Nutrient Agar	**Nutrient Agar + Ampicillin**	**Nutrient Agar + Kanamycin**
Cells with recombinant	Growth	Growth	No growth plasmid
Cells with original	Growth	Growth	Growth plasmid
Cells without plasmid	Growth	No growth	No growth

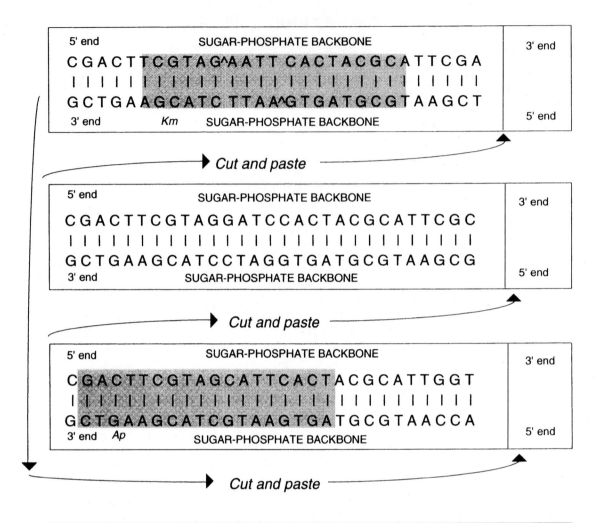

10

Classification of Microorganisms

LEARNING OBJECTIVES	CHECK YOUR UNDERSTANDING
10-1 Define *taxonomy*, *taxon*, and *phylogeny*.	Of what value are taxonomy and systematics?
10-2 Discuss the limitations of a two-kingdom classification system.	Why shouldn't bacteria be placed in the plant kingdom?
10-3 Identify the contributions of Linnaeus, von Nägeli, Chatton, Whittaker, and Woese.	
10-4 Discuss the advantages of the three-domain system.	What evidence supports classifying organisms into three domains?
10-5 List the characteristics of the Bacteria, Archaea, and Eukarya domains.	Compare archaea and bacteria; bacteria and eukarya; archaea and eukarya.
10-6 Explain why scientific names are used.	Using *Escherichia coli* and *Entamoeba coli* as examples, explain why the genus name must always be written out for the first use. Why is binomial nomenclature preferable to the use of common names?
10-7 List the major taxa.	Find the gram-positive bacterium *Staphylococcus* in Appendix F. To which bacterium is it most closely related: *Gemella* or *Streptococcus*?
10-8 Differentiate *culture*, *clone*, and *strain*.	Use the terms *species*, *culture*, *clone*, and *strain* in one sentence to describe growing methicillin-resistant *Staphylococcus aureus* (MRSA).
10-9 List the major characteristics used to differentiate the three kingdoms of multicellular Eukarya.	Assume you discovered a new organism: it is multicellular, nucleated, heterotrophic, and has cell walls. To what kingdom does it belong?
10-10 Define *protist*.	Write your own definition of *protist*.
10-11 Differentiate among eukaryotic, prokaryotic, and viral species.	Why wouldn't the definition of a viral species work for a bacterial species?
10-12 Compare and contrast classification and identification.	Is a cladogram used for identification or classification?
10-13 Explain the purpose of *Bergey's Manual*.	What is in *Bergey's Manual*?
10-14 Describe how staining and biochemical tests are used to identify bacteria.	Design a rapid test for a *Staphylococcus aureus*. (*Hint:* See Figure 6.10.)
10-15 Differentiate Western blotting from Southern blotting.	What is tested in Western blotting and Southern blotting?
10-16 Explain how serological tests and phage typing can be used to identify an unknown bacterium.	What is identified by phage typing?

10-17 Describe how a newly discovered microbe can be classified by DNA base composition, DNA fingerprinting, and PCR.

Why does PCR identify a microbe?

10-18 Describe how microorganisms can be identified by nucleic acid hybridization, Southern blotting, DNA chips, ribotyping, and FISH.

Which techniques involve nucleic acid hybridization?

10-19 Differentiate a dichotomous key from a cladogram.

Is a cladogram used for identification or classification?

NEW IN THIS EDITION

- Photos of fossil and living stromatolites
- Discussion of the use of transport media

CHAPTER SUMMARY

Introduction (p. 273)

1. Taxonomy is the science of the classification of organisms. Its goal is to show relationships among organisms.
2. Taxonomy also provides a means of identifying organisms.

The Study of Phylogenetic Relationships (pp. 274–278)

1. Phylogeny is the evolutionary history of a group of organisms.
2. The taxonomic hierarchy shows evolutionary, or phylogenetic, relationships among organisms.
3. Bacteria were separated into the Kingdom Prokaryotae in 1968.
4. Living organisms were divided into five kingdoms in 1969.

The Three Domains (pp. 274–277)

5. Living organisms are currently classified into three domains. A domain can be divided into kingdoms.
6. In this system, plants, animals, fungi, and protists belong to the Domain Eukarya.
7. Bacteria (with peptidoglycan) form a second domain.
8. Archaea (with unusual cell walls) are placed in the Domain Archaea.

A Phylogenetic Hierarchy (pp. 277–278)

9. Organisms are grouped into taxa according to phylogenetic relationships (from a common ancestor).
10. Some of the information for eukaryotic relationships is obtained from the fossil record.
11. Prokaryotic relationships are determined by rRNA sequencing.

Classification of Organisms (pp. 278–282)

Scientific Nomenclature (pp. 278–279)

1. According to scientific nomenclature, each organism is assigned two names, or a binomial: a genus and a specific epithet, or species.
2. Rules for the assignment of names to bacteria are established by the International Committee on Systematics of Prokaryotes.

3. Rules for naming fungi and algae are published in the *International Code of Botanical Nomenclature.*
4. Rules for naming protozoa are found in the *International Code of Zoological Nomenclature.*

The Taxonomic Hierarchy (p. 279)

5. A eukaryotic species is a group of organisms that interbreeds with each other but does not breed with individuals of another species.
6. Similar species are grouped into a genus; similar genera are grouped into a family; families, into an order; orders, into a class; classes, into a phylum; phyla, into a kingdom; and kingdoms, into a domain.

Classification of Prokaryotes (pp. 279–281)

7. *Bergey's Manual of Systematic Bacteriology* is the standard reference on bacterial classification.
8. A group of bacteria derived from a single cell is called a strain.
9. Closely related strains constitute a bacterial species.

Classification of Eukaryotes (pp. 281–282)

10. Eukaryotic organisms may be classified into the Kingdom Fungi, Plantae, or Animalia.
11. Protists are mostly unicellular organisms; these organisms are currently being assigned to kingdoms.
12. Fungi are absorptive chemoheterotrophs that develop from spores.
13. Multicellular photoautotrophs are placed in the Kingdom Plantae.
14. Multicellular ingestive heterotrophs are classified as Animalia.

Classification of Viruses (p. 282)

15. Viruses are not placed in a kingdom. They are not composed of cells and cannot grow without a host cell.
16. A viral species is a population of viruses with similar characteristics that occupies a particular ecological niche.

Methods of Classifying and Identifying Microorganisms (pp. 282–294)

1. *Bergey's Manual of Determinative Bacteriology* is the standard reference for laboratory identification of bacteria.
2. Morphological characteristics are useful in identifying microorganisms, especially when aided by differential staining techniques.
3. The presence of various enzymes, as determined by biochemical tests, is used in identifying microorganisms.
4. Serological tests, involving the reactions of microorganisms with specific antibodies, are useful in determining the identity of strains and species, as well as relationships among organisms. ELISA and Western blotting are examples of serological tests.
5. Phage typing is the identification of bacterial species and strains by determining their susceptibility to various phages.
6. Fatty acid profiles can be used to identify some organisms.
7. Flow cytometry measures physical and chemical characteristics of cells.
8. The percentage of GC base pairs in the nucleic acid of cells can be used in the classification of organisms.
9. The number and sizes of DNA fragments, or DNA fingerprints, produced by restriction enzymes are used to determine genetic similarities.

10. The polymerase chain reaction (PCR) can be used to amplify a small amount of microbial DNA in a sample. The presence or identification of an organism is indicated by amplified DNA.

11. Single strands of DNA, or of DNA and RNA, from related organisms will hydrogen-bond to form a double-stranded molecule; this bonding is called nucleic acid hybridization.

12. Southern blotting, DNA chips, and FISH are examples of nucleic acid hybridization techniques.

13. The sequence of bases in ribosomal RNA can be used in the classification of organisms.

14. Dichotomous keys are used for the identification of organisms. Cladograms show phylogenetic relationships among organisms.

THE LOOP

Chapter 10 can be assigned with other topics:

Scientific nomenclature (pp. 278–279)   with Chapter 1
Classification (pp. 278–282)   with evolution; as an introduction to Chapters 11, 12
Identification (pp. 282–294)   with unknown identification in the laboratory
Serotyping (p. 287)   with Chapter 18
Genetic analyses (pp. 288–293)   with Chapters 8 and 9

ANSWERS

Review

1. A and D appear to be most closely related because they have similar G-C moles %. No two are the same species.

2. A and D are most closely related.

3.

Gram reaction
+   −

Morphology   Acid from glucose

Coccus   Rod   −   +

Catalase?   Endospores?   C. fetus   Oxidase?

+   −   +   −   +   −

S. aureus   S. pyogenes   C. botulinum   L. monocytogenes   P. aeruginosa   Rod?

+   −

E. coli   M. pneumoniae

4.

% similarity
100   50

P. aeruginosa   <   79   >
E. coli
M. pneumoniae   <   65   >
C. botulinum   <   52   >

The purpose of a cladogram is to show the degree of relatedness between organisms. A dichotomous key can be used for identification but doesn't show relatedness like the cladogram. *Mycoplasma* and *Escherichia* are on one branch in the key, but the cladogram indicates *Mycoplasma* is more closely related to *Clostridium*.

Critical Thinking

1. Based on the nucleic acid composition, *Micrococcus* and *Staphylococcus* are not related. *Micrococcus* is in the phylum Actinobacteria; *Staphylococcus* is in the phylum Firmicutes.

2. DNA probe. Labeled DNA will hybridize with homologous DNA indicating (a) identity if the probe is known DNA and the homologous DNA is from an unknown bacterium, or (b) relatedness when the two organisms are known.

   PCR. The primer used in PCR will hybridize with homologous DNA so unrelated DNA will not be copied. Or, after making copies by PCR, a DNA probe can be used to locate specific DNA.

3. SF = *Streptococcus faecalis*. SF broth is used to culture *Enterococcus faecalis*.

Clinical Applications

1. The patient had plague. The *Yersinia* (gram-negative rod) was missed in the first Gram stain. After gram-negative rods were cultured, biochemical tests were not conclusive because *Yersinia* is biochemically inactive. Plague can be transmitted by the respiratory route, so the patient's contacts were given prophylactic antibiotic treatment.

2. Incorrect identification could be due to mutation to sucrose$^+$, misreading of the indicator in the sucrose fermentation test, or contamination by a sucrose$^+$ organism.

3. A key based on physical characteristics is most useful for laboratory identification. Such a key might look like this:

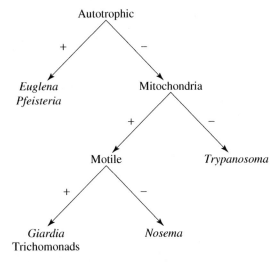

A key (or cladogram) based on rRNA is most useful for classification and is based on similarities in the rRNA sequences.

	% Similarity		% Similarity
Giardia—Euglena	40%	*Euglena—Trichomonas*	40%
Giardia—Trypanosoma	40%	*Euglena—Nosema*	40%
Giardia—Pfiesteria	40%	*Euglena—Pfiesteria*	75%
Giardia—Trichomonas	95%	*Euglena—Trichomonas*	40%
Giardia—Nosema	90%	*Euglena—Nosema*	40%
Giardia—Trypanosoma	90%	*Euglena—Trichomonas*	40%
Giardia—Pfiesteria	75%		

continues on next page

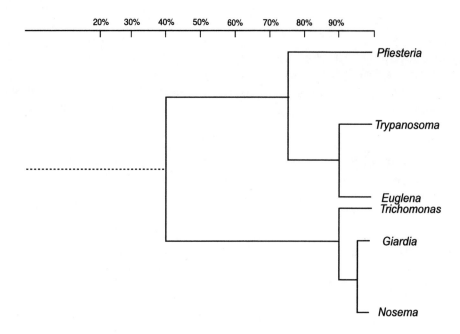

CASE STUDY: DESIGNING A TAXONOMIC KEY

Background

Classification is one of the fundamental concerns of science. Facts and objects must be arranged in an orderly fashion before unifying principles can be discovered and used as the basis for prediction. The purpose of taxonomy is to group objects according to degrees of relatedness. For example, all breeds of domestic dogs belong to one species; dogs differ from coyotes, but these two animals are similar enough to be included in the same genus. Wolves, dogs, and coyotes share enough numbers of characteristics to be included in one family. The dog family and cat family are grouped into the same order because of shared characteristics. Bacteria can also be grouped according to shared characteristics.

Data

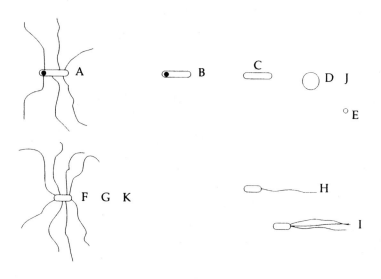

Figure	A	B	C	D	E	F	G	H	I	J	K
Catalase	−	+	−	+	+	+	+	+	+	+	+
G-C moles %	43	50	45	40	30	53	53	58	60	66	53
Gelatin hydrolyzed	+	+	+	−	−	+	+	+	−	−	−
Gram stain	+	+	+	+	−	−	−	−	−	+	−
H₂S produced	+	+	−	−	−	−	+	−	+	−	+
Indole produced	+	+	+	−	−	+	+	−	−	−	+
Lactose fermented	−	−	+	+	+	+	+	−	−	−	−
Metabolism	Anaerobe	Aerobe	Anaerobe	Facultative anaerobe	Facultative anaerobe	Facultative anaerobe	Facultative anaerobe	Aerobe	Aerobe	Aerobe	Facultative anaerobe
Methyl red	+	−	+	+	+	+	−	−	−	−	−
Sterols required	−	−	−	−	−	−	−	−	+	−	−
Voges–Proskauer	+	+	−	−	−	−	+	−	−	−	+
Glucose fermented	Acid & gas	Acid only	Acid only	Acid only	Acid only	Acid & gas	Acid & gas	−	Acid only	−	Acid & gas

Question

1. Design a classification system grouping related species, and, to the extent possible, show which groups are related.

The Solution

Students' schemes will vary; however, they should separate the following groups:

Wall-less   I
Gram-positive wall   A, B, C, D, J
Gram-negative wall   E, F, G, H, K

11

The Prokaryotes: Domains Bacteria and Archaea

LEARNING OBJECTIVES	CHECK YOUR UNDERSTANDING
11-1 Differentiate the alphaproteobacteria described in this chapter by drawing a dichotomous key.	Make a dichotomous key to distinguish among the alphaproteobacteria described in this chapter.
11-2 Differentiate the betaproteobacteria described in this chapter by drawing a dichotomous key.	Make a dichotomous key to distinguish among the betaproteobacteria described in this chapter.
11-3 Differentiate the gammaproteobacteria described in this chapter by drawing a dichotomous key.	Make a dichotomous key to distinguish among the orders of gammaproteobacteria described in this chapter.
11-4 Differentiate the deltaproteobacteria described in this chapter by drawing a dichotomous key.	Make a dichotomous key to distinguish among the deltaproteobacteria described in this chapter.
11-5 Differentiate the epsilonproteobacteria described in this chapter by drawing a dichotomous key.	Make a dichotomous key to distinguish among the epsilonproteobacteria described in this chapter.
11-6 Differentiate the groups of nonproteobacteria gram-negative bacteria described in this chapter by drawing a dichotomous key.	Make a dichotomous key to distinguish among the gram-negative nonproteobacteria described in this chapter.
11-7 Compare and contrast purple and green photosynthetic bacteria with the cyanobacteria.	Both the purple and green photosynthetic bacteria and the photosynthetic cyanobacteria use plantlike photosynthesis to make carbohydrates. In what way does the photosynthesis carried out by these two groups differ from plant photosynthesis?
11-8 Differentiate the genera of firmicutes described in this chapter by drawing a dichotomous key.	Make a dichotomous key to distinguish among the low G + C gram-positive bacteria described in this chapter.
11-9 Differentiate the actinobacteria described in this chapter by drawing a dichotomous key.	Make a dichotomous key to distinguish among the high G + C gram-positive bacteria described in this chapter.
11-10 Differentiate among chlamydias, spirochetes, Cytophaga, Bacteroidetes, and Fusobacteria by drawing a dichotomous key.	Make a dichotomous key to distinguish chlamydias, spirochetes, Cytophaga, Bacteroidetes, and Fusobacteria.
11-11 Name a habitat for each group of archaea.	What kind of archaea would populate solar evaporating ponds?
11-12 List two factors that contribute to the limits of our knowledge of microbial diversity.	How can you detect the presence of a bacterium that cannot be cultured?

NEW IN THIS EDITION

- Addition of several new bacterial groups: *Pelagibacter, Acinetobacter baumanii,* Planctomycetes, and *Gemmata obscuriglobus*
- Revised discussion of the theoretical minimal size of a bacterium and its genetic requirements

CHAPTER SUMMARY

Introduction (p. 299)

1. *Bergey's Manual* categorizes bacteria into taxa based on rRNA sequences.
2. *Bergey's Manual* lists identifying characteristics such as Gram stain reaction, cellular morphology, oxygen requirements, and nutritional properties.

The Prokaryotic Groups (p. 300)

1. Prokaryotic organisms are classified into two domains: Archaea and Bacteria.

DOMAIN BACTERIA (pp. 302–324)

1. Bacteria are essential to life on Earth.

The Proteobacteria (pp. 302–312)

1. Members of the phylum Proteobacteria are gram-negative.
2. Alphaproteobacteria include nitrogen-fixing bacteria, chemoautotrophs, and chemoheterotrophs.
3. The betaproteobacteria include chemoautotrophs and chemoheterotrophs.
4. Pseudomonadales, Legionellales, Vibrionales, Enterobacteriales, and Pasteurellales are classified as gammaproteobacteria.
5. Purple and green photosynthetic bacteria are photoautotrophs that use light energy and CO_2 and do not produce O_2.
6. *Myxococcus* and *Bdellovibrio* in the deltaproteobacteria prey on other bacteria.
7. Epsilonproteobacteria include *Campylobacter* and *Helicobacter*.

The Nonproteobacteria Gram-Negative Bacteria (pp. 313–315)

1. Several phyla of gram-negative bacteria are not related phylogenetically to the Proteobacteria.
2. Cyanobacteria are photoautotrophs that use light energy and CO_2 and do produce O_2.
3. Chemoheterotrophic examples are Planctomycetes, Chlamydiae, Spirochetes, Bacteroidetes, and Fusobacteria.

The Gram-Positive Bacteria (pp. 315–324)

1. In *Bergey's Manual,* gram-positive bacteria are divided into those that have low G + C ratio and those that have high G + C ratio.
2. Low G + C gram-positive bacteria include common soil bacteria, the lactic acid bacteria, and several human pathogens.
3. High G + C gram-positive bacteria include mycobacteria, corynebacteria, and actinomycetes.

DOMAIN ARCHAEA (p. 325)

1. Extreme halophiles, extreme thermophiles, and methanogens are included in the archaea.

MICROBIAL DIVERSITY (pp. 325–326)

1. Few of the total number of different prokaryotes have been isolated and identified.
2. PCR can be used to uncover the presence of bacteria that can't be cultured in the laboratory.

THE LOOP

The Study Questions do not ask students to recall characteristics of specific groups of bacteria. At Skyline College, this memorization is required during a study of Part Four and appropriate laboratory work. At this point, students are shown how bacteria are classified and identified. Review question 1 provides a preliminary key for identification of unknowns in the laboratory and provides names and characteristics of the large groups of bacteria.

ANSWERS

Check Your Understanding

There is no single correct solution to the Check Your Understanding questions that ask for a dichotomous key. Here are some to get you started.

1. Make a dichotomous key to distinguish among the alphaproteobacteria described in this chapter.

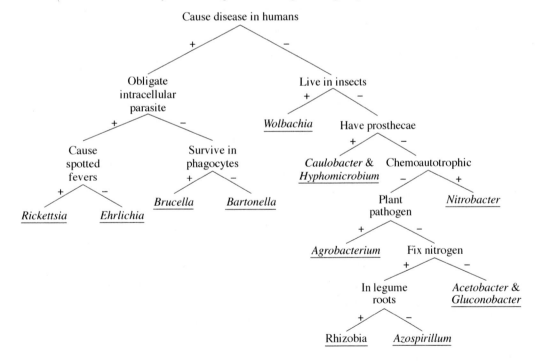

2. Make a dichotomous key to distinguish among the betaproteobacteria described in this chapter.

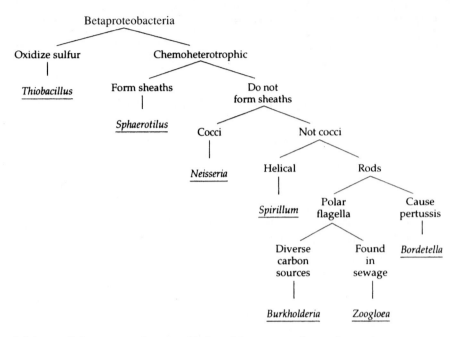

3. Make a dichotomous key to distinguish among the orders of gammaproteobacteria described in this chapter.

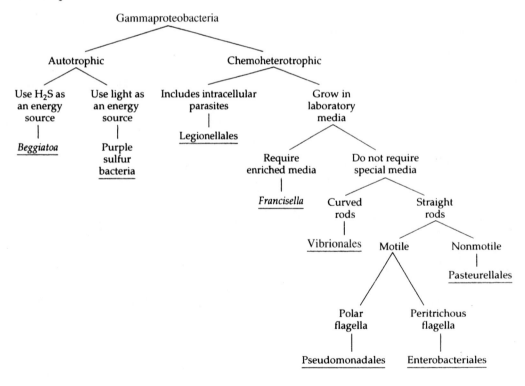

4.   Make a dichotomous key to distinguish among the deltaproteobacteria described in this chapter.

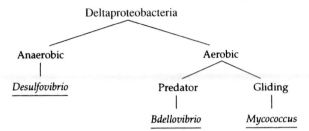

5.   Make a dichotomous key to distinguish among the epsilonproteobacteria described in this chapter.

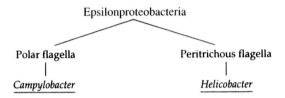

6.   Make a dichotomous key to distinguish among the gram-negative nonproteobacteria described in this chapter.

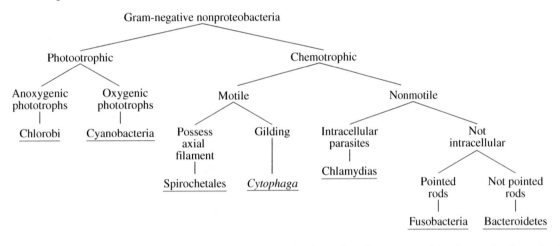

7.   Make a dichotomous key to distinguish among the low G + C gram-positive bacteria described in this chapter.

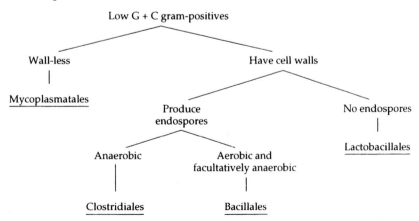

8. Make a dichotomous key to distinguish among the high G + C gram-positive bacteria described in this chapter.

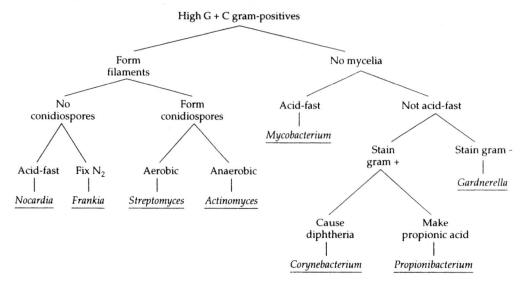

9. Make a dichotomous key to distinguish chlamydias, spirochetes, *Cytophaga*, Bacteroidetes, and Fusobacteria.

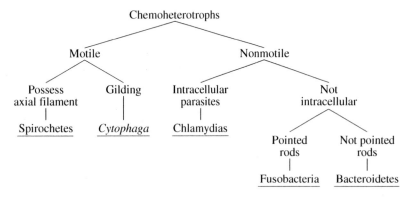

Review

1. a. *Clostridium*
   b. *Bacillus*
   c. *Streptomyces*
   d. *Mycobacterium*
   e. *Streptococcus*
   f. *Staphylococcus*
   g. *Treponema*
   h. *Spirillum*
   i. *Pseudomonas*
   j. *Escherichia*
   k. *Mycoplasma*
   l. *Rickettsia*
   m. *Chlamydia*

2. a. Both are oxygenic photoautotrophs. Cyanobacteria are prokaryotes; algae are eukaryotes.

    b. Both are chemoheterotrophs capable of forming mycelia; some form conidia. Actinomycetes are prokaryotes; fungi are eukaryotes.

    c. Both are large rod-shaped bacteria. *Bacillus* forms endospores, *Lactobacillus* is a fermentative non–endospore-forming rod.

    d. Both are small rod-shaped bacteria. *Pseudomonas* has an oxidative metabolism; *Escherichia* is fermentative. *Pseudomonas* has polar flagella; *Escherichia* has peritrichous flagella.

    e. Both are helical bacteria. *Leptospira* (a spirochete) has an axial filament. *Spirillum* has flagella.

    f. Both are gram-negative, rod-shaped bacteria. *Escherichia* are facultative anaerobes, and *Bacteroides* are anaerobes.

    g. Both are obligatory intracellular parasites. *Rickettsia* are transmitted by ticks; *Chlamydia* have a unique developmental cycle.

    h. Both lack peptidoglycan cell walls. *Ureaplasma* are archaea; *Mycoplasma* are bacteria (see Table 10.2).

3. There are many ways to draw a Key. Here's one example:

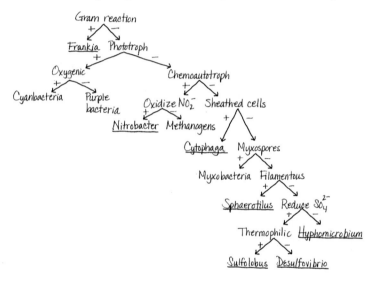

Critical Thinking

1. See Appendix F.

    a. Firmicutes, Actinobacteria

    b. Proteobacteria, nonproteobacteria except *Chlamydia*

    c. Archaea

    d. Mollicutes, *Chlamydia*

2. *Chromatium* and *Escherichia* are both classified as Proteobacteria.

3. a. *Methanobacterium*

    b. *Bacillus*

    c. *Lactobacillus*

    d. *Pseudomonas*

Clinical Applications

1. *Neisseria (meningitidis)*
2. *Salmonella (enterica)*
3. *Listeria (monocytogenes)*

CASE STUDY: MICROTRIVIOLOGY*

Students at Skyline College enjoy answering these trivia questions.

Trivia?! Certainly not a proper description of the science of microbiology! However, facts that are not common knowledge within the community of microbiologists could be described as microtrivia. Microtriviology is the study of these lesser known facts; the pursuit of microtriviology is intended to inform and entertain. You may want to give students 10 to 20 of the following questions.

Using your text, laboratory references, and the library, answer the following questions.

1. What color are the colonies of *Chromobacterium* spp.?
2. Which is larger in diameter, the "average" *Chlamydia* or the vaccinia virus?
3. What is the general nature of the pigment characteristically produced by *Bacteriodes melaninogenicus*?
4. Prior to 1992, *Burkholderia* bacteria were classified into what genus?
5. When was the first edition of *Bergey's Manual of Determinative Bacteriology* published? What edition of *Bergey's Manual of Determinative Bacteriology* is currently in use?
6. Who originally described the bacterium now known as *Escherichia coli (Bacterium coli commune)* and isolated its type species?
7. What is the current classification of bacteria formerly termed members of the Bethesda-Ballerup group?
8. Are the actinomycetes considered bacteria or fungi?
9. After whom was the genus *Erwinia* named?
10. How did *Salmonella* get its name?
11. With what group of bacteria is Runyan associated?
12. What bacterium fixes nitrogen in root nodules of nonleguminous plants?
13. What is the habitat of *Cristispira*?
14. What are X and V factors?
15. What is the *Serratia marcescens* red pigment characteristically produced at room temperature by many strains?
16. The two genera published simultaneously with *Legionella* that share its precedence for the appropriate bacteria are
    a. *Chainia* and *Wangiella*
    b. *Fluoribacter* and *Tatlockia*
    c. *Derxia* and *Gluconobacter*
    d. *Rickettsia* and *Bdellovibrio*
17. Name an endospore-forming coccus.
18. What two staining characteristics do vegetative cells of *Mycobacterium tuberculosis*, ascospores of *Sacchararomyces cerevisiae*, chlamydospores of *Candida albicans*, and endospores of *Bacillus subtilis* have in common?

---

* Philip A. Geis. "Microtriviology." A series of eight articles published in *SIM News*.

19. Match the following *Salmonella* serovars with the term that most closely describes the origin of the strain name.

    1. *S. verity*   a. The Mikado
    2. *S. gilbert*   b. A racehorse
    3. *S. oysterbeds*   c. Texas
    4. *S. manhattan*   d. Oysters Rockefeller
    5. *S. jukestown*   e. Truth
    6. *S. nashua*   f. Chinese egg
    7. *S. tejas*   g. New York
    8. *S. ank*   h. Netherlands
                            i. A jukebox in Georgetown
                            j. Address unknown
                            k. Kansas

20. Match the following microorganisms with the term that best describes the biological or geographical source of its original isolation.

    1. *Corynebacterium tritici*   a. Central Africa
    2. *Azotobacter vinelandii*   b. Wheat
    3. *Torulopsis apis*   c. Beetle
    4. *Dermatophilus congolensis*   d. Grapevine
    5. *Streptomyces bikiniensis*   e. Bee
                                       f. Swimming suits
                                       g. From a shore
                                       h. Vineland, New Jersey
                                       i. Bikini atoll

Answers

1. Violet
2. Vaccinia
3. Heme derivative
4. *Pseudomonas*
5. 1923; 9th
6. Theodor Escherich
7. *Citrobacter*
8. Bacteria
9. Erwin F. Smith
10. By Ligiéres for Daniel Salmon
11. *Mycobacteria*
12. *Frankia*
13. Crystalline styles of mollusks
14. X = heme derivatives; V = NAD$^+$ or NADP$^+$
15. Prodigiosin
16. B
17. *Sporosarcina*
18. Gram-positive and acid-fast
19. 1.e 2.a 3.d 4.k 5.i 6.b 7.c 8.j
20. 1.b 2.h 3.e 4.a 5.i

12 The Eukaryotes: Fungi, Algae, Protozoa, and Helminths

LEARNING OBJECTIVE	CHECK YOUR UNDERSTANDING
12-1 List the defining characteristics of fungi.	Assume you isolated a single-celled organism that has a cell wall. How would you determine that it is a fungus and not a bacterium?
12-2 Differentiate asexual from sexual reproduction, and describe each of these processes in fungi.	Contrast the mechanism of conidiospore and ascospore formation.
12-3 List the defining characteristics of the three phyla of fungi described in this chapter.	List the asexual and sexual spores made by Zygomycetes, Ascomycetes, and Basidiomycetes.
12-4 Identify two beneficial and two harmful effects of fungi.	Are yeasts beneficial or harmful?
12-5 List the distinguishing characteristics of lichens, and describe their nutritional needs.	What is the role of the lichens in nature?
12-6 Describe the roles of the fungus and the alga in a lichen.	What is the role of the fungus in a lichen?
12-7 List the defining characteristics of algae.	How do algae differ from bacteria? From fungi?
12-8 List the outstanding characteristics of the five phyla of algae discussed in this chapter.	List the cell wall composition and diseases caused by the following algae: diatoms, dinoflagellates, oomycotes.
12-9 Identify two beneficial and two harmful effects of algae.	
12-10 List the defining characteristics of protozoa.	Identify three differences between protozoa and animals.
12-11 Describe the outstanding characteristics of the seven phyla of protozoa discussed in this chapter, and give an example of each.	Do protozoa have mitochondria?
12-12 Differentiate an intermediate host from a definitive host.	Where does *Plasmodium* undergo sexual reproduction?
12-13 Compare and contrast cellular slime molds and plasmodial slime molds.	Why are slime molds classified with amoeba and not fungi?
12-14 List the distinguishing characteristics of parasitic helminths.	Why are the drugs used to treat parasitic helminths often toxic to the host?
12-15 Provide a rationale for the elaborate life cycle of parasitic worms.	Of what value is the complicated life cycle of parasitic helminths?
12-16 List the characteristics of the two classes of parasitic platyhelminths, and give an example of each.	Differentiate *Paragonimus* and *Taenia*.

12-17 Describe a parasitic infection in which humans serve as a definitive host, as an intermediate host, and as both.	What is the definitive host for *Enterobius*?
12-18 List the characteristics of parasitic nematodes, and give an example of infective eggs and infective larvae.	What stage of *Dirofilaria immitis* is infectious for dogs and cats?
12-19 Compare and contrast platyhelminths and nematodes.	You find a parasitic worm in a baby's diapers. How would you know whether it's a *Taenia* or a *Necator*?
12-20 Define *arthropod vector*.	Vectors can be divided into three major types, according to the roles they play for the parasite. List the three types of vectors and a disease transmitted by each.
12-21 Differentiate a tick from a mosquito, and name a disease transmitted by each.	Assume you see an arthropod on your arm. How will you determine whether it is a tick or a flea?

NEW IN THIS EDITION

- Discussion of new uses of fungi as pesticides
- Expanded discussion of the oomycotes, including the introduction of *Phytophthora* into the United States; a new figure illustrating *Phytophthora*'s life cycle
- Discussion of heartworm
- A new Clinical Focus (*MMWR*) box highlighting cryptosporidial diarrhea, the most common pathogen associated with swimming

CHAPTER SUMMARY

Fungi (pp. 330–339)

1. Mycology is the study of fungi.
2. The number of serious fungal infections is increasing.
3. Fungi are aerobic or facultatively anaerobic chemoheterotrophs.
4. Most fungi are decomposers, and a few are parasites of plants and animals.

Characteristics of Fungi (pp. 331–333)

5. A fungal thallus consists of filaments of cells called hyphae; a mass of hyphae is called a mycelium.
6. Yeasts are unicellular fungi. To reproduce, fission yeasts divide symmetrically, whereas budding yeasts divide asymmetrically.
7. Buds that do not separate from the mother cell form pseudohyphae.
8. Pathogenic dimorphic fungi are yeastlike at 37°C and moldlike at 25°C.
9. Fungi are classified according to rRNA.
10. Sporangiospores and conidiospores are produced asexually.
11. Sexual spores are usually produced in response to special circumstances, often changes in the environment.
12. Fungi can grow in acidic, low-moisture, aerobic environments.
13. They are able to metabolize complex carbohydrates.

Medically Important Phyla of Fungi (pp. 333–335)

14. The Zygomycota have coenocytic hyphae and produce sporangiospores and zygospores.

15. The Ascomycota have septate hyphae and produce ascospores and frequently conidiospores.

16. Basidiomycota have septate hyphae and produce basidiospores; some produce conidiospores.

17. Teleomorphic fungi produce sexual and asexual spores; anamorphic fungi produce asexual spores only.

Fungal Diseases (pp. 335–339)

18. Systemic mycoses are fungal infections deep within the body that affect many tissues and organs.

19. Subcutaneous mycoses are fungal infections beneath the skin.

20. Cutaneous mycoses affect keratin-containing tissues such as hair, nails, and skin.

21. Superficial mycoses are localized on hair shafts and superficial skin cells.

22. Opportunistic mycoses are caused by fungi that are not usually pathogenic.

23. Opportunistic mycoses can infect any tissues. However, they are usually systemic.

Economic Effects of Fungi (p. 339)

24. *Saccharomyces* and *Trichoderma* are used in the production of foods.

25. Fungi are used for the biological control of pests.

26. Mold spoilage of fruits, grains, and vegetables is more common than bacterial spoilage of these products.

27. Many fungi cause diseases in plants.

Lichens (pp. 339–340)

1. A lichen is a mutualistic combination of an alga (or a cyanobacterium) and a fungus.

2. The alga photosynthesizes, providing carbohydrates for the lichen; the fungus provides a holdfast.

3. Lichens colonize habitats that are unsuitable for either the alga or the fungus alone.

4. Lichens may be classified on the basis of morphology as crustose, foliose, or fruticose.

Algae (pp. 340–345)

1. Algae are unicellular, filamentous, or multicellular (thallic).

2. Most algae live in aquatic environments.

Characteristics of Algae (pp. 341–342)

3. Algae are eukaryotic; most are photoautotrophs.

4. The thallus of multicellular algae usually consists of a stipe, a holdfast, and blades.

5. Algae reproduce asexually by cell division and fragmentation.

6. Many algae reproduce sexually.

7. Photoautotrophic algae produce oxygen.

8. Algae are classified according to their structures and pigments.

Selected Phyla of Algae (pp. 342–344)

9. Brown algae (kelp) may be harvested for algin.

10. Red algae grow deeper in the ocean than other algae.

11. Green algae have cellulose and chlorophyll *a* and *b* and store starch.

12. Diatoms are unicellular and have pectin and silica cell walls; some produce a neurotoxin.

13. Dinoflagellates produce neurotoxins that cause paralytic shellfish poisoning and ciguatera.

14. The oomycotes are heterotrophic; they include decomposers and pathogens.

Roles of Algae in Nature (p. 344–345)

15. Algae are the primary producers in aquatic food chains.
16. Planktonic algae produce most of the molecular oxygen in the Earth's atmosphere.
17. Petroleum is the fossil remains of planktonic algae.
18. Unicellular algae are symbionts in such animals as *Tridacna*.

Protozoa (pp. 345–351)

1. Protozoa are unicellular, eukaryotic chemoheterotrophs.
2. Protozoa are found in soil and water and as normal microbiota in animals.

Characteristics of Protozoa (p. 346)

3. The vegetative form is called a trophozoite.
4. Asexual reproduction is by fission, budding, or schizogony.
5. Sexual reproduction is by conjugation.
6. During ciliate conjugation, two haploid nuclei fuse to produce a zygote.
7. Some protozoa can produce a cyst that provides protection during adverse environmental conditions.
8. Protozoa have complex cells with a pellicle, a cytostome, and an anal pore.

Medically Important Phyla of Protozoa (pp. 346–351)

9. Archaezoa lack mitochondria and have flagella; they include *Trichomonas* and *Giardia*.
10. Microsporidia lack mitochondria and microtubules; microsporans cause diarrhea in AIDS patients.
11. Amoebozoa are amoeba; they include *Entamoeba* and *Acanthamoeba*.
12. Apicomplexa have apical organelles for penetrating host tissue; they include *Plasmodium* and *Cryptosporidium*.
13. Ciliophora move by means of cilia; *Balantidium coli* is the human parasitic ciliate.
14. Euglenozoa move by means of flagella and lack sexual reproduction; they include *Trypanosoma*.

Slime Molds (pp. 351–352)

1. Cellular slime molds resemble amoebas and ingest bacteria by phagocytosis.
2. Plasmodial slime molds consist of a multinucleated mass of protoplasm that engulfs organic debris and bacteria as it moves.

Helminths (pp. 352–361)

1. Parasitic flatworms belong to the Phylum Platyhelminthes.
2. Parasitic roundworms belong to the Phylum Nematoda.

Characteristics of Helminths (pp. 353–355)

3. Helminths are multicellular animals; a few are parasites of humans.
4. The anatomy and life cycle of parasitic helminths are modified for parasitism.
5. The adult stage of a parasitic helminth is found in the definitive host.
6. Each larval stage of a parasitic helminth requires an intermediate host.
7. Helminths can be monoecious or dioecious.

Platyhelminths (pp. 356–358)

8. Flatworms are dorsoventrally flattened animals; parasitic flatworms may lack a digestive system.

9. Adult trematodes, or flukes, have an oral and ventral sucker with which they attach to host tissue.

10. Eggs of trematodes hatch into free-swimming miracidia that enter the first intermediate host; two generations of rediae develop; the rediae become cercariae that bore out of the first intermediate host and penetrate the second intermediate host; cercariae encyst as metacercariae; the metacercariae develop into adults in the definitive host.

11. A cestode, or tapeworm, consists of a scolex (head) and proglottids.

12. Humans serve as the definitive host for the beef tapeworm, and cattle are the intermediate host.

13. Humans serve as the definitive host and can be an intermediate host for the pork tapeworm.

14. Humans serve as the intermediate host for *Echinococcus granulosus;* the definitive hosts are dogs, wolves, and foxes.

Nematodes (pp. 358–361)

15. Roundworms have a complete digestive system.

16. The nematodes that infect humans with their eggs include (pinworm) *Ascaris.*

17. The nematodes that infect humans with their larvae include hookworm and *Trichinella.*

Arthropods as Vectors (pp. 361–363)

1. Jointed-legged animals, including ticks and insects, belong to the Phylum Arthropoda.

2. Arthropods that carry diseases are called vectors.

3. Vectorborne diseases are most effectively eliminated by controlling or eradicating the vectors.

THE LOOP

This chapter is divided so that you can select the units that meet the needs of your class.

Study Questions

Fungi (pp. 330–339) Review 1, 2, 4; Clinical 2
Algae (pp. 340–345) Review 3
Lichens (pp. 339–340) Review 3
Protozoa (pp. 345–351, 355) Review 5, 6; Critical Thinking 3; Clinical 3
Slime molds (pp. 351–352) Review 4; Critical Thinking 1
Helminths (pp. 352–361) Review 7, 8, 9; Critical Thinking 2; Clinical 1
Arthropods (pp. 361–363) Review 15

Detailed discussions of diseases caused by fungi, protozoa, and helminths appear in Part Four. If this chapter does not fit into the lecture portion of your course, you might assign it as self-study in conjunction with Part Four or laboratory exercises. Students might complete the Study Questions prior to the laboratory periods. The chapter test could be used as a posttest after students complete the laboratory exercises.

ANSWERS

Review

1. a. Systemic   c. Cutaneous   e. Systemic
   b. Subcutaneous   d. Superficial

2. a.   *E. coli*

    b.   *P. chrysogenum*

3. As the first colonizers on newly exposed rock or soil, lichens are responsible for the chemical weathering of large inorganic particles and the consequent accumulation of soil.

4. Cellular slime molds exist as individual amoeboid cells. Plasmodial slime molds are multinucleate masses of protoplasm. Both survive adverse environmental conditions by forming spores.

5. a.   Flagella   e.   Pseudopods   i.   Cilia

    b.   *Giardia*   f.   *Entamoeba*   j.   *Balantidium*

    c.   None   g.   None   k.   Flagella

    d.   *Nosema*   h.   *Plasmodium*   l.   *Trypanosoma*

6. *Trichomonas* cannot survive for long outside a host because it does not form a protective cyst. *Trichomonas* must be transferred from host to host quickly.

7. Ingestion.

8. Phylum: Platyhelminthes

    Class: Trematode

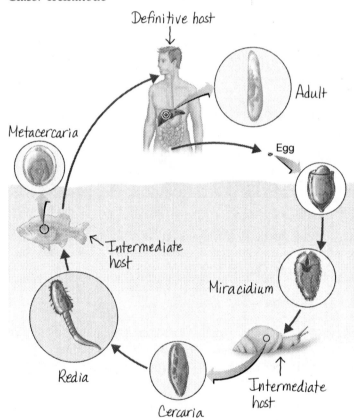

9. The male reproductive organs are in one individual, and the female reproductive organs in another. Nematodes belong to the Phylum Aschelminthes.

Critical Thinking

1. Plasmodial slime molds have an internal transport system, called protoplasmic streaming, to ensure circulation.

2. Fish (larva) $\dfrac{\text{Ingestion of fish}}{\text{Ingestion of eggs}}$ Mammal (adult)

    Mammals (e.g., bears) are a more likely part of the freshwater ecosystem, so parasites would evolve to use mammalian hosts.

3. Phylum: Protozoa
    Class: Mastigophora
    Host: Human
    Vector: Tsetse fly

Clinical Applications

1. *Taenia solium;* ingestion of tapeworm eggs excreted by a household member. Prevention: handwashing to break the fecal–oral cycle.
2. *Coccidioides immitis;* inhalation of arthrospores. Prevention: avoid working in contaminated soils.
3. Malaria; transmitted by bite of *Anopheles* mosquito.

CASE STUDY: THE UNFORTUNATE ALASKAN FISHING TRIP

Background

The Alaska Department of Public Health was notified that foodborne illness had occurred in fishermen aboard a fishing boat off the Alaska peninsula. The fishermen had eaten baked fish, steamed clams and mussels, boiled rice, boiled potatoes, and green salad. No alcohol was consumed.

Data

Case	Symptoms	Onset (hr)	Foods Eaten					
			Clams	Mussels	Salmon	Halibut	Rice	Potatoes
1	None	—	1			x		x
2	Vomiting; numbness around mouth; lower back pain	2.5	4–5			x	x	
3	None	—			x			x
4	Numbness of tongue and jaw; tingling of fingers	2	5			x		x
5	Numbness and tingling of face and hands; dizziness	1.5						
6	None	—		1 raw		x	x	
7	None	—	1			x	x	
8	None	—		1 raw	x			x

continues on next page

Case	Symptoms	Onset (hr)	Foods Eaten					
			Clams	Mussels	Salmon	Halibut	Rice	Potatoes
9	Numbness and tingling around mouth, face, and fingers; cardiopulmonary arrest. Died.	0.5	25–30			x		
10	Vomiting; numbness of lips and fingers; lower back pain	2		4–5		x		x
11	Vomiting; numbness of throat, toes, and fingers; perioral numbness	1		12			x	x
12	Lower back pain	2	6–7		x		x	
13	Nausea	0.5	2			x	x	
14	Numbness of face; paralysis of legs	1	20–25					x
15	Vomiting; numbness and tingling of jaws and arms; loss of consciousness	1		18–24				x
16	None	—	1					x
17	None	—				x		x
18	Vomiting; numbness of mouth; tingling of fingers and toes	2	3–4		x			x
19	Vomiting; tingling of mouth, face, and fingers	2	6–7				x	x
20	Numbness of face and hands; dizziness	1.5	10				x	
21	Paralysis of right arm; lower back pain	1.5	15–20					x

Questions

1. Identify the etiologic agent of this outbreak of food poisoning.
2. Was it food infection or intoxication?
3. How did the food get contaminated, and what item was contaminated?
4. Briefly explain how you arrived at your conclusion.

Hints

1. Make a summary table of the persons not ill.
2. Make a table of the onset of symptoms following eating.

The Solution

1. Paralytic shellfish poisoning (PSP) caused by *Alexandrium* toxin.
2. Intoxication.
3. Mollusks can become toxic when toxin-producing dinoflagellates create massive algal blooms known as "red tides."
4. The diagnosis of PSP is based on patient exposure history and clinical manifestations.

13

Viruses, Viroids, and Prions

LEARNING OBJECTIVE	CHECK YOUR UNDERSTANDING
13-1 Differentiate a virus from a bacterium.	How could the small size of viruses have helped researchers detect viruses before the invention of the electron microscope?
13-2 Describe the chemical and physical structure of both an enveloped and a nonenveloped virus.	Diagram a nonenveloped polyhedral virus that has spikes.
13-3 Define *viral species*.	How does a virus species differ from a bacterial species?
13-4 Give an example of a family, genus, and common name for a virus.	Attach the proper endings to *Papilloma-* to show the family and genus that includes HPV, the cause of cervical cancer.
13-5 Describe how bacteriophages are cultured.	What is the plaque method?
13-6 Describe how animal viruses are cultured.	Why are continuous cell lines of more practical use than primary cell lines for culturing viruses?
13-7 List three techniques used to identify viruses.	What tests could you use to identify influenza virus in a patient?
13-8 Describe the lytic cycle of T-even bacteriophages.	How do bacteriophages get nucleotides and amino acids if they don't have any metabolic enzymes?
13-9 Describe the lysogenic cycle of bacteriophage lambda.	*Vibrio cholerae* produces toxin and is capable of causing cholera only when it is lysogenic. What does this mean?
13-10 Compare and contrast the multiplication cycle of DNA and RNA-containing animal viruses.	Describe the principal events of attachment, entry, uncoating, biosynthesis, maturation, and release of an enveloped DNA-containing virus.
13-11 Define *oncogene* and *transformed cell*.	What is a provirus?
13-12 Discuss the relationship between DNA- and RNA-containing viruses and cancer.	How can an RNA virus cause cancer if it doesn't have DNA to insert into a cell's genome?
13-13 Provide an example of a patent viral infection.	Is shingles a persistent or latent infection?
13-14 Differentiate persistent viral infections from latent viral infections.	
13-15 Discuss how a protein can be infectious.	Contrast viroids and prions, and for each name a disease it causes.
13-16 Differentiate virus, viroid, and prion.	
13-17 Describe the lytic cycle for a plant virus.	How do plant viruses enter host cells?

NEW IN THIS EDITION

- Chapter-opening discussion of the use of retroviridae to genetically modify cells
- Discussion of bee colony collapse disease
- Updated Clinical Focus (*MMWR*) box on the evolution and occurrence of avian flu

CHAPTER SUMMARY

General Characteristics of Viruses (pp. 368–369)

1. Depending on one's viewpoint, viruses may be regarded as exceptionally complex aggregations of nonliving chemicals or as exceptionally simple living microbes.
2. Viruses contain a single type of nucleic acid (DNA or RNA) and a protein coat, sometimes enclosed by an envelope composed of lipids, proteins, and carbohydrates.
3. Viruses are obligatory intracellular parasites. They multiply by using the host cell's synthesizing machinery to cause the synthesis of specialized elements that can transfer the viral nucleic acid to other cells.

Host Range (pp. 368–369)

4. *Host range* refers to the spectrum of host cells in which a virus can multiply.
5. Most viruses infect only specific types of cells in one host species.
6. Host range is determined by the specific attachment site on the host cell's surface and the availability of host cellular factors.

Viral Size (p. 369)

7. Viral size is ascertained by electron microscopy.
8. Viruses range from 20 to 1000 nm in length.

Viral Structure (pp. 370–373)

1. A virion is a complete, fully developed viral particle composed of nucleic acid surrounded by a coat.

Nucleic Acid (pp. 371–372)

2. Viruses contain either DNA or RNA, never both, and the nucleic acid may be single- or double-stranded, linear or circular, or divided into several separate molecules.
3. The proportion of nucleic acid in relation to protein in viruses ranges from about 1% to about 50%.

Capsid and Envelope (pp. 372–373)

4. The protein coat surrounding the nucleic acid of a virus is called the capsid.
5. The capsid is composed of subunits, capsomeres, which can be a single type of protein or several types.
6. The capsid of some viruses is enclosed by an envelope consisting of lipids, proteins, and carbohydrates.
7. Some envelopes are covered with carbohydrate-protein complexes called spikes.

General Morphology (p. 373)

8. Helical viruses (for example, Ebola virus) resemble long rods, and their capsids are hollow cylinders surrounding the nucleic acid.

9. Polyhedral viruses (for example, adenovirus) are many-sided. Usually the capsid is an icosahedron.

10. Enveloped viruses are covered by an envelope and are roughly spherical but highly pleomorphic. There are also enveloped helical viruses (for example, influenza virus) and enveloped polyhedral viruses (for example, *Simplexvirus*).

11. Complex viruses have complex structures. For example, many bacteriophages have a polyhedral capsid with a helical tail attached.

Taxonomy of Viruses (pp. 373–374)

1. Classification of viruses is based on type of nucleic acid, strategy for replication, and morphology.

2. Virus family names end in -*viridae;* genus names end in -*virus.*

3. A viral species is a group of viruses sharing the same genetic information and ecological niche.

Isolation, Cultivation, and Identification of Viruses (pp. 374–379)

1. Viruses must be grown in living cells.

2. The easiest viruses to grow are bacteriophages.

Growing Bacteriophages in the Laboratory (pp. 374, 377)

3. The plaque method mixes bacteriophages with host bacteria and nutrient agar.

4. After several viral multiplication cycles, the bacteria in the area surrounding the original virus are destroyed; the area of lysis is called a plaque.

5. Each plaque originates with a single viral particle; the concentration of viruses is given as plaque-forming units.

Growing Animal Viruses in the Laboratory (pp. 377–379)

6. Cultivation of some animal viruses requires whole animals.

7. Simian AIDS and feline AIDS provide models for studying human AIDS.

8. Some animal viruses can be cultivated in embryonated eggs.

9. Cell cultures are cells growing in culture media in the laboratory.

10. Primary cell lines and embryonic diploid cell lines grow for a short time in vitro.

11. Continuous cell lines can be maintained in vitro indefinitely.

12. Viral growth can cause cytopathic effects in the cell culture.

Viral Identification (p. 379)

13. Serological tests are used most often to identify viruses.

14. Viruses may be identified by RFLPs and PCR.

Viral Multiplication (pp. 379–389)

1. Viruses do not contain enzymes for energy production or protein synthesis.

2. For a virus to multiply, it must invade a host cell and direct the host's metabolic machinery to produce viral enzymes and components.

Multiplication of Bacteriophages (pp. 379–382)

3. During the lytic cycle, a phage causes the lysis and death of a host cell.

4. Some viruses can either cause lysis or have their DNA incorporated as a prophage into the DNA of the host cell. The latter situation is called lysogeny.

5. During the attachment phase of the lytic cycle, sites on the phage's tail fibers attach to complementary receptor sites on the bacterial cell.

6. In penetration, phage lysozyme opens a portion of the bacterial cell wall, the tail sheath contracts to force the tail core through the cell wall, and phage DNA enters the bacterial cell. The capsid remains outside.

7. In biosynthesis, transcription of phage DNA produces mRNA coding for proteins necessary for phage multiplication. Phage DNA is replicated, and capsid proteins are produced. During the eclipse period, separate phage DNA and protein can be found.

8. During maturation, phage DNA and capsids are assembled into complete viruses.

9. During release, phage lysozyme breaks down the bacterial cell wall, and the new phages are released.

10. During the lysogenic cycle, prophage genes are regulated by a repressor coded for by the prophage. The prophage is replicated each time the cell divides.

11. Exposure to certain mutagens can lead to excision of the prophage and initiation of the lytic cycle.

12. Because of lysogeny, lysogenic cells become immune to reinfection with the same phage and may undergo phage conversion.

13. A lysogenic phage can transfer bacterial genes from one cell to another through transduction. Any genes can be transferred in generalized transduction, and specific genes can be transferred in specialized transduction.

Multiplication of Animal Viruses (pp. 382–389)

14. Animal viruses attach to the plasma membrane of the host cell.

15. Entry occurs by endocytosis or fusion.

16. Animal viruses are uncoated by viral or host cell enzymes.

17. The DNA of most DNA viruses is released into the nucleus of the host cell. Transcription of viral DNA and translation produce viral DNA and, later, capsid proteins. Capsid proteins are synthesized in the cytoplasm of the host cell.

18. DNA viruses include members of the families Adenoviridae, Poxviridae, Herpesviridae, Papovaviridae, and Hepadnaviridae.

19. Multiplication of RNA viruses occurs in the cytoplasm of the host cell. RNA-dependent RNA polymerase synthesizes a double-stranded RNA.

20. Picornaviridae + strand RNA acts as mRNA and directs the synthesis of RNA-dependent RNA polymerase.

21. Togaviridae + strand RNA acts as a template for RNA-dependent RNA polymerase, and mRNA is transcribed from a new – RNA strand.

22. Rhabdoviridae – strand RNA is a template for viral RNA-dependent RNA polymerase, which transcribes mRNA.

23. Reoviridae are digested in host cell cytoplasm to release mRNA for viral biosynthesis.

24. Retroviridae reverse transcriptase (RNA-dependent DNA polymerase) transcribes DNA from RNA.

25. After maturation, viruses are released. One method of release (and envelope formation) is budding. Nonenveloped viruses are released through ruptures in the host cell membrane.

Viruses and Cancer (pp. 389)

1. The earliest relationship between cancer and viruses was demonstrated in the early 1900s, when chicken leukemia and chicken sarcoma were transferred to healthy animals by cell-free filtrates.

The Transformation of Normal Cells into Tumor Cells (pp. 390–391)

2. When activated, oncogenes transform normal cells into cancerous cells.
3. Viruses capable of producing tumors are called oncogenic viruses.
4. Several DNA viruses and retroviruses are oncogenic.
5. The genetic material of oncogenic viruses becomes integrated into the host cell's DNA.
6. Transformed cells lose contact inhibition, contain virus-specific antigens (TSTA and T antigen), exhibit chromosome abnormalities, and can produce tumors when injected into susceptible animals.

DNA Oncogenic Viruses (p. 391)

7. Oncogenic viruses are found among the Adenoviridae, Herpesviridae, Poxviridae, and Papovaviridae.
8. The EB virus, a herpesvirus, causes Burkitt's lymphoma and nasopharyngeal carcinoma. *Hepadnavirus* causes liver cancer.

RNA Oncogenic Viruses (p. 391)

9. Among the RNA viruses, only retroviruses seem to be oncogenic.
10. HTLV-1 and HTLV-2 have been associated with human leukemia and lymphoma.
11. The virus's ability to produce tumors is related to the production of reverse transcriptase. The DNA synthesized from the viral RNA becomes incorporated as a provirus into the host cell's DNA.
12. A provirus can remain latent, can produce viruses, or can transform the host cell.

Latent Viral Infections (p. 392)

1. A latent viral infection is one in which the virus remains in the host cell for long periods without producing an infection.
2. Examples are cold sores and shingles.

Persistent Viral Infections (p. 392)

1. Persistent viral infections are disease processes that occur over a long period and are generally fatal.
2. Persistent viral infections are caused by conventional viruses; viruses accumulate over a long period.

Prions (pp. 392–393)

1. Prions are infectious proteins first discovered in the 1980s.
2. Prion diseases, such as CJD and mad cow disease, all involve the degeneration of brain tissue.
3. Prion diseases are the result of an altered protein; the cause can be a mutation in the normal gene for PrP^C or contact with an altered protein (PrP^{Sc}).

Plant Viruses and Viroids (pp. 393–395)

1. Plant viruses must enter plant hosts through wounds or with invasive parasites, such as insects.
2. Some plant viruses also multiply in insect (vector) cells.
3. Viroids are infectious pieces of RNA that cause some plant diseases, such as potato spindle tuber disease.

THE LOOP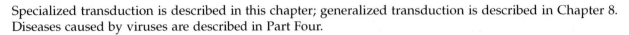

Specialized transduction is described in this chapter; generalized transduction is described in Chapter 8. Diseases caused by viruses are described in Part Four.

ANSWERS

Review

1. Viruses absolutely require living host cells to multiply.

2. A virus has the following properties:

   a. Contains DNA or RNA;

   b. Has a protein coat surrounding the nucleic acid;

   c. Multiplies inside a living cell using the synthetic machinery of the cell; and

   d. Causes the synthesis of virions. A virion is a fully developed virus particle that transfers the viral nucleic acid to other cells and initiates multiplication.

3. The capsid of a helical virus is a hollow cylinder with a helical shape, which surrounds the nucleic acid (see Figure 13.4). An example of a helical virus is tobacco mosaic virus. Polyhedral viruses are many-sided (Figure 13.2). A polyhedral virus in the shape of an icosahedron is adenovirus. Polyhedral or helical viruses surrounded by an envelope are called enveloped viruses. An example of an enveloped helical virus is *Influenzavirus* (Figure 13.3), and herpes simplex is an enveloped polyhedral virus.

4.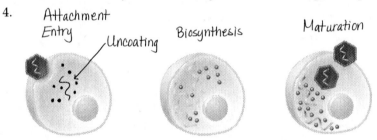

5. Both produce double-stranded RNA, with the – strand being the template for more + strands. + strands act as mRNA in both virus groups.

6. Antibiotic treatment of *S. aureus* can activate phage genes that encode P-V leukocidin.

7. a. Viruses cannot easily be observed in host tissues. Viruses cannot easily be cultured in order to be inoculated into a new host. Additionally, viruses are specific for their hosts and cells, making it difficult to substitute a laboratory animal for the third step of Koch's postulates.

   b. Some viruses can infect cells without inducing cancer. Cancer may not develop until long after infection. Cancers do not seem to be contagious.

8. a. subacute sclerosing panencephalitis

   b. common viruses

   c. persistent

9. a. plant cell walls

   b. vectors such as sap-sucking insects

   c. plant protoplasts and insect cell cultures

Critical Thinking

1. Outside living cells, viruses are inert. They cannot ingest and metabolize nutrients, and they cannot reproduce. These are descriptions one might use for chemicals, not living organisms. However, inside a living cell, viruses can multiply. Clinically, because they cause infection and disease, they might be considered alive.

2. A virus is small and cannot hold as much DNA as a cell. Genes that code for proteins that serve two functions conserve space on a viral nucleic acid.

3. These two diseases provide animal models for the study of acquired immunodeficiencies and treatments. Study of the viruses (SIV and FIV) can provide more information regarding the evolution of retroviruses.

4. A prophage, provirus, or plasmid begins as a strand of DNA outside the cell's chromosome that can be integrated into the chromosome. Like a plasmid, a prophage carries genes that can be used by the cell but are not essential. Prophages and proviruses are replicated with the cell's chromosome and remain in progeny cells. Prophage DNA will form a circle and replicate itself in the cell's cytoplasm. Unlike a plasmid, prophages and proviruses are not transferred in conjugation, and when they replicate themselves, viruses are produced that can destroy the host cell.

Clinical Applications

1. Cytomegalovirus. No bacteria or fungi were seen, which suggests a viral cause.

2. Herpes simplex virus. Presence of antibodies against this virus would confirm the etiology.

3. Hepatitis; these people acquired hepatitis A virus from contaminated ice-slushes.

Picornaviridae Hepatitis A Virus	Ingestion	+RNA, ss	Nonenveloped	
Hepadnaviridae Hepatitis B Virus	Injection	DNA, ds	Enveloped	Uses reverse transcriptase
Flaviviridae Hepatitis C Virus	Injection	+RNA, ss	Enveloped	

CASE STUDY: ENCEPHALITIS, TEXAS

Background

On May 30, a 22-year-old man complained of right hand weakness.

On June 1, he complained of right arm numbness.

On June 2, he exhibited several episodes of staring and unresponsiveness lasting 10 to 15 seconds. He consulted a physician in Mexico, who prescribed an unknown medication. That evening, he presented himself to a hospital emergency room in Texas complaining of right hand pain. He had been punctured by a catfish fin earlier in the week, so, based on this information, he was treated with ceftriaxone and tetanus toxoid.

On June 3, when he returned to the emergency room complaining of spasms, he was hyperventilating and had a white blood cell (WBC) count of 11,100 per µl. Although he was discharged after reporting some improvement, he began to have intermittent episodes of rigidity, breath holding, hallucinations, and difficulty swallowing. Eventually he refused liquids. That evening, he was admitted to the intensive-care unit of another hospital in Texas with a preliminary diagnosis of either encephalitis or tetanus. Manifestations included frequent spasms of the face, mouth, and neck; stuttering speech; hyperventilation; and a temperature of 37.8°C. His WBC count was 17,100 mm^3 with granulocytosis. He was sedated and observed.

On the morning of June 4, the patient was confused, disoriented, and areflexic (without reflexes). Although his neck was supple, muscle tonus was increased in his upper extremities. Analysis of cerebrospinal fluid indicated slightly elevated protein, slightly elevated glucose, and 1 WBC per 100 µl. An electroencephalogram showed abnormal activity. Because he had uncontrolled oral secretions, he was intubated. His temperature rose to 41.7°C, and he was sweating profusely.

On June 5, the man died.

The patient had worked as a phlebotomist for a blood bank and had donated blood on May 22. His platelets had been transfused before he became ill, but the remainder of his blood products were destroyed.

Questions

1. What was the purpose of the ceftriaxone? The tetanus toxoid?
2. What is granulocytosis?
3. What is the most likely cause of the man's illness and death?
4. What other information do you need to be sure?
5. How could he have been treated?
6. How should the recipient of the platelets be treated?

The Solution

1. To prevent tetanus.
2. An increase in granulocytes (neutrophils, eosinophils, and basophils).
3. Rabies. On June 4, the patient's supervisor from work reported to hospital authorities that the man had suffered a bat bite on the right index finger. CSF, serum, and skin biopsy were tested for rabies; all of these samples were negative. Postmortem samples of brain tissue were positive for rabies by direct immunofluorescent antibody test.
4. A fluorescent-antibody test would confirm the diagnosis of rabies.
5. Treatment with antibodies against rabies (rabies immune globulin) before the symptoms began could have saved him.
6. With rabies immune globulin.

14

Principles of Disease and Epidemiology

LEARNING OBJECTIVE	CHECK YOUR UNDERSTANDING
14-1 Define *pathology, etiology, infection,* and *disease.*	What are the objectives of pathology?
14-2 Define *normal* and *transient microbiota.*	How do normal microbiota differ from transient microbiota?
14-3 Compare commensalism, mutualism, and parasitism, and give an example of each.	Give several examples of microbial antagonism.
14-4 Contrast normal microbiota and transient microbiota with opportunistic microorganisms.	How can opportunistic pathogens cause infections?
14-5 List Koch's postulates.	Explain some exceptions to Koch's postulates.
14-6 Differentiate a communicable from a noncommunicable disease.	Does *Clostridium perfringens* (p. 646) cause a communicable disease?
14-7 Categorize diseases according to frequency of occurrence.	Distinguish the incidence from the prevalence of a disease.
14-8 Categorize diseases according to severity.	List two examples of acute and chronic diseases.
14-9 Define *herd immunity.*	How does herd immunity develop?
14-10 Identify four predisposing factors for disease.	What is a predisposing factor?
14-11 Put the following in proper sequence, according to the pattern of disease: period of decline, period of convalescence, period of illness, prodromal period, incubation period.	The incubation period for a cold is 3 days; the period of disease is usually 5 days. If the person next to you has a cold, when will you know if you contracted it?
14-12 Define *reservoir of infection.*	Why are carriers important reservoirs of infection?
14-13 Contrast human, animal, and nonliving reservoirs, and give one example of each.	How are zoonoses transmitted to humans?
14-14 Explain three methods of disease transmission.	Give an example of contact transmission, vehicle transmission, mechanical transmission, and biological transmission.
14-15 Define *nosocomial infections,* and explain their importance.	What interacting factors result in nosocomial infections?
14-16 Define *compromised host.*	What is a compromised host?
14-17 List several methods of disease transmission in hospitals.	How are nosocomial infections primarily transmitted, and how can they be prevented?
14-18 Explain how nosocomial infections can be prevented.	

14-19 List several probable reasons for emerging infectious diseases, and name one example for each reason.	Give several examples of emerging infectious diseases.
14-20 Define *epidemiology*, and describe three types of epidemiologic investigations.	After learning that 40 hospital employees developed nausea and vomiting, the hospital infection control officer determined that 39 ill people ate green beans in the hospital cafeteria compared to 34 healthy people who ate in the cafeteria the same day but did not eat green beans in the hospital cafeteria. What type of epidemiology is this?
14-21 Identify the function of the CDC.	What is the CDC's function?
14-22 Define the following terms: *morbidity, mortality,* and *notifiable infectious disease.*	In 2003, the morbidity of hemolytic uremic syndrome was 176, and the mortality was 29. The morbidity of listeriosis was 696; the mortality was 33. Which disease is more likely to be fatal?

NEW IN THIS EDITION

- Updated Clinical Focus (*MMWR*) box illustrating the emergence of hospital-acquired and community-acquired MRSA

CHAPTER SUMMARY

Introduction (p. 399)

1. Disease-causing microorganisms are called pathogens.
2. Pathogenic microorganisms have special properties that allow them to invade the human body or produce toxins.
3. When a microorganism overcomes the body's defenses, a state of disease results.

Pathology, Infection, and Disease (p. 400)

1. Pathology is the scientific study of disease.
2. Pathology is concerned with the etiology (cause), pathogenesis (development), and effects of disease.
3. Infection is the invasion and growth of pathogens in the body.
4. A host is an organism that shelters and supports the growth of pathogens.
5. Disease is an abnormal state in which part or all of the body is not properly adjusted or is incapable of performing normal functions.

Normal Microbiota (pp. 400–404)

1. Animals, including humans, are usually germfree in utero.
2. Microorganisms begin colonization in and on the surface of the body soon after birth.
3. Microorganisms that establish permanent colonies inside or on the body without producing disease make up the normal microbiota.
4. Transient microbiota are microbes that are present for various periods and then disappear.

Relationships between the Normal Microbiota and the Host (pp. 401–403)

5. The normal microbiota can prevent pathogens from causing an infection; this phenomenon is known as microbial antagonism.

6. Normal microbiota and the host exist in symbiosis (living together).

7. The three types of symbiosis are commensalism (one organism benefits, and the other is unaffected), mutualism (both organisms benefit), and parasitism (one organism benefits, and one is harmed).

Opportunistic Microorganisms (pp. 403–404)

8. Opportunistic pathogens do not cause disease under normal conditions but cause disease under special conditions.

Cooperation among Microorganisms (p. 404)

9. In some situations, one microorganism makes it possible for another to cause a disease or produce more severe symptoms.

The Etiology of Infectious Diseases (pp. 404–406)

Koch's Postulates (p. 404)

1. Koch's postulates are criteria for establishing that specific microbes cause specific diseases.

2. Koch's postulates have the following requirements: (1) the same pathogen must be present in every case of the disease; (2) the pathogen must be isolated in pure culture; (3) the pathogen isolated from pure culture must cause the same disease in a healthy, susceptible laboratory animal; and (4) the pathogen must be reisolated from the inoculated laboratory animal.

Exceptions to Koch's Postulates (pp. 404–406)

3. Koch's postulates are modified to establish etiologies of diseases caused by viruses and some bacteria, which cannot be grown on artificial media.

4. Some diseases, such as tetanus, have unequivocal signs and symptoms.

5. Some diseases, such as pneumonia and nephritis, may be caused by a variety of microbes.

6. Some pathogens, such as *S. pyogenes,* cause several different diseases.

7. Certain pathogens, such as HIV, cause disease in humans only.

Classifying Infectious Diseases (pp. 406–407)

1. A patient may exhibit symptoms (subjective changes in body functions) and signs (measurable changes), which a physician uses to make a diagnosis (identification of the disease).

2. A specific group of symptoms or signs that always accompanies a specific disease is called a syndrome.

3. Communicable diseases are transmitted directly or indirectly from one host to another.

4. A contagious disease is one that is easily spread from one person to another.

5. Noncommunicable diseases are caused by microorganisms that normally grow outside the human body and are not transmitted from one host to another.

Occurrence of a Disease (p. 406)

6. Disease occurrence is reported by incidence (number of people contracting the disease) and prevalence (number of cases at a particular time).

7. Diseases are classified by frequency of occurrence: sporadic, endemic, epidemic, and pandemic.

Severity or Duration of a Disease (pp. 406–407)

8. The scope of a disease can be defined as acute, chronic, subacute, or latent.

9. Herd immunity is the presence of immunity to a disease in most of the population.

Extent of Host Involvement (p. 407)

10. A local infection affects a small area of the body; a systemic infection is spread throughout the body via the circulatory system.

11. A primary infection is an acute infection that causes the initial illness.

12. A secondary infection can occur after the host is weakened from a primary infection.

13. An inapparent, or subclinical, infection does not cause any signs of disease in the host.

Patterns of Disease (pp. 408–409)

Predisposing Factors (p. 408)

1. A predisposing factor is one that makes the body more susceptible to disease or alters the course of a disease.

2. Examples include gender, climate, age, fatigue, and inadequate nutrition.

Development of Disease (pp. 408–409)

3. The incubation period is the interval between the initial infection and the first appearance of signs and symptoms.

4. The prodromal period is characterized by the appearance of the first mild signs and symptoms.

5. During the period of illness, the disease is at its height, and all disease signs and symptoms are apparent.

6. During the period of decline, the signs and symptoms subside.

7. During the period of convalescence, the body returns to its prediseased state, and health is restored.

The Spread of Infection (pp. 409–413)

Reservoirs of Infection (p. 409)

1. A continual source of infection is called a reservoir of infection.

2. People who have a disease or are carriers of pathogenic microorganisms are human reservoirs of infection.

3. Zoonoses are diseases that affect wild and domestic animals and can be transmitted to humans.

4. Some pathogenic microorganisms grow in nonliving reservoirs, such as soil and water.

Transmission of Disease (pp. 409–413)

5. Transmission by direct contact involves close physical contact between the source of the disease and a susceptible host.

6. Transmission by fomites (inanimate objects) constitutes indirect contact.

7. Transmission via saliva or mucus in coughing or sneezing is called droplet transmission.

8. Transmission by a medium such as water, food, or air is called vehicle transmission.

9. Airborne transmission refers to pathogens carried on water droplets or dust for a distance greater than 1 meter.

10. Arthropod vectors carry pathogens from one host to another by both mechanical and biological transmission.

Nosocomial (Hospital-Acquired) Infections (pp. 413–416)

1. A nosocomial infection is any infection that is acquired during the course of stay in a hospital, nursing home, or other health care facility.
2. About 5 to 15% of all hospitalized patients acquire nosocomial infections.

Microorganisms in the Hospital (p. 414)

3. Certain normal microbiota are often responsible for nosocomial infections when they are introduced into the body through such medical procedures as surgery and catheterization.
4. Opportunistic, drug-resistant gram-negative bacteria are the most frequent causes of nosocomial infections.

Compromised Host (p. 415)

5. Patients with burns, surgical wounds, and suppressed immune systems are the most susceptible to nosocomial infections.

Chain of Transmission (pp. 415–416)

6. Nosocomial infections are transmitted by direct contact between staff members and patients and between patients.
7. Fomites such as catheters, syringes, and respiratory devices can transmit nosocomial infections.

Control of Nosocomial Infections (p. 416)

8. Aseptic techniques can prevent nosocomial infections.
9. Hospital infection control staff members are responsible for overseeing the proper cleaning, storage, and handling of equipment and supplies.

Emerging Infectious Diseases (pp. 416–418)

1. New diseases and diseases with increasing incidences are called emerging infectious diseases (EIDs).
2. EIDs can result from the use of antibiotics and pesticides, climatic changes, travel, the lack of vaccinations, and improved case reporting.
3. The CDC, NIH, and WHO are responsible for surveillance and responses to emerging infectious diseases.

Epidemiology (pp. 418–422)

1. The science of epidemiology is the study of the transmission, incidence, and frequency of disease.
2. Modern epidemiology began in the mid-1800s with the works of Snow, Semmelweis, and Nightingale.
3. In descriptive epidemiology, data about infected people are collected and analyzed.
4. In analytical epidemiology, a group of infected people is compared with an uninfected group.
5. In experimental epidemiology, controlled experiments designed to test hypotheses are performed.
6. Case reporting provides data on incidence and prevalence to local, state, and national health officials.
7. The Centers for Disease Control and Prevention (CDC) is the main source of epidemiologic information in the United States.
8. The CDC publishes the *Morbidity and Mortality Weekly Report* to provide information on morbidity (incidence) and mortality (deaths).

THE LOOP

Prevention of nosocomial infections can be emphasized in an allied health class. The boxes in Chapters 6 and 7, "Delayed Bloodstream Infection Following Catheterization" (p. 164), and "Infection Following Steroid Injection" (p. 201), provide additional examples.

To expand on epidemiology, assign problems from the case histories of this guide. The following Clinical Focus boxes illustrate the work of epidemiologists:

Human Tuberculosis—New York City	*Mycobacterium bovis*	p. 144 (Chapter 5)
Delayed Bloodstream Infection Following Catheterization	*Pseudomonas fluorescens*	p. 164 (Chapter 6)
Infection Following Steroid Injection	Rapidly growing mycobacteria	p. 201 (Chapter 7)
Norovirus—Who Is Responsible for the Outbreak?	Norovirus	p. 266 (Chapter 9)
The Most Frequent Cause of Recreational Waterborne Diarrhea	*Cryptosporidium*	p. 355 (Chapter 12)
Nosocomial Infections	MRSA	p. 422 (Chapter 14)
A World Health Problem	Measles	p. 505 (Chapter 18)
Infections in the Gym	MRSA	p. 593 (Chapter 21)
A Neurological Disease	Rabies	p. 625 (Chapter 22)
A Sick Child	MRSA	p. 644 (Chapter 23)
Outbreak	*Legionella pneumophila*	p. 691 (Chapter 24)
A Foodborne Infection	*Salmonella enterica*	p. 715 (Chapter 25)
Survival of the Fittest	*Neisseria gonorrhoeae*	p. 751 (Chapter 26)

ANSWERS

Review

1. a. Etiology is the study of the cause of a disease, whereas pathogenesis is the manner in which the disease develops.

    b. Infection refers to the colonization of the body by a microorganism. Disease is any change from a state of health. A disease may, but does not always, result from infection.

    c. A communicable disease is a disease that is spread from one host to another, whereas a non-communicable disease is not transmitted from one host to another.

2. Symbiosis refers to different organisms living together. Commensalism is a symbiotic relationship in which one of the organisms is benefited and the other is unaffected. Corynebacteria living on the surface of the eye are commensals. Mutualism is a symbiosis in which both organisms are benefited. *E. coli* receives nutrients and a constant temperature in the large intestine and produces vitamin K and certain B vitamins that are useful for the human host. In parasitism, one organism benefits while the other is harmed. *Salmonella enterica* receives nutrients and warmth in the large intestine, and the human host experiences gastroenteritis or typhoid fever.

3.

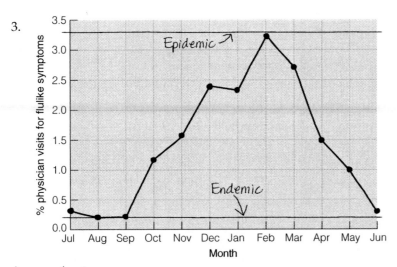

4. a. Acute

    b. Chronic

    c. Subacute

5. Hospital patients may be in a weakened condition and therefore predisposed to infection. Pathogenic microorganisms are generally transmitted to patients by contact and airborne transmission. The reservoirs of infection are the hospital staff, visitors, and other patients.

6. Changes in body function felt by the patient are called symptoms. Symptoms such as weakness or pain are not measurable by a physician. Objective changes that the physician can observe and measure are called signs.

7. When microorganisms causing a local infection enter a blood or lymph vessel and are spread throughout the body, a systemic infection can result.

8. Mutualistic microorganisms are providing a chemical or environment that is essential for the host. In a commensal relationship, the microorganisms are obtaining nutrients from sloughed-off cells and secretions, which benefits the host by removing materials that might be invaded by pathogens. These organisms, however, are not essential; another microorganism might serve the function as well.

9. Incubation period, prodromal period, period of illness, period of decline (may be crisis), period of convalescence.

Critical Thinking

1. Koch provided reproducible steps using scientific methodology. De Bary was correct but did not provide proof or experimental procedures that would provide proof. Recall that Koch also developed culturing and staining procedures.

2. Nightingale collected data on infected persons (descriptive epidemiology) and learned that the place of most infections was in the combat area. She compared two groups of soldiers, those at home (control) and those in battle (experimental) to determine what factors contributed to disease (analytical epidemiology). She then instituted sanitation measures in the Crimea, and the incidence of disease decreased (experimental epidemiology).

Disease	Transmission	Prevention
Cholera	Water	Proper disposal of sewage; disinfection of water.
Typhus	Body lice	Washing; disinfection of clothes and bedding.

Also see: I. B. Cohen, "Florence Nightingale." *Scientific American* 250:128–137, March 1984.

3. a. Malaria—Vector

    b. Tuberculosis—Airborne

    c. Nosocomial infections—Any method, although vectorborne is unlikely

    d. Salmonellosis—Common vehicle

    e. Streptococcal pharyngitis—Direct contact

    f. Mononucleosis—Droplet

    g. Measles—Direct contact; airborne

    h. Hepatitis A—Common vehicle; direct contact

    i. Tetanus—Indirect contact

    j. Hepatitis B—Indirect contact

    k. Chlamydial urethritis—Direct contact

4. Endemic level ≈ 400 cases or 0.15/100,000 per year. Information for the world population would have to be provided to indicate whether a pandemic state exists. Typhoid fever is transmitted by the fecal–oral route, usually through water.

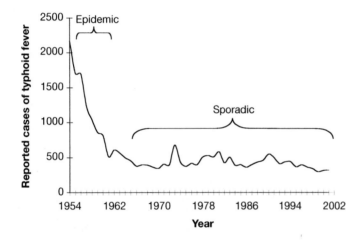

Clinical Applications

1. Mistakes: Exposure to nasopharyngeal secretions and failure to get antibiotic therapy.

    Meningitis is transmitted by the respiratory route.

2. Probable source: contaminated cleaning water.

    Burkholderia can tolerate a wide range of environmental conditions (e.g., low temperatures) and can grow on unusual carbon sources, including many detergents and disinfectants.

3. February 7 to March 9: incubation period.

    March 9: prodromal period.

    March 10 to March 17: period of illness.

    March 17: period of decline by crisis.

    Next 2 weeks: period of convalescence.

    Psittacosis is caused by *Chlamydophila psittaci.*

4. The infection is probably transmitted from patient to patient on the unwashed hands of hospital staff. Hospital staff must wash their hands between patients, wear gloves when appropriate, and wash their hands after removing gloves.

5. *Mycobacterium* is usually transmitted by the respiratory route. The hospital source seems to be the water system. The boiler and pipes need to be cleaned and disinfected. Biofilms must be prevented from growing in the boiler and pipes.

CASE STUDY: AN OUTBREAK OF FOOD POISONING, SAN FRANCISCO

Background

An outbreak of food poisoning occurred, affecting half the members of five families who ate at a restaurant in San Francisco at 3 p.m. on June 20.

On June 20, a woman was admitted to a hospital with "chilliness," nausea, abdominal cramps, and watery diarrhea. The next morning, she complained of limb numbness and difficulty swallowing and breathing. Examination was unremarkable except for slight weakness of the upper extremities and diminished deep tendon reflexes. Laboratory analysis yielded no viral or bacterial infection.

An investigation was started to trace her contacts. During the investigation, it became apparent that the symptoms were due to a meal shared by 32 persons on June 20. The restaurant purchased rice from a produce market in a 50-kg bag. The rice was boiled the morning of the dinner and kept warm in foil-covered pots. Chicken was purchased from a supermarket. The chicken was cut up, browned in oil, and boiled for 2 hours; the flesh was pulled from the bones. The chicken was mixed with rice noodles. A whole, gutted pig was roasted in a conventional hot-air oven until the meat was white. Rice noodles were purchased from a supermarket, boiled, and pan-fried. Whole, ungutted jackfish were purchased from a seaman who caught the fish at Midway Island. The fish were frozen in the ship's freezer until return to the Port of Oakland on June 19; they were gutted and cut into steaks, which were deep-fried and served in vinegar/herb sauce. The fish heads and viscera were boiled with vegetables for 15 minutes to make chowder (escabeche).

Questions

1. On one page, identify the etiologic agent of this outbreak of food poisoning.
2. Was it food infection or intoxication?
3. How did the food get contaminated, and what item was contaminated?
4. Briefly explain how you arrived at your conclusion. How did you eliminate the other major causes of food poisoning?

Hints

1. Make a summary table of the persons not ill.
2. Make a table of the onset of symptoms following eating.

Data

The data appear on page 122.

The Solution

1. Ciguatera poisoning.
2. Intoxication.
3. Ciguateratoxin is derived from the dinoflagellate *Gambierdiscus toxicus*, which herbivorous coral reef fish consume. Jackfish eat the herbivorous fish.
4. Diagnosis is clinical, based on the combination of gastrointestinal and neurological symptoms. The disease is endemic in many areas of the Caribbean and South Pacific.

| Case | Age | Sex | Symptoms | | | | | | | | Foods Eaten | | | | | | | Onset of Symptoms | | Duration |
			C	M	NV	A	B	R	N	V	1	2	3	4	5	6	7	Date	Hr	Days
1	66	M	x	x	x	x	x				x	x	x	x	x	x		20	7p	1
2	32	M		x	x	x					x			x	x	x	x	20	6p	1.5
3	29	F									x	x	x	x	x	x	x			
4	55	F											x	x	x	x	x			
5	39	F									x	x			x	x	x			
6	25	M									x	x			x	x	x			
7	32	M										x	x		x	x	x			
8		F	x		x		x			x	x	x			x	x		20	8p	1
9	25												x	x		x				
10	9	M		x	x	x	x				x		x	x		x	x			
11	10	M	x					x	x		x	x		x	x			21	8p	1
12	20	F										x	x	x		x	x	20	5p	14
13	34	F										x	x	x	x		x			
14	42	F									x		x	x						
15	13	F											x	x		x				
16	12	M												x	x	x	x			
17	66	F	x	x		x		x			x	x	x	x	x	x	x	20	6p	1
18	49	M		x	x	x					x			x	x	x		20	7p	1
19	32	F	x					x	x		x	x		x		x	x	20	5p	14
20	33	M	x	x		x	x				x	x	x		x		x	20	6p	1.5
21	25	M		x	x			x	x	x	x	x	x	x				21	6a	1.5
22	25	F	x		x	x				x	x	x	x	x	x	x	x	20	5p	0.5
23	40	F								x			x	x		x		22	11a	1
24	43	M	x	x	x	x	x	x	x	x	x	x		x		x	x	20	5p	14
25	30	F					x				x		x	x	x			20	5p	1
26	44	M		x	x	x					x	x		x	x	x	x	20	5p	3
27	49	F											x	x	x		x			
28	50	F										x	x	x	x	x	x			
29	32	M									x		x	x	x					
30	33	M	x		x				x	x	x	x			x		x	20	5p	14
31	52	F		x	x						x	x			x	x	x	20	7p	2
32	36	F	x	x	x	x					x	x		x		x	x	20	9p	11

Legend:
Symptoms: C = Chills, M = Malaise, NV = Nausea, vomiting, A = Abdominal pain, B = Blurred vision, R = Respiratory difficulty, N = Numbness, V = Vertigo.
Food: 1-Fried fish, 2-Chowder, 3-Pork, 4-Chicken/noodles, 5-Rice, 6-Fruit, 7-Chocolate cake.

15 Microbial Mechanisms of Pathogenicity

LEARNING OBJECTIVE	CHECK YOUR UNDERSTANDING
15-1 Identify the principal portals of entry.	List three portals of entry, and describe how microorganisms gain access through each.
15-2 Define ID_{50} and LD_{50}.	The LD_{50} of botulinum toxin is 0.03 ng/kg; the LD_{50} of *Salmonella* toxin is 12 mg/kg. Which is the more potent toxin?
15-3 Using examples, explain how microbes adhere to host cells.	How would a drug that binds mannose on human cells affect a pathogenic bacterium?
15-4 Explain how capsules and cell wall components contribute to pathogenicity.	What function do capsules and M proteins have in common?
15-5 Compare the effects of coagulases, kinases, hyaluronidase, and collagenase.	Would you expect a bacterium to make coagulase and kinase simultaneously?
15-6 Define and give an example of *antigenic variation*.	Many vaccines provide years of protection against a disease. Why doesn't the influenza vaccine offer more than a few months of protection?
15-7 Describe how bacteria use the host cell's cytoskeleton to enter the cell.	How does *E. coli* cause membrane ruffling?
15-8 Describe the function of siderophores.	Of what value are siderophores?
15-9 Provide an example of direct damage, and compare this to toxin production.	How does toxigenicity differ from direct damage?
15-10 Contrast the nature and effects of exotoxins and endotoxins.	Differentiate an exotoxin from an endotoxin.
15-11 Outline the mechanisms of action of A-B toxins, membrane-disrupting toxins, and superantigens. Classify diphtheria toxin, erythrogenic toxin, botulinum toxin, tetanus toxin, *Vibrio* enterotoxin, and staphylococcal enterotoxin.	Food poisoning can be divided into two categories: food infection and food intoxication. On the basis of toxin production by bacteria, explain the difference between these two categories.
15-12 Identify the importance of the LAL assay.	Washwater containing *Pseudomonas* was sterilized and used to wash cardiac catheters. Three patients developed fever, chills, and hypotension following cardiac catheterization. The water and catheters were sterile. Why did the patients show these reactions? How should the water have been tested?
15-13 Using examples, describe the roles of plasmids and lysogeny in pathogenicity.	How can lysogeny turn the normally harmless *E. coli* into a pathogen?

15-14 List nine cytopathic effects of viral infections.   Define *cytopathic effects,* and give five examples.

15-15 Discuss the causes of symptoms in fungal, protozoan, helminthic, and algal diseases.   Identify one virulence factors that contributes to the pathogenicity of each of the following diseases: fungal, protozoan, helminthic, and algal.

15-16 Differentiate portal of entry and portal of exit.   Which are the most often used portals of exit?

NEW IN THIS EDITION

- Revised discussion of A-B toxins
- A new Clinical Focus (*MMWR*) box showing the risk of contamination with endotoxins

CHAPTER SUMMARY

Introduction (p. 428)

1. Pathogenicity is the ability of a pathogen to produce a disease by overcoming the defenses of the host.
2. Virulence is the degree of pathogenicity.

How Microorganisms Enter a Host (pp. 429–432)

1. The specific route by which a particular pathogen gains access to the body is called its portal of entry.

Portals of Entry (p. 429)

2. Many microorganisms can penetrate mucous membranes of the conjunctiva and the respiratory, gastrointestinal, and genitourinary tracts.
3. Most microorganisms cannot penetrate intact skin; they enter hair follicles and sweat ducts.
4. Some microorganisms can gain access to tissues by inoculation through the skin and mucous membranes in bites, injections, and other wounds. This route of penetration is called the parenteral route.

The Preferred Portal of Entry (p. 429)

5. Many microorganisms can cause infections only when they gain access through their specific portal of entry.

Numbers of Invading Microbes (pp. 429–431)

6. Virulence can be expressed as LD_{50} (lethal dose for 50% of the inoculated hosts) or ID_{50} (infectious dose for 50% of the inoculated hosts).

Adherence (pp. 431–432)

7. Surface projections on a pathogen called adhesins (ligands) adhere to complementary receptors on the host cells.
8. Adhesins can be glycoproteins or lipoproteins and are frequently associated with fimbriae.
9. Mannose is the most common receptor.
10. Biofilms provide attachment and resistance to antimicrobial agents.

How Bacterial Pathogens Penetrate Host Defenses (pp. 432–434)

Capsules (p. 432)

1. Some pathogens have capsules that prevent them from being phagocytized.

Cell Wall Components (p. 432)

2. Proteins in the cell wall can facilitate adherence or prevent a pathogen from being phagocytized.

Enzymes (pp. 432–433)

3. Local infections can be protected in a fibrin clot caused by the bacterial enzyme coagulase.
4. Bacteria can spread from a focal infection by means of kinases (which destroy blood clots), hyaluronidase (which destroys a mucopolysaccharide that holds cells together), and collagenase (which hydrolyzes connective tissue collagen).
5. IgA proteases destroy IgA antibodies.

Antigenic Variation (p. 433)

6. Some microbes vary expression of antigens, thus avoiding the host's antibodies.

Penetration into the Host Cell Cytoskeleton (p. 433)

7. Bacteria may produce proteins that alter the actin of the host cell's cytoskeleton allowing bacteria into the cell.

How Bacterial Pathogens Damage Host Cells (pp. 434–441)

Using the Host's Nutrients: Siderophores (p. 434)

1. Bacteria get iron from the host using siderophores.

Direct Damage (p. 434)

2. Host cells can be destroyed when pathogens metabolize and multiply inside the host cells.

The Production of Toxins (pp. 434–439)

3. Poisonous substances produced by microorganisms are called toxins; toxemia refers to the presence of toxins in the blood. The ability to produce toxins is called toxigenicity.
4. Exotoxins are produced by bacteria and released into the surrounding medium. Exotoxins, not the bacteria, produce the disease symptoms.
5. Antibodies produced against exotoxins are called antitoxins.
6. A-B toxins consist of an active component that inhibits a cellular process and a binding component that attaches the two portions to the target cell, e.g., diphtheria toxin.
7. Membrane-disrupting toxins cause cell lysis, e.g., hemolysins.
8. Superantigens cause release of cytokines, which cause fever, nausea, and other symptoms; e.g., toxic shock syndrome toxin.
9. Endotoxins are lipopolysaccharides (LPS), the lipid A component of the cell wall of gram-negative bacteria.
10. Bacterial cell death, antibiotics, and antibodies may cause the release of endotoxins.
11. Endotoxins cause fever (by inducing the release of interleukin-1) and shock (because of a TNF-induced decrease in blood pressure).
12. Endotoxins allow bacteria to cross the blood–brain barrier.
13. The *Limulus* amoebocyte lysate (LAL) assay is used to detect endotoxins in drugs and on medical devices.

Plasmids, Lysogeny, and Pathogenicity (pp. 440–441)

14. Plasmids may carry genes for antibiotic resistance, toxins, capsules, and fimbriae.
15. Lysogenic conversion can result in bacteria with virulence factors, such as toxins or capsules.

Pathogenic Properties of Viruses (pp. 441–443)

1. Viruses avoid the host's immune response by growing inside cells.
2. Viruses gain access to host cells because they have attachment sites for receptors on the host cell.
3. Visible signs of viral infections are called cytopathic effects (CPE).
4. Some viruses cause cytocidal effects (cell death), and others cause noncytocidal effects (damage but not death).
5. Cytopathic effects include stopping mitosis, lysis, formation of inclusion bodies, cell fusion, antigenic changes, chromosomal changes, and transformation.

Pathogenic Properties of Fungi, Protozoa, Helminths, and Algae (pp. 443–444)

1. Symptoms of fungal infections can be caused by capsules, toxins, and allergic responses.
2. Symptoms of protozoan and helminthic diseases can be caused by damage to host tissue or by the metabolic waste products of the parasite.
3. Some protozoa change their surface antigens while growing in a host, thus avoiding destruction by the host's antibodies.
4. Some algae produce neurotoxins that cause paralysis when ingested by humans.

Portals of Exit (pp. 444–445)

1. Pathogens have definite portals of exit.
2. Three common portals of exit are the respiratory tract via coughing or sneezing, the gastrointestinal tract via saliva or feces, and the genitourinary tract via secretions from the vagina or penis.
3. Arthropods and syringes provide a portal of exit for microbes in blood.

THE LOOP ○━━━▭

Material in this chapter can be assigned with Chapter 4 to provide clinical information on cell structure. It can also be included with Part Four to provide information on how pathogens cause disease.

ANSWERS

Review

1. The ability of a microorganism to produce a disease is called pathogenicity. The degree of pathogenicity is virulence.
2. Encapsulated bacteria can resist phagocytosis and continue growing. *Streptococcus pneumoniae* and *Klebsiella pneumoniae* produce capsules that are related to their virulence. M protein found in the cell walls of *Streptococcus pyogenes* and A protein in the cell walls of *Staphylococcus aureus* help these bacteria resist phagocytosis.
3. Hemolysins are enzymes that cause the lysis of red blood cells; hemolysis might supply nutrients for bacterial growth. Leukocidins destroy neutrophils and macrophages that are active in phagocytosis; this decreases host resistance to infection. Coagulase is an enzyme that causes the fibrinogen

in blood to clot; the clot may protect the bacterium from phagocytosis and other host defenses. Bacterial kinases break down fibrin; kinases can destroy a clot that was made to isolate the bacteria, thus allowing the bacteria to spread. Hyaluronidase hydrolyzes the hyaluronic acid that binds cells together; this could allow the bacteria to spread through tissues. Siderophores take iron from host iron-transport proteins, thus allowing bacteria to get iron for growth. IgA proteases destroy IgA antibodies; IgA antibodies protect mucosal surfaces.

4. a. Would inhibit bacteria.

    b. Would prevent adherence of *N. gonorrhoeae*.

    c. *S. pyogenes* would not be able to attach to host cells and would be more susceptible to phagocytosis.

5.

	Exotoxin	Endotoxin
Bacterial source	Gram +	Gram −
Chemistry	Proteins	Lipid A
Toxigenicity	High	Low
Pharmacology	Destroy certain cell parts or physiological functions	Systemic, fever, weakness, aches, and shock
Example	Botulinum toxin	Salmonellosis

6.

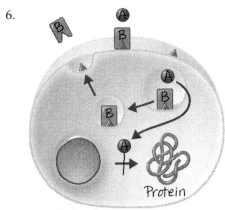

7. Pathogenic fungi do not have specific virulence factors; capsules, metabolic products, toxins, and allergic responses contribute to the virulence of pathogenic fungi. Some fungi produce toxins that, when ingested, produce disease. Protozoa and helminths elicit symptoms by destroying host tissues and producing toxic metabolic wastes.

8. *Legionella*.

9. Viruses avoid the host's immune response by growing inside host cells; some can remain latent in a host cell for prolonged periods. Some protozoa avoid the immune response by mutations that change their antigens.

Critical Thinking

1. Increased incidence in summer months suggests fecal–oral transmission while swimming. The disease is associated with the seasonal use of recreational waters and the lack of rainfall to provide clean water.

2. During the summer (highest light intensity), a smaller dose produces symptoms.

3. If normal microbiota are killed by the sulfonamide and the *Salmonella* are sulfonamide-resistant, the *Salmonella* have an easier time growing.

4.

Yersinia	Avoids destruction by complement	Plague
Helicobacter	Neutralizes stomach acid	Peptic disease syndrome
Rhinovirus	Gains access to host cells to avoid the immune response	Common cold

Clinical Applications

1. *Clostridium tetani* growing at the site of the wound produced an exotoxin. Her pain and spasms were due to an infection. This disease, tetanus, cannot be transmitted to another person.

2. a. Infection. *Vibrio parahaemolyticus.*

   b. Intoxication. Ciguatera.

3. *Salmonella* used the host's cytoskeleton to enter the cell. If the drug that inhibits cell division affects arrangement of the cytoskeleton, *Salmonella* will not be able to enter the cell.

CASE STUDY: FOOD POISONING, NEW MEXICO

Background

The New Mexico Health Department was consulted by an Albuquerque physician regarding two patients, a husband and wife, who had become ill within 45 minutes of eating dinner. Their symptoms included nausea, vomiting, diarrhea, headache, fever, flushing, and rapid pulse rate. An investigation found that the couple had shared a meal of grilled mahi mahi, pasta, salad, water, and wine. In a hospital emergency room, both patients were treated with antihistamines and ipecac. Their symptoms resolved within 36 hours of the onset of illness.

The fish had been imported from Taiwan through California and shipped frozen to the Albuquerque distributor, where it was thawed and sold from iced refrigerator cases. The patients had frozen the fish after they bought it. Later, they thawed it for 3 hours at room temperature and then grilled the still icy fish.

Questions

1. Identify the etiologic agent of this outbreak of food poisoning.

2. Was it food infection or intoxication?

3. How did the food get contaminated, and what item was contaminated?

4. Briefly explain how you arrived at your conclusion.

Data

Food Eaten	Husband	Wife	Daughter	Dog
Fish	x	x		x
Pasta	x	x	x	
Salad	x	x	x	
Wine	x	x	x	
Water	x	x	x	x
Ill	Yes	Yes	No	Yes

The Solution

1. Scombroid fish poisoning.

2. Intoxication.

3. Of all varieties of fish, the scombroid species and certain other dark-meat fish are the most likely to develop high levels of histamine. When fresh scombroid fish are not continuously iced or refrigerated, bacteria may convert the amino acid histidine, which occurs naturally in the muscle of the fish, to histamine. Because histamine is resistant to heat, cooking the fish generally will not prevent illness. Histamine levels may not be correlated with any obvious signs of decomposition of the fish. Thus, prompt and proper refrigeration or icing from the time the fish is caught until it is preserved, processed, or cooked is essential to prevent scombroid fish poisoning. Antihistamines may be useful for symptomatic treatment.

   Because histamine is metabolized by intestinal microbiota, even large doses of ingested pure histamine usually do not cause symptoms. Thus, although histamine is a marker for fish that could cause scombroid fish poisoning, the actual mechanism for the poisoning must depend on an additional cofactor. Experimental evidence indicates that other substances produced in fish by putrefactive bacteria inhibit the metabolism of histamine and permit its absorption and circulation.

4. Recovery after treatment with antihistamines. Fish samples obtained from the store yielded histamine levels of 3 mg/100 g of sample.

16

Innate Immunity: Nonspecific Defenses of the Host

LEARNING OBJECTIVES	CHECK YOUR UNDERSTANDING
16-1 Differentiate innate and adaptive immunity.	Which defense system, innate or adaptive immunity, prevents entry of microbes into the body?
16-2 Define *Toll-like receptors*.	What relationship do Toll-like receptors have to pathogen-associated molecular patterns?
16-3 Describe the role of the skin and mucous membranes in innate immunity.	Identify one physical factor and one chemical factor that prevent microbes from entering the body through skin and mucous membranes.
16-4 Differentiate physical from chemical factors, and list five examples of each.	Identify one physical factor and one chemical factor that prevent microbes from entering or colonizing the body through the eyes, digestive tract, and respiratory tract.
16-5 Describe the role of normal microbiota in innate immunity.	Distinguish microbial antagonism from commensalism.
16-6 Classify leukocytes, and describe the roles of granulocytes and monocytes.	Compare the structures and function of monocytes and neutrophils.
16-7 Define *differential white blood cell count*.	Describe the six different types of white blood cells, and name a function for each type.
16-8 Differentiate the lymphatic and blood circulatory systems.	What is the function of lymph nodes?
16-9 Define *phagocyte* and *phagocytosis*.	What do fixed and wandering macrophages do?
16-10 Describe the process of phagocytosis, and include the stages of adherence and ingestion.	What is the role of TLRs in phagocytosis?
16-11 Identify six mechanisms of avoiding destruction by phagocytosis.	How does each of these bacteria avoid destruction by phagocytes? *Streptococcus pneumoniae, Staphylococcus aureus, Listeria monocytogenes, Mycobacterium tuberculosis, Rickettsia*
16-12 List the stages of inflammation.	What purposes does inflammation serve?
16-13 Describe the roles of vasodilation, kinins, prostaglandins, and leukotrienes in inflammation.	What causes the redness, swelling, and pain associated with inflammation?
16-14 Describe phagocyte migration.	What is margination?
16-15 Describe the cause and effects of fever.	Why does a chill indicate that a fever is about to occur?
16-16 List the major components of the complement system.	What is complement?

16-17 Describe three pathways of activating complement.	List the steps of complementation activation via (1) the classical pathway, (2) the alternative pathway, and (3) the lectin pathway.
16-18 Describe three consequences of complement activation.	Summarize the major outcomes of complement activation.
16-19 Define *interferons.*	What is interferon?
16-20 Compare and contrast the actions of IFN-α and IFN-β with IFN-γ.	Why do IFN-α and IFN-β share the same receptor on target cells, yet IFN-γ has a different receptor?
16-21 Describe the role of iron-binding proteins in innate immunity.	What is the role of siderophores in infection?
16-22 Describe the role of antimicrobial peptides in innate immunity.	Why are scientists interested in AMPs?

NEW IN THIS EDITION

- Discussion of the roles that pathogen-associated molecules and biofilms play in infection
- Expanded discussions of physical and chemical factors in first line of defense and the lymphatic system
- Enhanced description of the roles of acute-phase proteins, complement, iron-binding proteins, and antimicrobial peptides
- New discussion of a test for complement in the Applications of Microbiology box describing serum and plasma collection

CHAPTER SUMMARY
Introduction (p. 449)

1. The ability to ward off disease through body defenses is called immunity.
2. Lack of immunity is called susceptibility.

The Concept of Immunity (p. 450)

1. Innate immunity refers to all body defenses that protect the body against any kind of pathogen.
2. Adaptive immunity refers to defenses (antibodies) against specific microorganisms.
3. Toll-like receptors are proteins in plasma membranes of macrophages and dendritic cells. TLRs bind to invading microbes.

FIRST LINE OF DEFENSE: SKIN AND MUCOUS MEMBRANES (pp. 450–453)

1. The body's first line of defense against infections is a physical barrier and the nonspecific chemicals of the skin and mucous membranes.

Physical Factors (pp. 451–452)

1. The structure of intact skin and the waterproof protein keratin provide resistance to microbial invasion.
2. Some pathogens can penetrate mucous membranes.
3. The lacrimal apparatus protects the eyes from irritating substances and microorganisms.

4. Saliva washes microorganisms from teeth and gums.

5. Mucus traps many microorganisms that enter the respiratory and gastrointestinal tracts; in the lower respiratory tract, the ciliary escalator moves mucus up and out.

6. The flow of urine moves microorganisms out of the urinary tract, and vaginal secretions move microorganisms out of the vagina.

Chemical Factors (p. 453)

1. Sebum contains unsaturated fatty acids, which inhibit the growth of pathogenic bacteria. Some bacteria commonly found on the skin can metabolize sebum and cause the inflammatory response associated with acne.

2. Perspiration washes microorganisms off the skin.

3. Lysozyme is found in tears, saliva, nasal secretions, and perspiration.

4. The high acidity (pH 1.2–3.0) of gastric juice prevents microbial growth in the stomach.

Normal Microbiota and Innate Immunity (p. 453)

1. Normal microbiota change the environment, a process that can prevent the growth of pathogens.

SECOND LINE OF DEFENSE (pp. 454–472)

1. A microbe's penetration of the first line of defense encourages production of phagocytes, inflammation, fever, and antimicrobial substances.

Formed Elements in Blood (pp. 454–456)

1. Blood consists of plasma (fluid) and formed elements (cells and cell fragments).

2. Leukocytes (white blood cells) are divided into granulocytes (neutrophils, basophils, eosinophils, and dendritic cells) and agranulocytes.

3. During many infections, the number of leukocytes increases (leukocytosis); some infections are characterized by leukopenia (decrease in leukocytes).

The Lymphatic System (p. 456–457)

1. The lymphatic system consists of lymph vessels, lymph nodes, and lymphoid tissue.

2. Interstitial fluid is returned to blood plasma via lymph vessels.

Phagocytes (pp. 457–460)

1. Phagocytosis is the ingestion of microorganisms or particulate matter by a cell.

2. Phagocytosis is performed by phagocytes, certain types of white blood cells or their derivatives.

Actions of Phagocytic Cells (p. 457)

3. Among the granulocytes, neutrophils are the most important phagocytes.

4. Enlarged monocytes become wandering macrophages and fixed macrophages.

5. Fixed macrophages are located in selected tissues and are part of the mononuclear phagocytic system.

6. Granulocytes predominate during the early stages of infection, whereas monocytes predominate as the infection subsides.

The Mechanism of Phagocytosis (pp. 458–459)

7. Chemotaxis is the process by which phagocytes are attracted to microorganisms.
8. Toll-like receptors on a phagocyte adhere to the microbial cells; adherence may be facilitated by opsonization—coating the microbe with serum proteins.
9. Pseudopods of phagocytes engulf the microorganism and enclose it in a phagosome to complete ingestion.
10. Many phagocytized microorganisms are killed by lysosomal enzymes and oxidizing agents.

Microbial Evasion of Phagocytosis (pp. 459–460)

11. Some microbes are not killed by phagocytes and can even reproduce in phagocytes.
12. Evasion mechanisms include M protein, capsules, leukocidins, membrane attack complexes, and prevention of phagolysosome formation.

Inflammation (pp. 460–463)

1. Inflammation is a bodily response to cell damage; it is characterized by redness, pain, heat, swelling, and sometimes the loss of function.
2. Tumor necrosis factor alpha (TNF-α) stimulates production of acute-phase proteins.

Vasodilation and Increased Permeability of Blood Vessels (p. 460–462)

3. The release of histamine, kinins, and prostaglandins causes vasodilation and increased permeability of blood vessels.
4. Blood clots can form around an abscess to prevent dissemination of the infection.

Phagocyte Migration and Phagocytosis (p. 462)

5. Phagocytes have the ability to stick to the lining of the blood vessels (margination).
6. They also have the ability to squeeze through blood vessels (diapedesis).
7. Pus is the accumulation of damaged tissue and dead microbes, granulocytes, and macrophages.

Tissue Repair (pp. 462–463)

8. A tissue is repaired when the stroma (supporting tissue) or parenchyma (functioning tissue) produces new cells.
9. Stromal repair by fibroblasts produces scar tissue.

Fever (p. 463)

1. Fever is an abnormally high body temperature produced in response to a bacterial or viral infection.
2. Bacterial endotoxins, interleukin-1, and tumor necrosis factor alpha can induce fever.
3. A chill indicates a rising body temperature; crisis (sweating) indicates that the body's temperature is falling.

Antimicrobial Substances (p. 463–472)

The Complement System (pp. 463–468)

1. The complement system consists of a group of serum proteins that activate one another to destroy invading microorganisms.
2. Complement proteins are activated in a cascade.
3. C3 activation can result in cell lysis, inflammation, and opsonization.
4. Complement is activated via the classical pathway, the alternative pathway, and the lectin pathway.
5. Complement is deactivated by host-regulatory proteins.
6. Complement deficiencies can result in an increased susceptibility to disease.
7. Some bacteria evade destruction by complement by means of capsules, surface lipid–carbohydrate complexes, and enzymatic destruction of C5a.

Interferons (pp. 468–470)

8. Interferons (IFNs) are antiviral proteins produced in response to viral infection.
9. There are three types of human interferon: IFN-α, IFN-β, and IFN-γ. Recombinant interferons have been produced.
10. The mode of action of IFN-α and IFN-β is to induce uninfected cells to produce antiviral proteins (AVPs) that prevent viral replication.
11. Interferons are host-cell–specific but not virus-specific.
12. Gamma interferon activates neutrophils and macrophages to kill bacteria.

Iron-Binding Proteins (p. 470)

13. Iron-binding proteins transport and store iron and deprive most pathogens of the available iron.

Antimicrobial Peptides (pp. 470–472)

14. Antimicrobial peptides (AMPs) inhibit cell wall synthesis; form pores in plasma membranes, resulting in lysis; and destroy DNA and RNA.
15. Antimicrobial peptides are produced by nearly all plants and animals, and bacterial resistance to AMPs has not yet been seen.

THE LOOP

If you prefer to include the complement system with antigen–antibody reactions, you can assign pages 463–468 with Chapter 17. Review questions 5 and 8, and Critical Thinking question 3, concerning complement, can be assigned when complement is covered.

ANSWERS

Review

1.
	Mechanical	**Chemical**
a.	Movement out	Lysozyme, acids
b.	Movement out	Acidic in female

2.

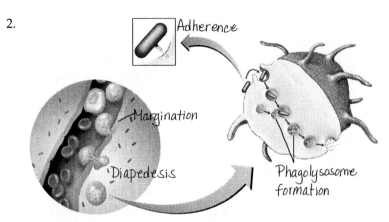

3. Inflammation is the body's response to tissue damage. The characteristic symptoms of inflammation are redness, pain, heat, and swelling.

4. Interferons are antiviral proteins produced by infected cells in response to viral infections. IFN-α and IFN-β induce uninfected cells to produce antiviral proteins. IFN-γ is produced by lymphocytes and activates neutrophils to kill bacteria.

5. Endotoxin binds C3b, which activates C5–C9 to cause cell lysis. This can result in free cell wall fragments, which bind more C3b, resulting in C5–C9 damage to host cell membranes.

6. Toxic oxygen products can kill pathogens.

7. The recipient's antibodies combine with donor antigens and fix complement; the activated complement causes hemolysis.

8. Inhibit formation of C3b, prevent MAC formation, hydrolyze C5a.

9. a. Innate. Facilitate adherence of phagocyte and pathogen.

   b. Innate. Bind iron.

   c. Innate. Kill or inhibit bacteria.

Critical Thinking

1. Transferrin binds available iron so bacteria can't have it to grow. A bacterium might respond with increased siderophores to take up iron.

2. The inflammatory response is usually a beneficial response. Exceptions to this are hypersensitivities and autoimmune diseases, which are discussed in Chapter 19. Each of the drugs has side effects; while the drag is reducing inflammation, another undesirable condition might result.

3.

Organism	How Does This Strategy Avoid Destruction by the Complement?	Disease
Group A streptococci	No C5–C9	Streptococcal sore throat
Haemophilus influenzae type b	Hides LPS, which can activate C	Meningitis
Pseudomonas aeruginosa	Binds C in solution instead of on cell surface	Septicemia; pyelonephritis
Trypanosoma cruzi	C5–C9 doesn't get activated	Chagas' disease

4.

Microorganisms	Effect	Disease
Influenzavirus	Kills host cell	Influenza
M. tuberculosis	Prevents digestion in phagocytes	Tuberculosis
T. gondii	Prevents digestion in phagocytes	Toxoplasmosis
Trichophyton	Digests keratin	Athlete's foot
T. cruzi	Prevents digestion in phagocytes	Chagas' disease

Clinical Applications

1. Kinins cause vasodilation and increased permeability of blood vessels. Symptoms should include increased secretions from the nose and eyes. Rhinoviruses cause the common cold.

2. The proportions of white blood cells may change during diseases. The results of a differential count can be used to diagnose diseases. A patient with mononucleosis will have an increased number of monocytes. Neutropenia: decreased neutrophils. Eosinophilia: increased eosinophils.

3. Phagocytosis is inhibited.

4. Neutrophils will not phagocytize and they will die prematurely.

5. a. Mannose-binding lectin binds with mannose on the surface of a broad range of microorganisms. However, the mannose recognition pattern is not normally exposed on human cells.

   b. Mannose-binding lectin deficiency results in increased susceptibility to infections in immuno-compromised individuals and in young children.

CASE STUDY: COMPLEMENT EVASION

The Problem

If a microbe is to be a successful parasite, it must avoid destruction by the host's complement system. The following list provides examples of known complement-evading techniques. Complete the table to identify the disease and method of action.

Organism	Strategy	Disease	How Does This Strategy Avoid Destruction by the Complement?
Legionella pneumophila	Uses C3b receptors to enter monocytes		
Pseudomonas aeruginosa	Produces proteases		
Salmonella enterica	Activates C3 on long-chain LPS molecules		
Schistosoma mansoni	Sheds glycocalyx molecules		

The Solution

Organism	Disease	How Does This Strategy Avoid Destruction by the Complement?
Legionella pneumophila	Legionellosis	Binds cells instead of C3
Pseudomonas aeruginosa	Opportunistic: sepsis, meningitis, cystitis	Degrades complement
Salmonella enterica	Salmonellosis	C5–C9 complex is too far away from cell surface to cause damage
Schistosoma mansoni	Schistosomiasis	Binds C in solution instead of on cell surface

17 Adaptive Immunity: Specific Defenses of the Host

LEARNING OBJECTIVE	CHECK YOUR UNDERSTANDING
17-1 Differentiate innate from adaptive immunity.	Is vaccination an example of innate or adaptive immunity?
17-2 Differentiate humoral from cellular immunity.	How was basic research on chicken diseases related to the discoveries of both humoral and cellular immunity?
17-3 Define *antigen*, *epitope*, and *hapten*.	Does an antibody necessarily react with a bacterium as an antigen or as an epitope?
17-4 Explain the function of antibodies, and describe their structural and chemical characteristics.	The original theoretical concepts of an antibody called for a rod with antigenic determinants at each end. What is the primary advantage of the Y-shaped structure that eventually emerged?
17-5 Name one function for each of the five classes of antibodies.	Which class of antibody is most likely to protect you from a common cold?
17-6 Compare and contrast T-dependent and T-independent antigens.	Would pneumococcal pneumonia (see Figure 24.13) require a T_H cell to stimulate a B cell to form antibodies?
17-7 Differentiate plasma cell from memory cell.	Plasma cells produce antibodies; do they also produce memory cells?
17-8 Describe clonal selection.	In what way does a B cell that encounters an antigen function as an antigen-presenting cell?
17-9 Describe how a human can produce different antibodies.	On what part of the antibody molecule do we find the genetic information that makes the huge genetic diversity of antibody production possible?
17-10 Describe four outcomes of an antigen–antibody reaction.	Antibodies and what other component of the immune system are required for the lysis of a target antigenic cell?
17-11 Describe at least one function of each of the following: M cells, T_H1 cells, T_H2 cells, T_C cells, T_{reg} cells, CTL, NK cells.	What antibody is the primary one produced when an antigen is taken up by an M cell?
17-12 Differentiate T helper, T cytotoxic, and T regulatory cells.	Which T cell is generally involved when a B cell reacts with an antigen and produces antibodies against the antigen?
17-13 Differentiate T_H1 and T_H2 cells.	Which is the T cell type that is generally involved in allergic reactions?
17-14 Define *apoptosis*.	What is another name for apoptosis, one that describes its function?

17-15 Define *antigen-presenting cell.*	Are dendritic cells considered primarily part of the humoral or the cellular immune system?
17-16 Describe the function of natural killer cells.	How does the natural killer cell respond if the target cell does not have MHC class I molecules on its surface?
17-17 Describe the role of antibodies and natural killer cells in antibody-dependent cell-mediated cytotoxicity.	What makes a natural killer cell, which is not immunologically specific, attack a particular target cell?
17-18 Identify at least one function of each of the following cytokines: interleukins, chemokines, interferons, TNF, and hematopoietic cytokines.	What is the function of cytokines?
17-19 Distinguish a primary from a secondary immune response.	Is the anamnestic response primary or secondary?
17-20 Contrast the four types of adaptive immunity.	What type of adaptive immunity is involved when gamma globulin is injected into a person?

NEW IN THIS EDITION

- Extensive revision of Figure 17.4, the activation of B cells to produce antibodies, for accuracy and clarity
- Figure 17.9, illustrating M cells that are found within Peyer's patches
- Completely revised discussions of the major histocompatibility complex and T cells
- Completely rewritten discussion of dendritic cells
- Completely rewritten discussion of cytokines

CHAPTER SUMMARY

The Adaptive Immune System (p. 477)

1. An individual's genetically predetermined resistance to certain diseases is called innate immunity.
2. Adaptive immunity is the ability of the body to specifically react to a microbial infection.

Dual Nature of the Adaptive Immune System (pp. 477–478)

1. Red bone marrow stem cells produce lymphocytes. Lymphocytes that mature in bone marrow become B cells.
2. Humoral immunity involves antibodies, which are found in serum and lymph and are produced by B cells.
3. Lymphocytes that migrate through the thymus become T cells. Cellular immunity involves T cells.
4. T cell receptors recognize antigens.

Antigens and Antibodies (pp. 478–482)

The Nature of Antigens (pp. 478–479)

1. An antigen (or immunogen) is a chemical substance that causes the body to produce specific antibodies.

2. As a rule, antigens are proteins or large polysaccharides. Antibodies are formed against specific regions on antigens called epitopes, or antigenic determinants.

3. A hapten is a low-molecular-weight substance that cannot cause the formation of antibodies unless combined with a carrier molecule; haptens react with their antibodies independently of the carrier molecule.

The Nature of Antibodies (pp. 479–482)

4. An antibody, or immunoglobulin, is a protein produced by B cells in response to an antigen and is capable of combining specifically with that antigen.

5. Typical monomers consist of four polypeptide chains: two heavy chains and two light chains.

6. Within each chain is a variable (V) region that binds the epitope and a constant (C) region that distinguishes the different classes of antibodies.

7. An antibody monomer is Y-shaped or T-shaped: the V regions form the tips, the C regions form the base and F_C (stem) region.

8. The F_C region can attach to a host cell or to complement.

9. IgG antibodies are the most prevalent in serum; they provide naturally acquired passive immunity, neutralize bacterial toxins, participate in complement fixation, and enhance phagocytosis.

10. IgM antibodies consist of five monomers held by a joining chain; they are involved in agglutination and complement fixation.

11. Serum IgA antibodies are monomers; secretory IgA antibodies are dimers that protect mucosal surfaces from invasion by pathogens.

12. IgD antibodies are on B cells; they may delete B cells that produce antibodies against self.

13. IgE antibodies bind to mast cells and basophils and are involved in allergic reactions.

B Cells and Humoral Immunity (pp. 482–486)

Clonal Selection of Antibody-Producing Cells (pp. 482–488)

1. Red bone marrow stem cells give rise to B cells with IgM and IgD on their surfaces, which recognize specific epitopes.

2. For T-dependent antigens, B cells are selected by antigens with repeating epitopes.

3. For T-independent antigens, B cells are activated by a T cell. The T cell was activated by an antigenic fragment presented with host MHC II.

4. Activated B cells differentiate into plasma cells and memory cells.

5. B cells that recognize self are eliminated by clonal deletion.

The Diversity of Antibodies (p. 484)

6. During development, the genes in embryonic B cells recombine so that mature B cells each have different genes for the V region of their antibodies.

Antigen–Antibody Binding and Its Results (pp. 484–486)

1. An antigen–antibody complex forms when an antibody binds to its specific epitopes on an antigen.

2. Agglutination results when an antibody combines with epitopes on two different cells.

3. Opsonization enhances phagocytosis of the antigen.

4. Antibodies that attach to microbes or toxins cause neutralization.

5. Complement activation results in cell lysis.

T Cells and Cellular Immunity (pp. 486–489)

1. Red bone marrow stem cells give rise to T cells, which mature in the thymus gland. Thymic selection removes T cells that don't recognize MHC-self molecules.
2. T-cell receptors on T cells recognize antigens.
3. T cells recognize antigens processed by antigen-presenting cells.
4. T cells recognize antigens in association with MHC on an APC.

Classes of T Cells (p. 487)

5. T cells are classified according to their functions and cell-surface glycoproteins called CDs.

T Helper Cells (CD4$^+$ T Cells) (pp. 487–488)

6. T_H1 cells activate cells involved in cellular immunity.
7. T_H2 cells are associated with allergic reactions and parasitic infections.
8. T helper cells, or CD4$^+$ T cells, are activated by MHC class II on APCs. After binding an APC, CD4$^+$ T cells secrete cytokines that activate other T cells and B cells.

T Cytotoxic Cells (CD8$^+$ T Cells) (pp. 488–489)

9. T cytotoxic cells (T_C), or CD8$^+$ T cells, are activated by endogenous antigens and MHC class I on a target cell and are transformed into a CTL.
10. CTLs lyse or induce apoptosis in the target cell.

T Regulatory Cells (p. 489)

11. T regulatory cells (T_{reg}) suppress T cells against self.

Antigen-Presenting Cells (APCs) (pp. 489–490)

1. APCs include B cells, dendritic cells, and macrophages.
2. Dendritic cells are the primary APCs.
3. Activated macrophages are effective phagocytes and APCs.
4. APCs carry antigens to lymphoid tissues where T cells that recognize the antigen are located.

Extracellular Killing by the Immune System (p. 491)

1. Natural killer (NK) cells lyse virus-infected cells, tumor cells, and parasites. They kill cells that do not express MHC class I antigens.

Antibody-Dependent Cell-Mediated Cytotoxicity (pp. 491–492)

1. In ADCC, NK cells and macrophages lyse antibody-coated cells.

Cytokines: Chemical Messengers of Immune Cells (pp. 492–493)

1. Cells of the immune system communicate with each other by means of chemicals called cytokines.
2. Interleukins (IL) are cytokines that serve as communicators between leukocytes.
3. Chemokines cause leukocytes to migrate to an infection.

4. Alpha interferon and IFN-β protect cells against viruses. Gamma interferon increases phagocytosis.
5. Tumor necrosis factor promotes the inflammatory reaction.
6. Hematopoietic cytokines promote development of white blood cells.
7. Overproduction of cytokines leads to a cytokine storm, which results in tissue damage.

Immunological Memory (pp. 493–494)

1. The relative amount of antibody in serum is called the antibody titer.
2. The response of the body to the first contact with an antigen is called the primary response. It is characterized by the appearance of IgM followed by IgG.
3. Subsequent contact with the same antigen results in a very high antibody titer and is called the secondary, anamnestic, or memory response. The antibodies are primarily IgG.

Types of Adaptive Immunity (pp. 494–496)

1. Immunity resulting from infection is called naturally acquired active immunity; this type of immunity may be long-lasting.
2. Antibodies transferred from a mother to a fetus (transplacental transfer) or to a newborn in colostrum results in naturally acquired passive immunity in the newborn; this type of immunity can last up to a few months.
3. Immunity resulting from vaccination is called artificially acquired active immunity and can be long-lasting.
4. Artificially acquired passive immunity refers to humoral antibodies acquired by injection; this type of immunity can last for a few weeks.
5. Serum containing antibodies is often called antiserum.
6. When serum is separated by gel electrophoresis, antibodies are found in the gamma fraction of the serum and are termed immune serum globulin, or gamma globulin.

THE LOOP

Complement is included in Chapter 16 (pp. 463–468), but can be assigned with this chapter.

ANSWERS

Review

1. a. Adaptive immunity is the resistance to infection obtained during the life of the individual. Adaptive immunity results from the production of antibodies and T cells. Innate immunity refers to the resistance of species or individuals to certain diseases that is not dependent on antigen-specific immunity.

    b. Humoral immunity is due to antibodies (and B cells). Cellular immunity is due to T cells.

    c. Active immunity refers to antibodies produced by the individual who carries them. Passive immunity refers to antibodies produced by another source and then transferred to the individual who needs the antibodies.

    d. T_H1 cells produce cytokines that activate T cells. Cytokines produced by T_H2 cells activate B cells.

    e. Natural immunity is acquired naturally, i.e., from mother to newborn, or following an infection. Artificial immunity is acquired from medical treatment, i.e., by injection of antibodies or by vaccination.

  f. T-dependent antigens: Certain antigens must combine with self-antigens to be recognized by T_H cells and then by B cells. T-independent antigens can elicit an antibody response without T cells.

  g. T cells can be classified by their surface antigens: T_H cells possess the CD4 antigen; T_C cells have the CD8 antigen.

  h. Immunoglobins = antibodies; TCRs = antigen-receptors on T cells.

2. The major histocompatability complex (MHC) are self-antigens. T_H cells react with MHC II; T_C cells react with MHC I.

3.

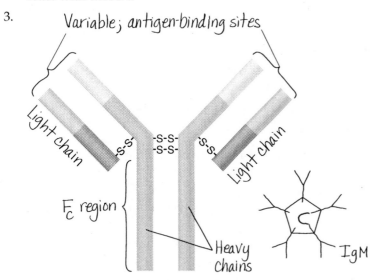

4. See Figure 17.19.

5. T cytotoxic cells (T_C) destroy target cells upon contact. T helper cells (T_H) interact with an antigen to "present" it to a B cell for antibody formation. T_{reg} cells suppress the immune response. Cytokines are chemicals released by cells that initiate a response by other cells.

6.

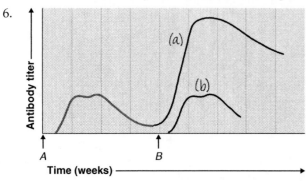

7. Both would prevent attachment of the pathogen; (a) interferes with the attachment site on the pathogen and (b) interferes with the pathogen's receptor site.

8. Rearrangement of the V region genes during embryonic development produces B cells with different antibody genes.

9. The person recovered because he or she produced antibodies against the pathogen. The memory response will continue to protect the person against that pathogen.

Critical Thinking

1. T_C cells secreted TNF and IFN, which diffuse through liver cells and stimulate these cells to produce antiviral proteins.

2. Dietary amino acids are necessary to make antibodies (proteins) and new (T) cells.

3. Having had an *M. tuberculosis* infection and recovered (naturally acquired active immunity); vaccination with BCG (artificially acquired passive immunity).

4. Antivenin = antibodies against the snake venom; obtained from the serum of a vaccinated horse or mouse (see monoclonal antibodies, pp. 507–509).

Clinical Applications

1. Antibiotics and immunity can cause gram-negative cells to lyse, releasing cell wall fragments. This exposes the body to more endotoxin. The woman's life-threatening condition was due to endotoxin shock. Monoclonal antibodies removed the cell walls.

2. Increased susceptibility to infection due to decreased antibody formation.

3. He could not produce the secretory component of IgA.

4. The mechanism is called antibody enhancement. Immune complexes of antibodies and viruses attach to cells, facilitating viral penetration.

5. B cells are in the lymph nodes and the spleen.

CASE STUDY: JULES BORDET'S DISCOVERY

Background

In 1885, Jules Bordet tested the effects of immune serum on a bacterial culture. He took goat serum from an animal vaccinated against *Vibrio cholerae* cells. He then heated the goat serum to 58°C for 1 hour. Guinea pig serum was from a nonimmune animal. Each tube contained 12 drops of the specified serum and about 9000 *V. cholerae* cells. Plate counts were made at intervals to determine the number of bacteria in each tube.

Data

| | Number of *V. cholerae* | | |
Hour of counting	Heated goat serum	Guinea pig serum	8 drops guinea pig + 4 drops goat serum
6:00 PM	8640	9600	10,200
7:30 PM	4320	2160	0
10:00 PM	6480	3600	0
10:00 AM	very high	very high	0

Questions

1. How is serum obtained from blood?
2. What accounts for the results Bordet observed?

The Solution

1. Serum is the fluid left after blood clots.
2. Bordet discovered complement. Goat serum antibodies alone or guinea pig serum alone did not kill the bacteria overnight. Goat serum antibodies acted with guinea pig complement to kill the bacteria within 1.5 hours.

18

Practical Applications of Immunology

LEARNING OBJECTIVE	CHECK YOUR UNDERSTANDING
18-1 Define *vaccine*.	What is the etymology (origin) of the word *vaccine*?
18-2 Explain why vaccination works.	Vaccination is often the only feasible way to control most viral diseases; why is this?
18-3 Differentiate the following, and provide an example of each: attenuated, inactivated, toxoid, subunit, and conjugated vaccines.	Experience has shown that attenuated vaccines tend to be more effective than inactivated vaccines. Why?
18-4 Contrast subunit vaccines and nucleic acid vaccines.	Which is more likely to be useful in preventing a disease caused by an encapsulated bacterium such as the pneumococcus: a subunit vaccine or a nucleic acid vaccine?
18-5 Compare and contrast the production of whole-agent vaccines, recombinant vaccines, and DNA vaccines.	Which type of vaccine did Louis Pasteur develop: whole-agent, recombinant, or DNA?
18-6 Define *adjuvant*.	What is the derivation of the word *adjuvant*?
18-7 Explain the value of vaccines, and discuss acceptable risks for vaccines.	What is the name of a currently used oral vaccine that occasionally causes the disease it is intended to prevent?
18-8 Differentiate sensitivity from specificity in a diagnostic test.	What property of the immune system suggested its use as an aid for diagnosing disease: specificity or sensitivity?
18-9 Define *monoclonal antibodies*, and identify their advantage over conventional antibody production.	The blood of an infected cow would have a considerable amount of antibodies against the infectious pathogen in its blood. How would an equivalent amount of monoclonal antibodies be more useful?
18-10 Explain how precipitation reactions and immunodiffusion tests work.	Why does the reaction of a precipitation test become visible only in a narrow range?
18-11 Differentiate direct from indirect agglutination tests.	Why wouldn't a direct agglutination test work very well with viruses?
18-12 Differentiate agglutination from precipitation tests.	Which test detects soluble antigens, agglutination or precipitation?
18-13 Define *hemagglutination*.	Certain diagnostic tests require red blood cells that clump visibly. What are these tests called?
18-14 Explain how a neutralization test works.	In what way is there a connection between hemagglutination and certain viruses?
18-15 Differentiate precipitation from neutralization tests.	Which of these tests is an antigen–antibody reaction: precipitation or viral hemagglutination?

18-16 Explain the basis for the complement-fixation test.	Why is complement given its name?
18-17 Compare and contrast direct and indirect fluorescent-antibody tests.	Which test is used to detect antibodies against a pathogen: the direct or the indirect fluorescent-antibody test?
18-18 Explain how direct and indirect ELISA tests work.	Which test is used to detect antibodies against a pathogen: the direct or the indirect ELISA test?
18-19 Explain how Western blotting works.	How are antibodies detected in Western blotting?
18-20 Explain the importance of monoclonal antibodies.	How has the development of monoclonal antibodies revolutionized diagnostic immunology?

NEW IN THIS EDITION

- Revised and updated discussions of adjuvants and nucleic acid vaccines
- Updated tables of vaccine schedules
- A new Clinical Focus (*MMWR*) box describing delayed hypersensitivity to penicillin
- A new Clinical Focus (*MMWR*) box describing the impact of vaccination using measles as an example

CHAPTER SUMMARY

Vaccines (pp. 501–506)

1. Edward Jenner developed the modern practice of vaccination when he inoculated people with cowpox virus to protect them against smallpox.

Principles and Effects of Vaccination (p. 501)

2. Herd immunity results when most of a population is immune to a disease.

Types of Vaccines and Their Characteristics (pp. 501–505)

3. Attenuated whole-agent vaccines consist of attenuated (weakened) microorganisms; attenuated virus vaccines generally provide lifelong immunity.
4. Inactivated whole-agent vaccines consist of killed bacteria or viruses.
5. Toxoids are inactivated toxins.
6. Subunit vaccines consist of antigenic fragments of a microorganism; these include recombinant vaccines and acellular vaccines.
7. Conjugated vaccines combine the desired antigen with a protein that boosts the immune response.
8. Nucleic acid vaccines, or DNA vaccines, cause the recipient to make the antigenic protein.

The Development of New Vaccines (pp. 505–506)

9. Viruses for vaccines may be grown in animals, cell cultures, or chick embryos.
10. Recombinant vaccines and nucleic acid vaccines do not need to be grown in cells or animals.
11. Genetically modified plants may someday provide edible vaccines.
12. Adjuvants improve the effectiveness of some antigens.

Safety of Vaccines (p. 506)

13. Vaccines are the safest and most effective means of controlling infectious diseases.

Diagnostic Immunology (p. 507)

Immunologic-Based Diagnostic Tests (p. 507)

1. Many tests based on the interactions of antibodies and antigens have been developed to determine the presence of antibodies or antigens in a patient.

2. The sensitivity of a diagnostic test is determined by the percentage of positive samples it correctly detects; and its specificity is determined by the percentage of false positive results it gives.

Monoclonal Antibodies (pp. 507–509)

3. Hybridomas are produced in the laboratory by fusing a cancerous cell with an antibody-secreting plasma cell.

4. A hybridoma cell culture produces large quantities of the plasma cell's antibodies, called monoclonal antibodies.

5. Monoclonal antibodies are used in serological identification tests, to prevent tissue rejections, and to make immunotoxins to treat cancer.

Precipitation Reactions (pp. 509–510)

6. The interaction of soluble antigens with IgG or IgM antibodies leads to precipitation reactions.

7. Precipitation reactions depend on the formation of lattices and occur best when antigen and antibody are present in optimal proportions. Excesses of either component decrease lattice formation and subsequent precipitation.

8. The precipitin ring test is performed in a small tube.

9. Immunodiffusion procedures are precipitation reactions carried out in an agar gel medium.

10. Immunoelectrophoresis combines electrophoresis with immunodiffusion for the analysis of serum proteins.

Agglutination Reactions (pp. 510–512)

11. The interaction of particulate antigens (cells that carry antigens) with antibodies leads to agglutination reactions.

12. Diseases may be diagnosed by combining the patient's serum with a known antigen.

13. Diseases can be diagnosed by a rising titer or seroconversion (from no antibodies to the presence of antibodies).

14. Direct agglutination reactions can be used to determine antibodytiter.

15. Antibodies cause visible agglutination of soluble antigens affixed to latex spheres in indirect or passive agglutination tests.

16. Hemagglutination reactions involve agglutination reactions using red blood cells. Hemagglutination reactions are used in blood typing, the diagnosis of certain diseases, and the identification of viruses.

Neutralization Reactions (p. 512)

17. In neutralization reactions, the harmful effects of a bacterial exotoxin or virus are eliminated by a specific antibody.

18. An antitoxin is an antibody produced in response to a bacterial exotoxin or a toxoid that neutralizes the exotoxin.

19. In a virus neutralization test, the presence of antibodies against a virus can be detected by the antibodies' ability to prevent cytopathic effects of viruses in cell cultures.

20. Antibodies against certain viruses can be detected by their ability to interfere with viral hemagglutination in viral hemagglutination inhibition tests.

Complement-Fixation Reactions (pp. 512–513)

21. Complement-fixation reactions are serological tests based on the depletion of a fixed amount of complement in the presence of an antigen–antibody reaction.

Fluorescent-Antibody Techniques (pp. 513–514)

22. Fluorescent-antibody techniques use antibodies labeled with fluorescent dyes.

23. Direct fluorescent-antibody tests are used to identify specific microorganisms.

24. Indirect fluorescent-antibody tests are used to demonstrate the presence of antibody in serum.

25. A fluorescence-activated cell sorter can be used to detect and count cells labeled with fluorescent antibodies.

Enzyme-Linked Immunosorbent Assay (ELISA) (pp. 514–516)

26. ELISA techniques use antibodies linked to an enzyme.

27. Antigen–antibody reactions are detected by enzyme activity. If the indicator enzyme is present in the test well, an antigen–antibody reaction has occurred.

28. The direct ELISA is used to detect antigens against a specific antibody bound in a test well.

29. The indirect ELISA is used to detect antibodies against an antigen bound in a test well.

Western Blotting (Immunoblotting) (p. 516)

30. Serum antibodies separated by electrophoresis are identified with an enzyme-linked antibody.

The Future of Diagnostic Immunology (p. 516–518)

31. The use of monoclonal antibodies will continue to make new diagnostic tests possible.

THE LOOP

This chapter can be used as a reference for Part Four or with Chapter 9 in a discussion of biotechnology.

ANSWERS

Review

1. a. Whole-agent. Live, avirulent virus that can cause the disease if it mutates back to its virulent state.
   b. Whole-agent; (heat-) killed bacteria.
   c. Subunit; (heat- or formalin-) inactivated toxin.
   d. Subunit
   e. Subunit

    f. Conjugated

    g. Nucleic acid

2.   If excess antibody is present, an antigen will combine with several antibody molecules. Excess antigen will result in an antibody combining with several antigens. Refer to Figure 18.3.

3.   Particulate antigens react in agglutination reactions. The antigens can be cells or soluble antigens bound to synthetic particles. Soluble antigens take part in precipitation reactions.

4.   a. Some viruses are able to agglutinate red blood cells. This is used to detect the presence of large numbers of virions capable of causing hemagglutination (e.g., *Influenzavirus*).

    b. Antibodies produced against viruses that are capable of agglutinating red blood cells will inhibit the agglutination. Hemagglutination inhibition can be used to detect the presence of antibodies against these viruses.

    c. This is a procedure to detect antibodies that react with soluble antigens by first attaching the antigens to insoluble latex spheres. This procedure may be used to detect the presence of antibodies that develop during certain mycotic or helminthic infections.

5.

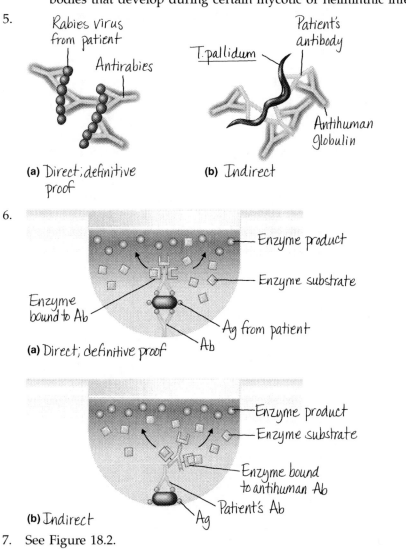

(a) Direct; definitive proof

(b) Indirect

6.

(a) Direct; definitive proof

(b) Indirect

7.   See Figure 18.2.

8.   a. 5   c. 1   e. 6

    b. 4, 6   d. 3   f. 2, 4

9.   a. 5   c. 1   e. 2

    b. 3   d. 6   f. 4

Critical Thinking

1. The live vaccine may revert to a more virulent form; exogenous protein contaminants in viral vaccines; the inherent instability of certain live viral preparations.

2. Traditionally, by vaccinating a large animal such as a horse or a goat, and purifying the antibodies from its blood. Now these antibodies can be obtained in vitro by monoclonal antibody techniques.

3. The antibodies (called reagin) are not specific. The disease is syphilis.

Clinical Applications

1. (a) is proof of a disease state. (b) could indicate disease, prior disease and recovery, or vaccination. The disease is tuberculosis.

2. No reaction; the antibodies will neutralize the toxin. This is a neutralization reaction. The disease is scarlet fever.

3. Patient A probably has the disease. Patient B does not have and never had the disease. Patient C recovered from the disease. Patient D acquired the disease between days 7 and 14; an example of seroconversion. The disease is legionellosis.

4. Students should include the value of herd immunity in their answer.

CASE STUDY: *PSEUDOMONAS*

Background

Pseudomonas aeruginosa is able to colonize the respiratory mucosa and cause recurring pneumonia in cystic fibrosis patients. The following experiments were performed to determine how *P. aeruginosa* can colonize mucous membranes.

0.1 ml broth culture was added to 0.4 ml serum and incubated for 1 hour; 0.1 ml of the same broth culture was added to 0.4 ml isotonic saline and incubated for 1 hour. Plate counts were performed on 1-ml samples to determine the number of bacteria.

Dilution	*Serratia* in serum Number of colonies	*Serratia* in saline Number of colonies
$1:10^2$	92	Too many to count
$1:10^4$	10	Too many to count
$1:10^6$	0	293

Dilution	*Pseudomonas* in serum Number of colonies	*Pseudomonas* in saline Number of colonies
$1:10^2$	Too many to count	Too many to count
$1:10^4$	600	150
$1:10^6$	65	12

Immunoelectrophoresis was then used to compare normal serum to the serum incubated with *Serratia* and *Pseudomonas* (see figure on the next page). Serum was placed in a well in agarose. Serum components were separated by electrophoresis. After electrophoresis, antihuman serum was added to the center trough. As antibodies diffused out of the trough, precipitation bands formed at zones of equivalence. The dark band at the cathode end of the gel is albumin; other bands indicate other serum proteins, such as the various immunoglobulins.

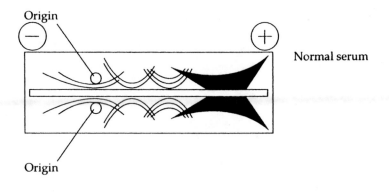

Normal serum

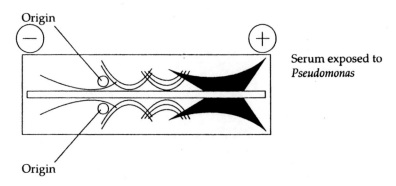

Serum exposed to *Pseudomonas*

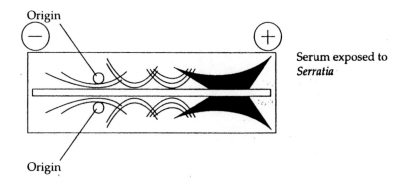

Serum exposed to *Serratia*

Questions

1. Calculate the number of bacteria in each serum and saline sample.
2. What was the purpose of the saline?
3. Provide an explanation for the ability of *Pseudomonas* to colonize mucous membranes.

The Solution

1. $\text{Bacteria/ml} = \dfrac{\text{Number of Colonies}}{\text{Dilution} \times \text{Amount plated}}$

	Serum	Saline
Serratia sample	9.2×10^3	2.93×10^8
Pseudomonas sample	6.5×10^7	1.50×10^6

2. Saline was the control.
3. The IgA band is missing from the serum exposed to *Pseudomonas*. *P. aeruginosa* can degrade IgA antibodies found on mucous membranes.

19

Disorders Associated with the Immune System

LEARNING OBJECTIVES	CHECK YOUR UNDERSTANDING
19-1 Define *hypersensitivity*.	Are all immune responses beneficial?
19-2 Describe the mechanism of anaphylaxis.	In what tissues do we find the mast cells that are major contributors to allergic reactions such as hay fever?
19-3 Compare and contrast systemic and localized anaphylaxis.	Which is the more dangerous to life, systemic or localized anaphylaxis?
19-4 Explain how allergy skin tests work.	How can we tell whether a person is sensitive to a particular allergen, such as a tree pollen?
19-5 Define *desensitization* and *blocking antibody*.	Which antibody types need to be blocked to desensitize a person subject to allergies?
19-6 Describe the mechanism of cytotoxic reactions and how drugs can induce them.	What, besides an allergen and an antibody, is required to precipitate a cytotoxic reaction?
19-7 Describe the basis of the ABO and Rh blood group systems.	What are the antigens located on the cell membranes of type O blood?
19-8 Explain the relationship among blood groups, blood, transfusions, and hemolytic disease of the newborn.	If a fetus that is Rh⁺ can be damaged by anti-Rh antibodies of the mother, why does such damage never happen during the first such pregnancy?
19-9 Describe the mechanism of immune complex reactions.	Are the antigens causing immune complex reactions soluble or insoluble?
19-10 Describe the mechanism of delayed cell-mediated reactions, and name two examples.	What is the primary reason for the delay in a delayed cell-mediated reaction?
19-11 Describe a mechanism for self-tolerance.	What is the importance of clonal deletion in the thymus?
19-12 Give an example of immune complex, cytotoxic, and cell-mediated autoimmune diseases.	What organ is affected in Graves' disease?
19-13 Define *HLA complex*, and explain its importance in disease susceptibility and tissue transplants.	What is the relationship between the major histocompatibility complex in humans and the human leukocyte antigen complex?
19-14 Explain how a transplant is rejected.	What immune system cells are involved in the rejection of nonself transplants?
19-15 Define *privileged site*.	Why is a transplanted cornea usually not rejected as nonself?
19-16 Discuss the role of stem cells in transplantation.	Differentiate an embryonic stem cell from an adult stem cell.
19-17 Define *autograft, isograft, allograft,* and *xeno-transplant*.	Which type of transplant is most subject to hyperacute rejection?

19-18 Explain how graft-versus-host disease occurs.	When red bone marrow is transplanted, many immunocompetent cells are included. How can this be bad?
19-19 Explain how rejection of a transplant is prevented.	What cytokine is usually the target of immunosuppressant drugs intended to block transplant rejection?
19-20 Describe how the immune system responds to cancer and how cells evade immune responses.	What is the function of tumor-associated antigens in the development of cancer?
19-21 Give two examples of immunotherapy.	Give an example of a prophylactic cancer vaccine that is in current use.
19-22 Compare and contrast congenital and acquired immunodeficiencies.	Is AIDS an acquired or a congenital immunodeficiency?
19-23 Give two examples of how infectious diseases emerge.	On what continent did the HIV-1 virus arise?
19-24 Explain the attachment of HIV to a host cell.	What is the primary receptor on host cells to which HIV attaches?
19-25 List two ways in which HIV avoids the host's antibodies.	Would an antibody against the coat of HIV be able to react with a provirus?
19-26 Describe the stages of HIV infection.	Would a $CD4^+$ T-cell count of 300 cells/µl be diagnostic of AIDS?
19-27 Describe the effects of HIV infection on the immune system	Which cells of the immune system are the main target of an HIV infection?
19-28 Describe how HIV infection is diagnosed.	What form of nucleic acid is detected in a PVL test for HIV?
19-29 List the routes of HIV transmission.	What is considered to be the most dangerous form of sexual contact for transmission of HIV?
19-30 Identify geographic patterns of HIV transmission.	What is the most common mode, worldwide, by which HIV is transmitted?
19-31 List the current methods of preventing and treating HIV infection.	Does circumcision make a man more or less likely to acquire HIV infection?

NEW IN THIS EDITION

- Discussion of the relationship between certain blood groups, their relative resistance or susceptibility to certain diseases, and the blood groups found in certain geographical areas
- Discussion of the autoimmune disease psoriasis and its associated arthritis, along with current treatments involving monoclonal antibodies
- Updated discussion of stem cells and a new figure (Figure 19.10) illustrating the derivation of stem cells and stem cell lines
- Updated discussion of HIV and AIDS
- A new Clinical Focus (*MMWR*) box describing delayed hypersensitivity to penicillin

CHAPTER SUMMARY

Introduction (p. 522)

1. Hay fever, transplant rejection, and autoimmunity are examples of harmful immune reactions.
2. Immunosuppression is failure of the immune system.
3. Superantigens activate many T-cell receptors that can cause adverse host responses.

Hypersensitivity (pp. 523–531)

1. Hypersensitivity reactions represent immunological responses to an antigen (allergen) that lead to tissue damage rather than immunity.
2. Hypersensitivity reactions occur when a person has been sensitized to an antigen.
3. Hypersensitivity reactions can be divided into four classes: types I, II, and III are immediate reactions based on humoral immunity, and type IV is a delayed reaction based on cell-mediated immunity.

Type I (Anaphylactic) Reactions (pp. 523–526)

4. Anaphylactic reactions involve the production of IgE antibodies that bind to mast cells and basophils to sensitize the host.
5. The binding of two adjacent IgE antibodies to an antigen causes the target cell to release chemical mediators, such as histamine, leukotrienes, and prostaglandins, which cause the observed allergic reactions.
6. Systemic anaphylaxis may develop in minutes after injection or ingestion of the antigen; this may result in circulatory collapse and death.
7. Localized anaphylaxis is exemplified by hives, hay fever, and asthma.
8. Skin testing is useful in determining sensitivity to an antigen.
9. Desensitization to an antigen can be achieved by repeated injections of the antigen, which leads to the formation of blocking (IgG) antibodies.

Type II (Cytotoxic) Reactions (pp. 526–528)

10. Type II reactions are mediated by IgG or IgM antibodies and complement.
11. The antibodies are directed toward foreign cells or host cells. Complement fixation may result in cell lysis. Macrophages and other cells may also damage the antibody-coated cells.

The ABO Blood Group System (pp. 526–527)

12. Human blood may be grouped into four principal types, designated A, B, AB, and O.
13. The presence or absence of two carbohydrate antigens designated A and B on the surface of the red blood cell determines a person's blood type.
14. Naturally occurring antibodies are present in serum against the opposite AB antigen.
15. Incompatible blood transfusions lead to the complement-mediated lysis of the donor red blood cells.

The Rh Blood Group System (pp. 527–528)

16. Approximately 85% of the human population possesses another blood group antigen, designated the Rh antigen; these individuals are designated Rh^+.
17. The absence of this antigen in certain individuals (Rh^-) can lead to sensitization upon exposure to it.
18. An Rh^+ person can receive Rh^+ or Rh^- blood transfusions.
19. When an Rh^- person receives Rh^+ blood, that person will produce anti-Rh antibodies.
20. Subsequent exposure to Rh^+ cells will result in a rapid, serious hemolytic reaction.
21. An Rh^- mother carrying an Rh^+ fetus will produce anti-Rh antibodies.

22. Subsequent pregnancies involving Rh incompatibility may result in hemolytic disease of the newborn.

23. The disease may be prevented by passive immunization of the mother with anti-Rh antibodies.

Drug-Induced Cytotoxic Reactions (p. 528)

24. In the disease thrombocytopenic purpura, platelets are destroyed by antibodies and complement.

25. Agranulocytosis and hemolytic anemia result from antibodies against one's own blood cells coated with drug molecules.

Type III (Immune Complex) Reactions (pp. 528–529)

26. Immune complex diseases occur when IgG antibodies and soluble antigen form small complexes that lodge in the basement membranes of cells.

27. Subsequent complement fixation results in inflammation.

28. Glomerulonephritis is an immune complex disease.

Type IV (Delayed Cell-Mediated) Reactions (pp. 529–531)

29. Delayed cell-mediated hypersensitivity reactions are due primarily to T_D cell proliferation.

30. Sensitized T cells secrete cytokines in response to the appropriate antigen.

31. Cytokines attract and activate macrophages and initiate tissue damage.

32. The tuberculin skin test and allergic contact dermatitis are examples of delayed hypersensitivities.

Autoimmune Diseases (pp. 532–533)

1. Autoimmunity results from a loss of self-tolerance.

2. Self-tolerance occurs during fetal development; T cells that will target host cells are eliminated (clonal deletion) or inactivated.

3. Autoimmunity may be due to antibodies against infectious agents.

4. Graves' disease and myasthenia gravis are cytotoxic autoimmune reactions in which antibodies react to cell-surface antigens.

5. Systemic lupus erythematosus and rheumatoid arthritis are immune complex autoimmune reactions in which the deposition of immune complexes results in tissue damage.

6. Multiple sclerosis, insulin-dependent diabetes mellitus, and psoriasis are cell-mediated autoimmune reactions mediated by T cells.

Reactions Related to the Human Leukocyte Antigen (HLA) Complex (pp. 533–537)

1. Histocompatibility self molecules located on cell surfaces express genetic differences among individuals; these antigens are coded for by MHC or HLA gene complexes.

2. To prevent the rejection of transplants, HLA and ABO blood group antigens of the donor and recipient are matched as closely as possible.

3. Transplants recognized as foreign antigens may be lysed by T cells and attacked by macrophages and complement-fixing antibodies.

4. Transplantation to a privileged site (such as the cornea) or of a privileged tissue (such as pig heart valves) does not cause an immune response.

5. Pluripotent stem cells differentiate into a variety of tissues that may provide tissues for transplant.

6. Four types of transplants have been defined on the basis of genetic relationships between the donor and the recipient: autografts, isografts, allografts, and xenotransplants.

7. Bone marrow (with immunocompetent cells) can cause graft-versus-host disease.

8. Successful transplant surgery often requires immunosuppressant drugs to prevent an immune response to the transplanted tissue.

The Immune System and Cancer (pp. 537–538)

1. Cancer cells are normal cells that have undergone transformation, divide uncontrollably, and possess tumor-associated antigens.
2. The response of the immune system to cancer is called immunological surveillance.
3. TC cells recognize and lyse cancerous cells.
4. Cancer cells can escape detection and destruction by the immune system.
5. Cancer cells may grow faster than the immune system can respond.

Immunotherapy for Cancer (p. 538)

6. Vaccines against liver and cervical cancer are available.
7. Herceptin consists of monoclonal antibodies against a breast cancer growth factor.
8. Immunotoxins are chemical poisons linked to a monoclonal antibody; the antibody selectively locates the cancer cell for release of the poison.

Immunodeficiencies (p. 538)

1. Immunodeficiencies can be congenital or acquired.
2. Congenital immunodeficiencies are due to defective or absent genes.
3. A variety of drugs, cancers, and infectious diseases can cause acquired immunodeficiencies.

Acquired Immunodeficiency Syndrome (AIDS) (pp. 539–548)

The Origin of AIDS (p. 540)

1. HIV is thought to have originated in central Africa and was brought to other countries by modern transportation and unsafe sexual practices.

HIV Infection (pp. 540–545)

2. AIDS is the final stage of HIV infection.
3. HIV is a retrovirus with single-stranded RNA, reverse transcriptase, and a phospholipid envelope with gp120 spikes.
4. HIV spikes attach to $CD4^+$ and coreceptors on host cells; the $CD4^+$ receptor is found on T helper cells, macrophages, and dendritic cells.
5. Viral RNA is transcribed to DNA by reverse transcriptase. The viral DNA becomes integrated into the host chromosome to direct synthesis of new viruses or to remain latent as a provirus.
6. HIV evades the immune system in latency, in vacuoles, by using cell–cell fusion, and by antigenic change.
7. Genetically distinct groups of HIV are classified into clades.
8. HIV infection is categorized by symptoms: phase 1 (asymptomatic) and phase 2 (selected symptoms) are reported as AIDS if $CD4^+$ T-cells fall below 200 cells/μl; phase 3 (AIDS indicator conditions) is reported as AIDS.
9. HIV infection is also categorized by $CD4^+$ T-cell numbers: 200 $CD4^+$ cells/μl is reported as AIDS.
10. The progression from HIV infection to AIDS takes about 10 years.
11. The life of an AIDS patient can be prolonged by the proper treatment of opportunistic infections.
12. People lacking CCR5 are resistant to HIV infection.

Diagnostic Methods (p. 545)

13. HIV antibodies are detected by ELISA and Western blotting.

14. Plasma viral load tests detect viral nucleic acid and are used to quantify HIV in blood.

HIV Transmission (pp. 545–546)

15. HIV is transmitted by sexual contact, breast milk, contaminated needles, transplacental infection, artificial insemination, and blood transfusion.

16. In developed countries, blood transfusions are not a likely source of infection because blood is tested for HIV antibodies.

AIDS Worldwide (p. 546)

17. Heterosexual intercourse is the primary method of HIV transmission.

Preventing and Treating AIDS (pp. 547–548)

20. The use of condoms and sterile needles prevents the transmission of HIV.

21. Vaccine development is difficult because the virus remains inside host cells.

22. Current chemotherapeutic agents target the virus enzymes, including reverse transcriptase, integrase, and protease.

THE LOOP

This chapter can be assigned with pages 21 and 387–340 for coverage of AIDS.

ANSWERS

Review

1.

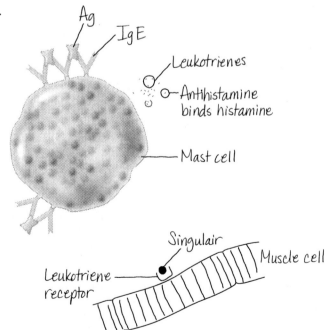

2. Recipient's serum contains complement; activated complement causes hemolysis.

3. Recipient's antibodies will react with donor's tissues.

4. Refer to Figure 19.7.

    a. The observed symptoms are due to lymphokines.

    b. When a person contacts poison oak initially, the antigen (catechols on the leaves) binds to tissue cells, is phagocytized by macrophages, and is presented to receptors on the surface of T cells. Contact between the antigen and the appropriate T cell stimulates the T cell to proliferate and become sensitized. Subsequent exposure to the antigen results in sensitized T cells releasing lymphokines, and a delayed hypersensitivity occurs.

    c. Small repeated doses of the antigen are believed to cause the production of IgG (blocking) antibodies.

5. Lupus patients have antibodies directed at their own DNA.

6. Cytotoxic   Antibodies react with cell-surface antigens.

    Immune complex   Antibody–complement complexes deposit in tissues.

    Cell-mediated   T cells destroy self cells.

    See Table 19.3.

7. Natural

    Inherited

    Viral infections, most notably HIV

    Artificial

    Induced by immunosuppression drugs

    Result: Increased susceptibility to various infections depending on the type of immune deficiency.

8. Tumor cells have tumor-specific antigens such as TSTA and T antigen. Sensitized T_C cells may react with tumor-specific antigens, initiating lysis of the tumor cells.

9. Some malignant cells can escape the immune system by antigen modulation or immunological enhancement. Immunotherapy might trigger immunological enhancement. The body's defense against cancer is cell-mediated and not humoral. Transfer of lymphocytes could cause graft-versus-host disease.

Critical Thinking

1. During embryonic development, clones of lymphocytes called forbidden clones react with "self" antigens. These forbidden clones are suppressed by specific classes of T lymphocytes. Lymphocytes that can react with foreign ("nonself") antigens are left to function in the mature immune system.

2. When a human is passively immunized with horse serum, antibodies may be produced against the horse immunoglobulns (antibodies). Immune complexes form between horse immunoglobulins and the antibodies formed against them. Symptoms are due to complement fixation.

3. Yes, they make antibodies. They are more likely to have T-independent antibodies. Their anti-HIV antibodies are ineffective because the virus can remain in the host cell, can be transmitted by cell-to-cell fusion, and can undergo antigenic changes to its surface proteins.

4. Anti-AIDS drugs are nucleoside analogs or enzyme inhibitors.

Clinical Applications

1. The infections are long-lasting, allowing sufficient time for sensitizing and shocking exposures to the fungal antigens.

2. a. An immediate hypersensitivity.

    b. The mediators of anaphylaxis; refer to Review question 2.

c. Skin tests.

d. Some workers will not produce IgE antibodies against the conidiospores.

3. Epinephrine is used to treat symptoms of type I hypersensitivity, systemic anaphylaxis. People with hypersensitivity to eggs may experience anaphylaxis from this vaccine.

4. The woman made IgG antibodies in response to the B antigen in the transfusion. IgG antibodies can cross the placenta. A normal type A+ person has anti-B antibodies of the IgM type that cannot cross the placenta.

CASE STUDY: HIV TRANSMISSION

Background

A dentist showed symptoms of HIV infection in late 1986 and was diagnosed with AIDS in 1987. At the time of the AIDS diagnosis, AZT therapy was begun, discontinued for a short period in late 1987, then restarted and continued until his practice closed in 1989. All of the dentist's employees, including the dental hygienists, tested negative for HIV antibodies.

The dentist wrote an open letter to his former patients, which prompted 591 persons to be tested for HIV antibodies. The following list summarizes the seropositive individuals.

Patient	Sex	Clinical Status	HIV Risk Factor	Dental Visits No.	Dental Visits Dates
A	F	AIDS	No	6	1987–89
B	F	$CD4^+<500/mm^3$	No	21	1987–89
C	M	$CD4^+<200/mm^3$	Unknown	14	1984–89
D	M	AIDS	Yes	19	1985–89
E	F	$CD4^+<500/mm^3$	No*	10	1988
F	M	AIDS	Yes†	5	1988
G	M	$CD4^+<400/mm^3$	No	2	1988

* Patient F was an infrequent sex partner of patient E. Their last contact was in the fall of 1988.
† Tested seronegative in October and December 1988, positive in December 1990.

Questions

1. Analyses of DNA and amino acid sequences from HIV isolated from the patients strongly suggest that five of the patients were infected by the dentist. Which two were not? How did you arrive at your conclusion?

2. How can transmission of HIV and hepatitis B by health care workers be prevented?

The Solution

1. Patients D and F were probably not infected by the dentist.

2. See Universal Precautions (Table 19.6, page 546).

20 Antimicrobial Drugs

LEARNING OBJECTIVES	CHECK YOUR UNDERSTANDING
20-1 Identify the contributions of Paul Ehrlich and Alexander Fleming to chemotherapy.	Who coined the term *magic bullet*?
20-2 Name the microbes that produce the most antibiotics.	More than half our antibiotics are produced by a certain species of bacteria. What is it?
20-3 Describe the problems of chemotherapy for viral, fungal, protozoan, and helminthic infections.	Identify at least one reason why it is so difficult to target a pathogenic virus without damaging the host's cells.
20-4 Define the following terms: *spectrum of activity, broad-spectrum antibiotic, superinfection.*	Why are antibiotics with a very broad spectrum of activity not as useful as one might first think?
20-5 Identify five modes of action of antimicrobial drugs.	What cellular function is inhibited by tetracyclines?
20-6 Explain why the drugs described in this section are specific for bacteria.	One of the most successful groups of antibiotics targets the synthesis of bacterial cell walls; why does the antibiotic not affect the mammalian cell?
20-7 List the advantages of each of the following over penicillin: semisynthetic penicillins, cephalosporins, and vancomycin.	What phenomenon prompted the development of the first semisynthetic antibiotics, such as methicillin?
20-8 Explain why isoniazid (INH) and ethambutal are antimycobacterial agents.	In what genus of bacteria do we find mycolic acids in the cell wall?
20-9 Describe how each of the following inhibits protein synthesis: aminoglycosides, tetracyclines, chloramphenicol, macrolides.	Why does erythromycin, a macrolide antibiotic, have a spectrum of activity largely limited to gram-positive bacteria, even though its mode of action is similar to that of the broad-spectrum tetracyclines?
20-10 Compare the mode of action of polymyxin B, bacitracin, and neomycin.	Of the three drugs often found in over-the-counter antiseptic creams—polymyxin B, bacitracin, and neomycin—which has a mode of action most similar to that of penicillin?
20-11 Describe how rifamycins and quinolones kill bacteria.	What group of antibiotics interfere with the DNA-replicating enzyme DNA gyrase?
20-12 Describe how sulfa drugs inhibit microbial growth.	Both humans and bacteria need the essential nutrient para-aminobenzoic acid; why, then, are only bacteria affected by sulfa drugs?
20-13 Explain the modes of action of currently used antifungal drugs.	What sterol in the cell membrane of fungi is the most common target for antifungal action?

20-14 Explain the modes of action of currently used antiviral drugs.	One of the most widely used antivirals, acyclovir, inhibits the synthesis of DNA. Humans also synthesize DNA, so why is the drug still useful in treating viral infections?
20-15 Explain the modes of action of currently used antiprotozoan and antihelminthic drugs.	What was the first drug available for use against parasitic infections?
20-16 Describe the two tests for microbial susceptibility to chemotherapeutic agents.	In the disk-diffusion (Kirby-Bauer) test, the zone of inhibition indicating sensitivity around the disk varies with the antibiotic. Why?
20-17 Describe the mechanisms of drug resistance.	What is the most common mechanism that a bacterium uses to resist the effects of penicillin?
20-18 Compare and contrast synergism and antagonism.	Tetracycline sometimes interferes with the activity of penicillin. How?
20-19 Identify three areas of research on new chemotherapeutic agents.	Why is the positive electric charge on antimicrobial peptides such a probable factor in the mode of action?

NEW IN THIS EDITION

- Revised discussion of the sulfa drugs, giving more prominence to their historical importance
- Discussion of the current methods used for the discovery of new antibiotics, most specifically, rapid throughput methods
- New figure illustrating antibiotic-resistance mechanisms

CHAPTER SUMMARY

Introduction (p. 553)

1. An antimicrobial drug is a chemical substance that destroys pathogenic microorganisms with minimal damage to host tissues.
2. Chemotherapeutic agents include chemicals that combat disease in the body.

The History of Chemotherapy (pp. 554–555)

1. Paul Ehrlich developed the concept of chemotherapy to treat microbial diseases; he predicted the development of chemotherapeutic agents, which would kill pathogens without harming the host.
2. Sulfa drugs came into prominence in the late 1930s.
3. Alexander Fleming discovered the first antibiotic, penicillin, in 1929; its first clinical trials were done in 1940.

The Spectrum of Antimicrobial Activity (p. 555)

1. Antibacterial drugs affect many targets in a prokaryotic cell.
2. Fungal, protozoan, and helminthic infections are more difficult to treat because these organisms have eukaryotic cells.
3. Narrow-spectrum drugs affect only a select group of microbes—gram-positive cells, for example; broad-spectrum drugs affect a more diverse range of microbes.
4. Small, hydrophilic drugs can affect gram-negative cells.
5. Antimicrobial agents should not cause excessive harm to normal microbiota.

6. Superinfections occur when a pathogen develops resistance to the drug being used or when normally resistant microbiota multiply excessively.

The Action of Antimicrobial Drugs (pp. 555–559)

1. General action is either by directly killing microorganisms (bactericidal) or by inhibiting their growth (bacteriostatic).
2. Some agents, such as penicillin, inhibit cell wall synthesis in bacteria.
3. Other agents, such as chloramphenicol, tetracyclines, and streptomycin, inhibit protein synthesis by acting on 70S ribosomes.
4. Antifungal agents target plasma membranes.
5. Some agents inhibit nucleic acid synthesis.
6. Agents such as sulfanilamide act as antimetabolites by competitively inhibiting enzyme activity.

A Survey of Commonly Used Antimicrobial Drugs (pp. 559–572)

Antibacterial Antibiotics: Inhibitors of Cell Wall Synthesis (pp. 559–563)

1. All penicillins contain a β-lactam ring.
2. Natural penicillins produced by *Penicillium* are effective against gram-positive cocci and spirochetes.
3. Penicillinases (β-lactamases) are bacterial enzymes that destroy natural penicillins.
4. Semisynthetic penicillins are made in the laboratory by adding different side chains onto the β-lactam ring made by the fungus.
5. Semisynthetic penicillins are resistant to penicillinases and have a broader spectrum of activity than natural penicillins.
6. Carbapenems are broad-spectrum antibiotics that inhibit cell wall synthesis.
7. The monobactam aztreonam affects only gram-negative bacteria.
8. Cephalosporins inhibit cell wall synthesis and are used against penicillin-resistant strains.
9. Polypeptides such as bacitracin inhibit cell wall synthesis primarily in gram-positive bacteria.
10. Vancomycin inhibits cell wall synthesis and may be used to kill penicillinase-producing staphylococci.

Antimycobacterial Antibiotics (p. 563)

11. Isoniazid (INH) and ethambutol inhibit cell wall synthesis in mycobacteria.

Inhibitors of Protein Synthesis (pp. 563–566)

12. Chloramphenicol, aminoglycosides, tetracyclines, macrolides, and streptogramins inhibit protein synthesis at 70S ribosomes.
13. Oxazolidinones prevent formation of 70S ribosomes.

Injury to the Plasma Membrane (pp. 566–567)

14. A new class of antibiotics inhibits fatty-acid synthesis, essential for plasma membranes.
15. Polymyxin B and bacitracin cause damage to plasma membranes.

Inhibitors of Nucleic Acid (DNA/RNA) Synthesis (p. 567)

16. Rifamycin inhibits mRNA synthesis; it is used to treat tuberculosis.
17. Quinolones and fluoroquinolones inhibit DNA gyrase for treating urinary tract infections.

Competitive Inhibitors of the Synthesis of Essential Metabolites (p. 567)

18. Sulfonamides competitively inhibit folic acid synthesis.
19. TMP-SMZ competitively inhibits dihydrofolic acid synthesis.

Antifungal Drugs (pp. 567–569)

20. Polyenes, such as nystatin and amphotericin B, combine with plasma membrane sterols and are fungicidal.
21. Azoles and allylamines interfere with sterol synthesis and are used to treat cutaneous and systemic mycoses.
22. Echinocandins interfere with fungal cell wall synthesis.
23. The antifungal agent flucytosine is an antimetabolite of cytosine.
24. Griseofulvin interferes with eukaryotic cell division and is used primarily to treat skin infections caused by fungi.

Antiviral Drugs (pp. 569–571)

25. Nucleoside and nucleotide analogs, such as acyclovir and zidovudine, inhibit DNA or RNA synthesis.
26. Inhibitors of viral enzymes are used to treat influenza and HIV infection.
27. Alpha interferons inhibit the spread of viruses to new cells.

Antiprotozoan and Antihelminthic Drugs (pp. 571–572)

28. Chloroquine, quinacrine, diiodohydroxyquin, pentamidine, and metronidazole are used to treat protozoan infections.
29. Antihelminthic drugs include mebendazole, praziquantel, and ivermectin.

Tests to Guide Chemotherapy (pp. 572–573)

1. Tests are used to determine which chemotherapeutic agent is most likely to combat a specific pathogen.
2. These tests are used when susceptibility cannot be predicted or when drug resistance arises.

The Diffusion Methods (p. 572)

3. In the disk-diffusion test, also known as the Kirby-Bauer test, a bacterial culture is inoculated on an agar medium, and filter paper disks impregnated with chemotherapeutic agents are overlaid on the culture.
4. After incubation, the diameter of the zone of inhibition is used to determine whether the organism is sensitive, intermediate, or resistant to the drug.
5. MIC is the lowest concentration of drug capable of preventing microbial growth; MIC can be estimated using the E test.

Broth Dilution Tests (pp. 572–573)

6. In a broth dilution test, the microorganism is grown in liquid media containing different concentrations of a chemotherapeutic agent.
7. The lowest concentration of a chemotherapeutic agent that kills bacteria is called the minimum bactericidal concentration (MBC).

Resistance to Antimicrobial Drugs (pp. 573–576)

1. Hereditary drug resistance (R) factors are carried by plasmids and transposons.
2. Resistance may be due to enzymatic destruction of a drug, prevention of penetration of the drug to its target site, cellular or metabolic changes at target sites, or rapid efflux of the antibiotic.

3. Resistance can be minimized by the discriminating use of drugs in appropriate concentrations and dosages.

Antibiotic Safety (pp. 576–578)

1. The risk (e.g., side effects) versus the benefit (e.g., curing an infection) must be evaluated prior to using antibiotics.

Effects of Combinations of Drugs (p. 578)

1. Some combinations of drugs are synergistic; they are more effective when taken together.
2. Some combinations of drugs are antagonistic; when taken together, both drugs become less effective than when taken alone.

The Future of Chemotherapeutic Agents (pp. 578–580)

1. Many bacterial diseases, previously treatable with antibiotics, have become resistant to antibiotics.
2. Chemicals produced by plants and animals are providing new antimicrobial agents called antimicrobial peptides.
3. Protein synthesis in pathogens can be blocked by siRNAs.
4. New agents may inhibit bacterial virulence factors.

THE LOOP

This chapter can be covered with disinfectants, antiseptics, and physical methods of controlling microorganisms (Chapter 7).

ANSWERS

Review

1.

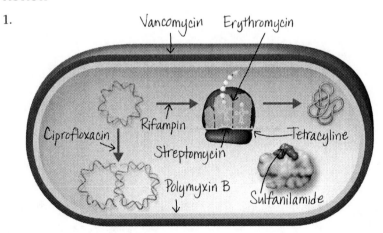

2. The drug (1) should exhibit selective toxicity; (2) should have a broad spectrum; (3) should not produce hypersensitivity in the host; (4) should not produce drug resistance; and (5) should not harm normal microbiota.
3. Because a virus uses the host cell's metabolic machinery, it is difficult to damage the virus without damaging the host. Fungi, protozoa, and helminths possess eukaryotic cells. Therefore, antiviral, antifungal, antiprotozoan, and antihelminthic drugs must also affect eukaryotic cells.

4. Drug resistance is the lack of susceptibility of a microorganism to a chemotherapeutic agent. Drug resistance may develop when microorganisms are constantly exposed to an antimicrobial agent. The development of drug-resistant microorganisms can be minimized by judicious use of antimicrobial agents; following directions on the prescription; or by administering two or more drugs simultaneously.

5. Simultaneous use of two agents can prevent the development of resistant strains of microorganisms; take advantage of the synergistic effect; provide therapy until a diagnosis is made; and lessen the toxicity of individual drugs by reducing the dosage of each in combination. One problem that can result from simultaneous use of two agents is the antagonistic effect.

6. a. Like polymyxin B, causes leaks in the plasma membrane.

   b. Interferes with translation.

7. a. Inhibits formation of peptide bond.

   b. Prevents translocation of ribosome along mRNA.

   c. Interferes with attachment of tRNA to mRNA-ribosome complex.

   d. Changes shape of 30S portion of ribosome, resulting in misreading mRNA.

   e. Prevents 70S ribosomal subunits from forming.

   f. Prevents release of peptide from ribosome.

8. DNA polymerase adds bases to the 3′–OH.

9. a. Penicillin inhibits bacterial cell wall synthesis. Echinocandin inhibits fungal cell wall synthesis.

   b. Imidazole interferes with fungal plasma membrane synthesis. Polymyxin B disrupts any plasma membrane.

Critical Thinking

1. a. No. Human cells lack cell walls.

   b. No. It inhibits a viral enzyme.

   c. Yes. It affects mitochondrial ribosomes.

   d. Probably not. Sterols protect human membranes.

2. Cells infected by viruses may be rapidly metabolizing (anabolizing) in order to synthesize viruses. These cells are more likely to incorporate base analogs than normal, uninfected cells.

3. The carbon source can't enter the cells.

4. a. A and D were equally effective.

   b. A or D would be recommended, depending on their respective side effects.

   c. You can't tell. A subculture from the zone of inhibition would have to be done to determine whether A was bactericidal or bacteriostatic.

5. *S. griseus* makes streptomycin during idiophase. The inactivating enzyme is necessary to protect the bacterium from the streptomycin.

6. MIC, 50 µg/ml; MBC, 25 µg/ml.

Clinical Applications

1. Tetracycline induces lag phase, and penicillin requires log phase. In some infections, streptomycin enters more easily through a penicillin-damaged cell wall.

2. The bacteria were resistant to nalidixic acid but susceptible to sulfonamide.

3. Many bacteria were killed initially, so the patient started to feel better. Recall that bacteria die logarithmically, so it takes quite a while to kill an entire population. The concentration of penicillin dropped in his body when he stopped taking penicillin, so the surviving bacteria were able to grow.

CASE STUDY: DETERMINING THE METHOD OF ACTION

Background

Assume you have discovered a new antibiotic. The effectiveness of this drug is shown below. To determine the method of action of this chemical, you culture a bacterium in two bioreactors containing nutrient broth, add the new drug to the test broth after 20 hours, and analyze both media. Protease activity is easily measured because protease is an extracellular enzyme.

Data

Antibiotic Disk Test	
Bacterium	**Zone of Inhibition (mm)**
Bacillus subtilis	0
Escherichia coli	10
Mycobacterium phlei	0
Pseudomonas aeruginosa	8
Salmonella typhimurium	9
Staphylococcus aureus	5
Streptococcus pyogenes	5

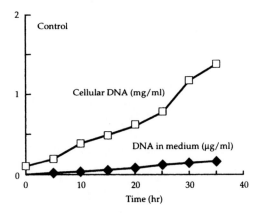

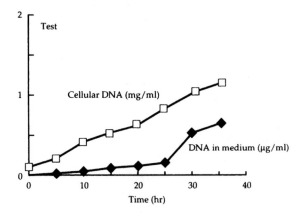

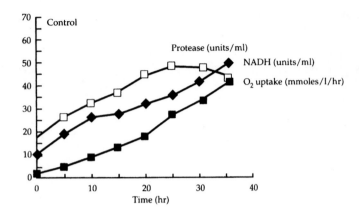

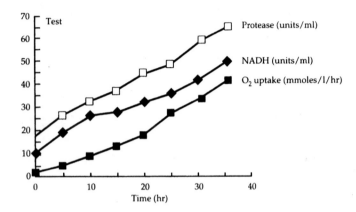

Questions

1. What bacterium did you use as your test organism?
2. Why were these particular parameters measured? What do they tell you about cell activity?
3. What is the method of action of this antibiotic? How can you tell?

The Solution

1. The test organism should be gram-negative because the drug is much less effective against gram-positives.
2. Cellular DNA is proportional to growth.

   Extracellular DNA indicates cells are lysing.

   The concentration of this protein is proportional to the rate of transcription.

   The concentration of NADH indicates the rate of catabolism.

   The rate of oxygen uptake is a measure of electron transport activity.
3. The decrease in protease suggests that protein synthesis is stopped.

21

Microbial Diseases of the Skin and Eyes

LEARNING OBJECTIVES	CHECK YOUR UNDERSTANDING
21-1 Describe the structure of the skin and mucous membranes and the ways pathogens can invade the skin.	The moisture provided by perspiration encourages microbial growth on skin. What factors in perspiration discourage microbial growth?
21-2 Provide examples of normal skin microbiota, and state the general locations and ecological roles of its members.	Are skin bacteria more likely to be gram-positive or gram-negative?
21-3 Differentiate staphylococci from streptococci, and name several skin infections caused by each.	Which bacterial species features the virulence factor M protein?
21-4 List the causative agent, mode of transmission. and clinical symptoms of *Pseudomonas* dermatitis, otitis externa, acne, and Buruli ulcer.	What is the common name for otitis externa?
21-5 List the causative agent, mode of transmission, and clinical symptoms of these skin infections: warts, smallpox, monkeypox, chickenpox, shingles, cold sores, measles, rubella, fifth disease, and roseola.	How did the odd designation of "fifth disease" arise?
21-6 Differentiate cutaneous from subcutaneous mycoses, and provide an example of each.	How do sporotrichosis and athlete's foot differ? In what ways are they similar?
21-7 List the causative agent and predisposing factors for candidiasis.	How might the use of penicillin result in a case of candidiasis?
21-8 List the causative agent, mode of transmission, clinical symptoms, and treatment for scabies and pediculosis.	What diseases, if any, are spread by head lice, such as *Pediculus humanus capitis*?
21-9 Define *conjunctivitis*.	What is the common name of inclusion conjunctivitis?
21-10 List the causative agent, mode of transmission, and clinical symptoms of these eye infections: ophthalmia neonatorum, inclusion conjunctivitis, trachoma.	Why have antibiotics almost entirely replaced the less expensive use of silver nitrate for preventing ophthalmia neonatorum?
21-11 List the causative agent, mode of transmission, and clinical symptoms of these eye infections: herpetic keratitis, *Acanthamoeba* keratitis.	Of the two eye diseases herpetic keratitis and *Acanthamoeba* keratitis, which is the more likely to be caused by an organism actively reproducing in saline solutions for contact lenses?

NEW IN THIS EDITION

- Completely rewritten discussion of *Staphylococcus aureus*, emphasizing the importance of methicillin-resistant *S. aureus*
- New discussion of the global health threat Buruli ulcer
- An updated Clinical Focus (*MMWR*) box describing community-acquired MRSA

CHAPTER SUMMARY

Introduction (p. 584)

1. The skin is a physical barrier against microorganisms.
2. Moist areas of the skin (such as the armpit) support larger populations of bacteria than dry areas (such as the scalp).
3. Human skin produces antibiotics called defensins.

Structure and Function of the Skin (p. 585)

1. The outer portion of the skin (epidermis) contains keratin, a waterproof coating.
2. The inner portion of the skin, the dermis, contains hair follicles, sweat ducts, and oil glands that provide passageways for microorganisms.
3. Sebum and perspiration are secretions of the skin that can inhibit the growth of microorganisms.
4. Sebum and perspiration provide nutrients for some microorganisms.
5. Body cavities are lined with epithelial cells. When these cells secrete mucus, they constitute the mucous membrane.

Normal Microbiota of the Skin (pp. 585–586)

1. Microorganisms that live on skin are resistant to desiccation and high concentrations of salt.
2. Gram-positive cocci predominate on the skin.
3. The normal skin microbiota are not completely removed by washing.
4. Members of the genus *Propionibacterium* metabolize oil from the oil glands and colonize hair follicles.
5. *Malassezia furfur* yeast grows on oily secretions and may be the cause of dandruff.

Microbial Diseases of the Skin (pp. 586–603)

1. Vesicles are small fluid-filled lesions; bullae are vesicles larger than 1 cm; macules are flat, reddened lesions; papules are raised lesions; and pustules are raised lesions containing pus.

Bacterial Diseases of the Skin (pp. 586–598)

Staphylococcal Skin Infections (pp. 586–589)

2. Staphylococci are gram-positive bacteria that often grow in clusters.
3. The majority of skin microbiota consist of coagulase-negative *Staphylococcus epidermidis*.
4. Almost all pathogenic strains of S. aureus produce coagulase.
5. Pathogenic *S. aureus* can produce enterotoxins, leukocidins, and exfoliative toxin.
6. Localized infections (sties, pimples, and carbuncles) result from *S. aureus* entering openings in the skin.
7. Impetigo is a highly contagious superficial skin infection caused by *S. aureus*.
8. Toxemia occurs when toxins enter the bloodstream; staphylococcal toxemias include scalded skin syndrome and toxic shock syndrome.

Streptococcal Skin Infections (pp. 589–591)

9. Streptococci are gram-positive cocci that often grow in chains.

10. Streptococci are classified according to their hemolytic enzymes and cell wall antigens.

11. Group A beta-hemolytic streptococci (including *Streptococcus pyogenes*) are the pathogens most important to humans.

12. Group A beta-hemolytic streptococci produce a number of virulence factors: M protein, erythrogenic toxin, deoxyribonuclease, streptokinases, and hyaluronidase.

13. Erysipelas is caused by *S. pyogenes.*

14. Invasive group A beta-hemolytic streptococci cause severe and rapid tissue destruction.

Infections by Pseudomonads (pp. 591–594)

15. Pseudomonads are gram-negative rods. They are aerobes found primarily in soil and water that are resistant to many disinfectants and antibiotics.

16. *Pseudomonas aeruginosa* produces an endotoxin and several exotoxins.

17. Diseases caused by *P. aeruginosa* include otitis externa, respiratory infections, burn infections, and dermatitis.

18. Infections have a characteristic blue-green pus caused by the pigment pyocyanin.

19. Quinolones are useful in treating *P. aeruginosa* infections.

Buruli Ulcer (p. 594)

20. *Mycobacterium ulcerans* causes deep-tissue ulceration.

Acne (p. 594)

21. *Propionibacterium acnes* can metabolize sebum trapped in hair follicles.

22. Metabolic end-products (fatty acids) cause inflammatory acne.

23. Tretinoin, benzoyl peroxide, erythromycin, and light therapy are used to treat acne.

Viral Diseases of the Skin (pp. 595–600)

Warts (p. 595)

24. Papillomaviruses cause skin cells to proliferate and produce a benign growth called a wart or papilloma.

25. Warts are spread by direct contact.

26. Warts may regress spontaneously or be removed chemically or physically.

Smallpox (Variola) (pp. 595–596)

27. Variola virus causes two types of skin infections: variola major and variola minor.

28. Smallpox is transmitted by the respiratory route, and the virus is moved to the skin via the bloodstream.

29. The only host for smallpox is humans.

30. Smallpox has been eradicated as a result of a vaccination effort by the World Health Organization.

Chickenpox (Varicella) and Shingles (Herpes Zoster) (pp. 596–597)

31. Varicella-zoster virus is transmitted by the respiratory route and is localized in skin cells, causing a vesicular rash.

32. Complications of chickenpox include encephalitis and Reyes syndrome.

33. After chickenpox, the virus can remain latent in nerve cells and subsequently activate as shingles.

34. Shingles (herpes zoster) is characterized by a vesicular rash along the affected cutaneous sensory nerves.

35. The virus can be treated with acyclovir. An attenuated live vaccine is available.

Herpes Simplex (pp. 597–598)

36. Herpes simplex infection of mucosal cells results in cold sores and occasionally encephalitis.

37. The virus remains latent in nerve cells, and cold sores can recur when the virus is activated.

38. HSV-1 is transmitted primarily by oral and respiratory routes.

39. Herpes encephalitis occurs when herpes simplex viruses infect the brain.

40. Acyclovir has proven successful in treating herpes encephalitis.

Measles (Rubeola) (pp. 598–599)

41. Measles is caused by measles virus and is transmitted by the respiratory route.

42. Vaccination provides effective long-term immunity.

43. After the virus has incubated in the upper respiratory tract, macular lesions appear on the skin, and Koplik's spots appear on the oral mucosa.

44. Complications of measles include middle ear infections, pneumonia, encephalitis, and secondary bacterial infections.

Rubella (pp. 599–600)

45. The rubella virus is transmitted by the respiratory route.

46. An infected individual might experience a red rash and light fever or be asymptomatic.

47. Congenital rubella syndrome can affect a fetus when a woman contracts rubella during the first trimester of her pregnancy.

48. Damage from congenital rubella syndrome includes stillbirth, deafness, eye cataracts, heart defects, and mental retardation.

49. Vaccination with live rubella virus provides immunity of unknown duration.

Other Viral Rashes (p. 600)

50. Human parvovirus B19 causes fifth disease, and HHV-6 causes roseola.

Fungal Diseases of the Skin and Nails (pp. 600–602)

Cutaneous Mycoses (pp. 600–601)

51. Fungi that colonize the outer layer of the epidermis cause dermatomycoses.

52. *Microsporum, Trichophyton,* and *Epidermophyton* cause dermatomycoses called ringworm, or tinea.

53. These fungi grow on keratin-containing epidermis, such as hair, skin, and nails.

54. Ringworm and athlete's foot are usually treated with topical antifungal chemicals.

55. Diagnosis is based on the microscopic examination of skin scrapings or fungal culture.

Subcutaneous Mycoses (p. 601)

56. Sporotrichosis results from a soil fungus that penetrates the skin through a wound.

57. The fungi grow and produce subcutaneous nodules along the lymphatic vessels.

Candidiasis (pp. 601–602)

58. *Candida albicans* causes infections of mucous membranes and is a common cause of thrush (in oral mucosa) and vaginitis.

59. *C. albicans* is an opportunistic pathogen that may proliferate when the normal bacterial microbiota are suppressed.

60. Topical antifungal chemicals may be used to treat candidiasis.

Parasitic Infestation of the Skin (pp. 602–603)

61. Scabies is caused by a mite burrowing and laying eggs in the skin.
62. Pediculosis is an infestation by *Pediculus humanus*.

Microbial Diseases of the Eye (pp. 603–605)

1. The mucous membrane lining the eyelid and covering the eyeball is the conjunctiva.

Inflammation of the Eye Membranes: Conjunctivitis (p. 603)

2. Conjunctivitis is caused by several bacteria and can be transmitted by improperly disinfected contact lenses.

Bacterial Diseases of the Eye (pp. 603–605)

3. Bacterial microbiota of the eye usually originate from the skin and upper respiratory tract.
4. Ophthalmia neonatorum is caused by the transmission of *Neisseria gonorrhoeae* from an infected mother to an infant during its passage through the birth canal.
5. All newborn infants are treated with an antibiotic to prevent *Neisseria* and *Chlamydia* infection.
6. Inclusion conjunctivitis is an infection of the conjunctiva caused by *Chlamydia trachomatis*. It is transmitted to infants during birth and is transmitted in unchlorinated swimming water.
7. In trachoma, which is caused by *C. trachomatis*, scar tissue forms on the cornea.
8. Trachoma is transmitted by hands, fomites, and perhaps flies.

Other Infectious Diseases of the Eye (p. 605)

9. *Fusarium* and *Aspergillus* fungi can infect the eye.
10. Herpetic keratitis causes corneal ulcers. The etiology is HSV-1 that invades the central nervous system and can recur.
11. *Acanthamoeba* protozoa, transmitted via water, can cause a serious form of keratitis.

THE LOOP

For a taxonomic approach, pages can be assigned as follows:

ANSWERS

Diseases in Focus 21.1: Macular Rashes

A 4-year-old boy with a history of cough, conjunctivitis, and fever (38.3°C) now has a macular rash that starts on his face and neck and is spreading to the rest of his body. The macular rash that appears on the face and then spreads to the rest of the body following a period of coldlike symptoms differentiates measles from the other macular rashes. The boy in the photograph is actually infected with measles virus. The presence of Koplik's spots inside the mouth is diagnostic for measles.

Diseases in Focus 21.2: Vesicular and Pustular Rashes

An 8-year-old boy has a rash consisting of vesicular lesions of 5 days' duration on his neck and stomach. Within 5 days, 73 students in his elementary school had illness matching the case definition for this disease. Vesicles on the upper body distinguish chickenpox from other vesicular rashes. The body in the photograph is actually infected with chickenpox virus (human herpesvirus-3). Diagnosis is based on the appearance of the rash. Vesicles due to shingles, also caused by HHV-3, appear along a nerve and are not disseminated over the body. Smallpox vesicles first appear on the face and then down the trunk. Smallpox vesicles are more deeply embedded in the skin and are in a similar stage of development in each area of the body. Laboratory confirmation of chickenpox, by the presence of antibodies, is rarely done.

Diseases in Focus 21.3: Patchy Redness and Pimple-Like Conditions

An 11-month-old boy came to clinic with a 1-week history of an itchy red rash under his arms. He seemed more bothered at night and had no fever. The fact that the itchy rash is localized (under the patient's arms, in this case) and the size of the lesions (1 mm) suggest scabies. Scabies is not associated with fever. Scabies is the only papular rash in the table. Toxic shock syndrome and erysipelas cause widespread red rash accompanied by fever. The child in the photo has scabies. Diagnosis is by microscopic examination of skin scrapings for the mite.

Diseases in Focus 21.4: Microbial Diseases of the Eye

A 20-year-old man has eye redness with dried mucus crust in the morning. The condition resolved with topical antibiotic treatment. The red inflamed conjunctiva shown in the photo is characteristic of conjunctivitis rather than a corneal infection. Also, the mucus crust suggests an infection. In this case, diagnosis of bacterial conjunctivitis was confirmed by recovery following antibiotic therapy. If the condition had not resolved, an eye swab could be cultured to look for specific bacteria (but not viruses).

Review

1. Bacteria usually enter through inapparent openings in the skin. Fungal pathogens (except subcutaneous) often grow on the skin itself. Viral infections of the skin (except warts and herpes simplex) most often gain access to the body through the respiratory tract.

2. *Staphylococcus aureus; Streptococcus pyogenes.*

3.

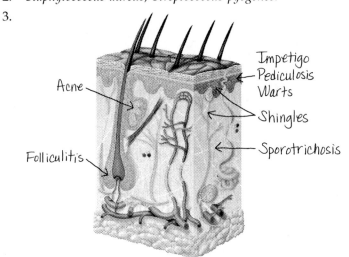

4.

Disease	Etiological Agent	Clinical Symptoms	Method of Transmission
Acne	*P. acnes*	Infected oil glands	Direct contact
Pimples	*S. aureus*	Infected hair follicles	Direct contact
Warts	Papovavirus	Benign tumor	Direct contact
Chickenpox	Herpesvirus	Vesicular rash	Respiratory route
Fever blisters	Herpesvirus	Recurrent "blisters"	Direct contact
Measles	Paramyxovirus	Papular rash, Koplik's spots	Respiratory route
Rubella	Togavirus	Macular rash	Respiratory route

5. The test determines the woman's susceptibility to rubella. If the test is negative, she is susceptible to the disease. If she acquires the disease during pregnancy, the fetus could become infected. A susceptible woman should be vaccinated.

6.

Symptoms	Disease
Koplik's spots	Measles
Macular rash	Measles
Vesicular rash	Chickenpox
Small, spotted rash	German measles
"Blisters"	Cold sore
Corneal ulcer	Keratoconjunctivitis

7. The central nervous system can be invaded following keratoconjunctivitis; this results in encephalitis.

8. Attenuated measles, mumps, and rubella viruses.

9. Scabies is an infestation of mites in the skin. It is treated with permethrin insecticide or gamma benzene hexachloride. The presence of a six-legged arthropod (insect) indicates pediculosis (lice).

Critical Thinking

1. *S. aureus* is adapted for surviving on the human skin, which has a high concentration of NaCl. Microorganisms that are not adapted to this hypertonic environment will not be able to tolerate the 7.5% NaCl in mannitol salt agar.

2. Most warts regress spontaneously. Warts are usually removed for cosmetic reasons. Occasionally warts are painful when they are located where pressure is placed on them (e.g., plantar warts on the sole of the foot).

3. The infections were transmitted by the contact lenses or cosmetics. Cosmetics are inoculated with microbes each time they are used. Some of the microbes grow, resulting in large inoculations of the eyes. Contact lenses can cause infection if they are improperly cleaned (i.e., without using an antiseptic) or contaminated by fingers.

4. The virus had one host—humans. It was not found in soil, water, or nonhuman organisms. Polio and measles meet this criterion.

Clinical Applications

1. *Pseudomonas aeruginosa*. This bacterium is common in soil and is resistant to many antibiotics.

2. Toxic shock syndrome due to growth of *Staphylococcus* at the injection site.

3. The symptoms of toxic shock syndrome were caused by toxins produced from the secondary infection *(S. aureus)*.

CASE STUDY: WRESTLING WITH SKIN INFECTIONS

Background

A wrestling camp held July 2 through July 28 was attended by 175 male high school wrestlers from throughout the United States. On July 19, seven wrestlers were referred to a local urgent care facility because of complaints of painful vesicles on various parts of their bodies [head or neck (3), extremities (2), trunk (1)] and conjunctiva (1). Bacterial and fungal cultures from the skin lesions were negative.

A questionnaire was administered to wrestlers by telephone following the conclusion of camp. Sixty-one wrestlers met the case definition of the presence of cutaneous vesicles. Onset occurred during the camp session or within 1 week after the athletes left camp (see the figure).

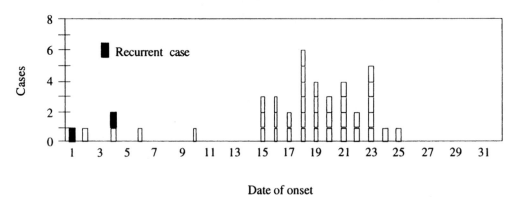

Date of onset

Athletes who reported wrestling with a participant with a rash were more likely to have the infection. Thirty-eight wrestlers interviewed reported a past history of oral cold sores. The attack rate was 24% for wrestlers who reported a past history of oral cold sores and 38% for wrestlers without a history of oral cold sores.

Questions

1. What diseases do you suspect?
2. How was this disease transmitted?
3. How is this disease treated?
4. Provide a possible explanation of the lower attack rate in wrestlers with a history of oral cold sores.
5. How can such outbreaks be prevented?

The Solution

1. Herpes gladiatorum
2. Direct contact
3. Acyclovir
4. Individuals with a history of oral herpes may have circulating antibodies that will prevent a new infection or recurrence.
5. Control methods should include education of athletes and trainers regarding herpes gladiatorum, routine skin examinations before wrestling contact, and exclusion of wrestlers with suspicious skin lesions. This outbreak might have been prevented if athletes with such lesions had been promptly excluded from contact competition.

22

Microbial Diseases of the Nervous System

LEARNING OBJECTIVES	CHECK YOUR UNDERSTANDING
22-1 Define *central nervous system and blood–brain barrier*.	Why can the antibiotic chloramphenicol readily cross the blood–brain barrier, whereas most other antibiotics cannot?
22-2 Differentiate meningitis from encephalitis.	Encephalitis is an inflammation of what organ or organ structure?
22-3 Discuss the epidemiology of meningitis caused by *Haemophilus influenzae, Neisseria meningitidis, Streptococcus pneumoniae,* and *Listeria monocytogenes*.	Why is meningitis caused by the pathogen *Listeria monocytogenes* frequently associated with ingestion of refrigerated foods?
22-4 Explain how bacterial meningitis is diagnosed and treated.	What body fluid is sampled to diagnose bacterial meningitis?
22-5 Discuss the epidemiology of tetanus, including mode of transmission, etiology, disease symptoms, and preventive measures.	Is the tetanus vaccine directed at the bacterium or the toxin produced by the bacterium?
22-6 State the causative agent, symptoms, suspect foods, and treatment for botulism.	The very name *botulism* is derived from the fact that sausage was the most common food causing the disease. Why is sausage now rarely a cause of botulism?
22-7 Discuss the epidemiology of leprosy, including mode of transmission, etiology, disease symptoms, and preventive measures.	Why are nude mice and armadillos important in the study of leprosy?
22-8 Discuss the epidemiology of poliomyelitis, rabies, and arboviral encephalitis, including mode of transmission, etiology, and disease symptoms.	Why is paralytic polio more likely than a mild or asymptomatic infection in areas with high standards of sanitation?
22-9 Compare the Salk and Sabin polio vaccines.	Why is the Sabin oral polio vaccine more effective than the injected Salk polio vaccine?
22-10 Compare the preexposure and postexposure treatments for rabies.	Why is postexposure vaccination for rabies a practical option?
22-11 Explain how arboviral encephalitis can be prevented.	When there are serious local outbreaks of arboviral encephalitis, what is the usual reponse to minimize its transmission?
22-12 Identify the causative agent, reservoir, symptoms, and treatment for cryptococcosis.	What is the most common source of airborne cryptococcal infection?
22-13 Identify the causative agent, vector, symptoms, and treatment for African trypanosomiasis and amebic meningoencephalitis.	What insect is the vector for African typanosomiasis?

22-14	List the characteristics of diseases caused by prions.	What are the recommendations for sterilizing reusable surgical instruments when prion contamination might be a factor?
22-15	List some possible causes of chronic fatigue syndrome.	Name one common disease that may be associated with chronic fatigue syndrome.

NEW IN THIS EDITION

- A new figure illustrating the performance of a spinal tap, which is used in diagnosing many nervous system diseases
- Inclusion of a newer pathogen in the discussion of cryptococcosis
- A brief description of prions supplementing that given in Chapter 13
- Revised discussion of chronic fatigue syndrome, which now includes the CDC's diagnostic definition and the alternative name of myalgic encephalomyelitis
- A new Clinical Focus (*MMWR*) box describing a recent case of human rabies

CHAPTER SUMMARY

Structure and Function of the Nervous System (p. 611)

1. The central nervous system (CNS) consists of the brain, which is protected by the skull bones, and the spinal cord, which is protected by the backbone.
2. The peripheral nervous system (PNS) consists of the nerves that branch from the CNS.
3. The CNS is covered by three layers of membranes called meninges: the dura mater, arachnoid mater, and pia mater. Cerebrospinal fluid (CSF) circulates between the arachnoid mater and the pia mater in the subarachnoid space.
4. The blood–brain barrier normally prevents many substances, including antibiotics, from entering the brain.
5. Microorganisms can enter the CNS through trauma, along peripheral nerves, and through the bloodstream and lymphatic system.
6. An infection of the meninges is called meningitis. An infection of the brain is called encephalitis.

Bacterial Diseases of the Nervous System (pp. 611–620)

Bacterial Meningitis (pp. 612–615)

1. Meningitis can be caused by viruses, bacteria, fungi, and protozoa.
2. The three major causes of bacterial meningitis are *Haemophilus influenzae, Streptococcus pneumoniae,* and *Neisseria meningitidis.*
3. Nearly 50 species of opportunistic bacteria can cause meningitis.

Haemophilus influenzae *Meningitis (p. 613)*

4. *H. influenzae* is part of the normal throat microbiota.
5. *H. influenzae* requires blood factors for growth; serotypes are based on capsules.
6. *H. influenzae* type b is the most common cause of meningitis in children under 4 years old.
7. A conjugated vaccine directed against the capsular polysaccharide antigen is available.

Neisseria *Meningitis (Meningococcal Meningitis) (p. 613)*

8. *N. meningitidis* causes meningococcal meningitis. This bacterium is found in the throats of healthy carriers.

9. The bacteria probably gain access to the meninges through the bloodstream. The bacteria may be found in leukocytes in CSF.

10. Symptoms are due to endotoxin. The disease occurs most often in young children.

11. Purified capsular polysaccharide vaccine against serotypes A, C, Y, and W-135 is available.

Streptococcus pneumoniae Meningitis (Pneumococcal Meningitis) (p. 614)

12. *S. pneumoniae* is commonly found in the nasopharynx.

13. Young children are most susceptible to *S. pneumoniae* meningitis. Untreated, it has a high mortality rate.

14. A conjugated vaccine is available.

Diagnosis and Treatment of the Most Common Types of Bacterial Meningitis (p. 614)

15. Diagnosis is based on Gram stain, cultures, and serological tests of the bacteria in CSF.

16. Cephalosporins may be administered before the pathogen is identified.

Listeriosis (pp. 614–615)

17. *Listeria monocytogenes* causes meningitis in newborns, the immunosuppressed, pregnant women, and cancer patients.

18. Acquired by ingestion of contaminated food, it may be asymptomatic in healthy adults.

19. *L. monocytogenes* can cross the placenta and cause spontaneous abortion and stillbirth.

Tetanus (pp. 615–616)

20. Tetanus is caused by a localized infection of a wound by *Clostridium tetani.*

21. *C. tetani* produces the neurotoxin tetanospasmin, which causes the symptoms of tetanus: spasms, contraction of muscles controlling the jaw, and death resulting from spasms of respiratory muscles.

22. *C. tetani* is an anaerobe that will grow in deep, unclean wounds.

23. Acquired immunity results from DTaP immunization.

24. Following an injury, an immunized person may receive a booster of tetanus toxoid. An unimmunized person may receive (human) tetanus immune globulin.

25. Debridement (removal of tissue) and antibiotics may be used to control the infection.

Botulism (pp. 616–619)

26. Botulism is caused by an exotoxin produced by *C. botulinum* growing in foods.

27. Serological types of botulinum toxin vary in virulence; type A is the most virulent.

28. The toxin is a neurotoxin that inhibits the transmission of nerve impulses.

29. Blurred vision occurs in 1 to 2 days; progressive flaccid paralysis follows for 1 to 10 days, possibly resulting in death from respiratory and cardiac failure.

30. *C. botulinum* will not grow in acidic foods or in an aerobic environment.

31. Endospores are killed by proper canning. The addition of nitrites to foods inhibits growth of *C. botulinum.*

32. The toxin is heat labile and is destroyed by boiling (100°C) for 5 minutes.

33. Infant botulism results from the growth of *C. botulinum* in an infant's intestines.

34. Wound botulism occurs when *C. botulinum* grows in anaerobic wounds.

35. For diagnosis, mice protected with antitoxin are inoculated with toxin from the patient or foods.

Leprosy (pp. 619–620)

36. *Mycobacterium leprae* causes leprosy, or Hansen's disease.

37. *M. leprae* has never been cultured on artificial media. It can be cultured in armadillos and mouse footpads.

38. The tuberculoid form of the disease is characterized by loss of sensation in the skin surrounded by nodules.

39. In the lepromatous form, disseminated nodules and tissue necrosis occur.

40. Leprosy is not highly contagious and is spread by prolonged contact with exudates.

41. Untreated individuals often die of secondary bacterial complications, such as tuberculosis.

42. Laboratory diagnosis is based on observations of acid-fast rods in a skin biopsy.

43. Patients with leprosy are treated with sulfone drugs.

Viral Diseases of the Nervous System (pp. 620–626)

Poliomyelitis (pp. 620–622)

1. The symptoms of poliomyelitis are usually sore throat and nausea, and occasionally paralysis (fewer than 1% of cases).

2. Poliovirus is transmitted by the ingestion of water contaminated with feces.

3. Poliovirus first invades lymph nodes of the neck and small intestine. Viremia and spinal cord involvement may follow.

4. Diagnosis is based on isolation of the virus from feces and throat secretions.

5. The Salk vaccine (an inactivated polio vaccine) involves the injection of formalin-inactivated viruses and boosters every few years. The Sabin vaccine (an oral polio vaccine) contains three live, attenuated strains of poliovirus and is administered orally.

6. Polio is a good candidate for elimination through vaccination.

Rabies (pp. 622–624)

7. Rabies virus (Lyssavirus) causes an acute, usually fatal, encephalitis called rabies.

8. Rabies may be contracted through the bite of a rabid animal or invasion through skin. The virus multiplies in skeletal muscle and connective tissue.

9. Encephalitis occurs when the virus moves along peripheral nerves to the CNS.

10. Symptoms of rabies include spasms of mouth and throat muscles followed by extensive brain and spinal cord damage and death.

11. Laboratory diagnosis may be made by DFA tests of saliva, serum, and CSF or brain smears.

12. Reservoirs for rabies in the United States include skunks, bats, foxes, and raccoons. Domestic cattle, dogs, and cats may get rabies. Rodents and rabbits seldom get rabies.

13. Postexposure treatment includes administration of human rabies immune globulin (RIG) along with multiple intramuscular injections of vaccine.

14. Preexposure treatment consists of vaccination.

15. Other genotypes of *Lyssavirus* cause rabies-like diseases.

Arboviral Encephalitis (pp. 624–626)

16. Symptoms of encephalitis are chills, headache, fever, and eventually coma.

17. Many types of viruses (called arboviruses) transmitted by mosquitoes cause encephalitis.

18. The incidence of arboviral encephalitis increases in the summer months, when mosquitoes are most numerous.

19. Notifiable arboviral infections are eastern equine encephalitis (EEE), western equine encephalitis (WEE), St. Louis encephalitis (SLE), California encephalitis (CE), and West Nile virus (WNV).

20. Diagnosis is based on serological tests.

21. Control of the mosquito vector is the most effective way to control encephalitis.

Fungal Disease of the Nervous System (pp. 626–627)

Cryptococcus neoformans Meningitis (Cryptococcosis) (pp. 626–627)

1. *Cryptococcus* spp. are encapsulated yeastlike fungi that cause cryptococcosis.
2. The disease may be contracted by inhaling dried infected pigeon or chicken droppings.
3. The disease begins as a lung infection and may spread to the brain and meninges.
4. Immunosuppressed individuals are most susceptible to cryptococcosis.
5. Diagnosis is based on latex agglutination tests for cryptococcal antigens in serum or CSF.

Protozoan Diseases of the Nervous System (pp. 627–629)

African Trypanosomiasis (pp. 627–629)

1. African trypanosomiasis is caused by the protozoa *Trypanosoma brucei gambiense* and *T.b. rhodesiense* and is transmitted by the bite of the tsetse fly.
2. The disease affects the nervous system of the human host, causing lethargy and eventually coma. It is commonly called sleeping sickness.
3. Vaccine development is hindered by the protozoan's ability to change its surface antigens.

Amebic Meningoencephalitis (p. 629)

4. Encephalitis caused by the protozoan *Naegleria fowleri* is almost always fatal.
5. Granulomatous amebic encephalitis, caused by *Acanthamoeba* spp. and *Balamuthia mandrillaris*, is a chronic disease.

Nervous System Diseases Caused by Prions (pp. 629–632)

1. Prions are self-replicating proteins with no detectable nucleic acid.
2. Diseases of the CNS that progress slowly and cause spongiform degeneration are caused by prions.
3. Transmissible spongiform encephalopathies are caused by prions that are transferable from one animal to another.
4. Creutzfeldt-Jakob disease and kuru are human diseases similar to scrapie. They are transmitted between humans.

Disease Caused by Unidentified Agents (p. 633)

Chronic Fatigue Syndrome (p. 633)

1. Chronic fatigue syndrome (CFS) may be triggered by a microbial infection.

THE LOOP

For a taxonomic approach, pages can be assigned as follows:

ANSWERS

Diseases in Focus 22.1: Meningitis and Encephalitis

A worker in a day-care center in eastern North Dakota became ill with fever, rash, headache, and abdominal pain. The patient had a precipitous clinical decline and died on the first day of hospitalization. Diagnosis was confirmed by Gram staining of cerebrospinal fluid. Diagnosis of nonviral meningitis is based on microscopic examination or culture of cerebrospinal fluid. In this case, the gram-negative diplococci shown in the photo are *Neisseria meningitidis*. This will be confirmed by culture characteristics.

Diseases in Focus 22.2: Types of Arboviral Encephalitis

An 8-year-old girl in rural Wisconsin has chills, headache, and fever and reports having been bitten by mosquitoes. Chills, fever, headache, and mosquitoes indicate arboviral encephalitis. WEE, SLE, CE, or WN are possible in the patient's Wisconsin location. Indirect testing of the patient's serum for antibodies against the viruses is necessary to confirm diagnosis.

Diseases in Focus 22.3: Microbial Diseases with Neurological Symptoms or Paralysis

After eating canned chili, two children experienced cranial nerve paralysis followed by descending paralysis. The children are on mechanical ventilation. Leftover canned chili was tested by mouse bioassay. Leprosy is characterized by loss of sensation in areas of the skin, and tetanus causes uncontrolled muscle contractions. Early symptoms of poliomyelitis include sore throat and nausea. Rabies, sleeping sickness, and CJD do not cause paralysis. (It is important to consider the *most likely* diseases first, and there is no indication that the patients traveled to trypanosome-endemic areas.) The progressive (descending) paralysis is characteristic of botulism. The photo shows endospore-forming rods cultured from the canned chili. The presence of botulinal toxin in the chili or in the patient's feces is confirmed by mouse bioassay. This can take several days, so the initial clinical findings are usually diagnostic.

Review

1. The symptoms of tetanus are due, not to bacterial growth (infection and inflammation), but to neurotoxin.
2. a. Vaccination with tetanus toxoid.
   b. Immunization with antitetanus toxin antibodies.
3. "Improperly cleaned" because *C. tetani* is found in soil that might contaminate a wound. "Deep puncture" because it is likely to be anaerobic. "No bleeding" because a flow of blood ensures an aerobic environment and some cleansing.
4. Etiology—Picornavirus (poliovirus).

   Transmission—Ingestion of contaminated water.

   Symptoms—Headache, sore throat, fever, nausea; rarely paralysis.

   Prevention—Sewage treatment.

   These vaccinations provide artificially acquired active immunity because they cause the production of antibodies, but they do not prevent or reverse damage to nerves.

5.

Causative Agent	Susceptible Population	Mode of Transmission	Treatment
N. meningitidis	Children; military recruits	Respiratory	Penicillin
H. influenzae	Children	Respiratory	Rifampin
S. pneumoniae	Children; elderly	Respiratory	Penicillin
L. monocytogenes	Anyone	Foodborne	Penicillin
C. neoformans	Immunosuppressed individuals	Respiratory	Amphotericin B

6.

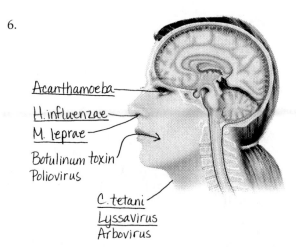

Acanthamoeba
H. influenzae
M. leprae
Botulinum toxin
Poliovirus
C. tetani
Lyssavirus
Arbovirus

7. Postexposure treatment—Passive immunization with antibodies followed by active immunization with HDCV. Preexposure treatment—Active immunization with HDCV.

Following exposure to rabies, antibodies are needed immediately to inactivate the virus. Passive immunization provides these antibodies. Active immunization will provide antibodies over a longer period of time, but they are not formed immediately.

8.

Disease	Etiology	Vector	Symptoms	Treatment
Arboviral encephalitis	Togaviruses, Arboviruses	Mosquitoes (*Culex*)	Headache, fever, coma	Immune serum
African trypanosomiasis	*Trypanosoma brucei gambiense*, *T. b. rhodesiense*	Tsetse fly	Decreased physical activity and mental acuity	Suramm; melarsoprol
Botulism	*C. botulinum*	Ingestion	Flaccid paralysis	Antitoxin
Leprosy	*M. leprae*	Direct contact	Areas of sensation loss in skin	Dapsone

9. The causative agent of Creutzfeldt–Jakob disease (CJD) is transmissible. Although there is some evidence for an inherited form of the disease, it has been transmitted by transplants. Similarities with viruses are that (1) the prion cannot be cultured by conventional bacteriological techniques and (2) the prion is not readily seen in patients with CJD.

Critical Thinking

1. The term "rusty nail" implies that the sharp object has been contaminated with soil and possibly *C. tetani*. *C. tetani* can grow in deep puncture wounds, and a nail is capable of producing such a wound.

2. The only cases of polio in the United States during the last 10 years have been caused by OPV.

Clinical Applications

1. *Haemophilus influenzae* meningitis, treated with rifampin.

2. *Cryptococcus neoformans.* Need microscopic observation of the fungus from cerebrospinal fluid or culture.

3. Primary amebic meningoencephalitis or granulomatous amebic encephalitis; treated with amphotericin B.

CASE STUDY: AN OUTBREAK OF FOOD POISONING

Background

On October 15, a 40-year-old man was admitted to the hospital. He had a "splitting" headache, his legs were unsteady, and his vision was blurred. During examination, it was apparent that there was something wrong with his throat. It wasn't sore, but it felt stiff and tight, and it was almost impossible for him to speak.

Over the next 7 days, 28 persons with similar symptoms were admitted to the hospital. Twelve of these patients required ventilatory support; no deaths were reported. During the investigation, it became apparent that the illnesses were due to meals consumed between October 14 and 16 at one restaurant. Detailed food histories were obtained from the patients. An additional case-control study was conducted on well people who had consumed food at the restaurant during the same 3-day period. Repeated news media announcements helped health personnel locate 18 other people who had eaten virtually the same foods at the restaurant.

The meals consisted of the following foods:

Patty Melt. Frozen hamburger patties purchased from a restaurant distributor. Patties were removed from the freezer and fried as ordered. Presliced pasteurized American cheese purchased from a distributor was kept refrigerated, and a slice was melted on each cooked hamburger patty. Meat and cheese were served on rye bread purchased from a local bakery.

Sautéed Onions. Onions were purchased fresh from a farmer. Fresh whole onions were sliced and then sautéed with margarine, paprika, garlic salt, and a chicken-based powder. After the initial cooking, the onions were held uncovered in a pan on a warm stove ($<60°C$) along with a large volume of melted margarine; they were not reheated before serving.

French-Fried Potatoes. Precut frozen potatoes were deep-fried in two- or three-serving batches as needed.

Potato Salad. Potatoes were purchased from a farmer. They had been stored in a root cellar and were transported loose in a pickup truck. The potatoes were washed, peeled, diced, and boiled. Cooled, drained potato cubes were mixed with oil, vinegar, dry mustard, and garlic salt and were kept refrigerated. Individual servings were removed from the container as needed.

Lettuce and Tomato Salad. Produce was delivered every other day. Lettuce and tomatoes were cut in the morning, refrigerated, and mixed with oil and vinegar for serving.

Questions

1. On one page, identify the etiologic agent of this outbreak of food poisoning.
2. Was it food infection or intoxication?
3. What item was contaminated, and how did it become contaminated?
4. Briefly explain how you arrived at your conclusion. How did you eliminate the other major causes of food poisoning?

Hints

1. Make a summary table of the persons not ill.
2. Make a table of the onset of symptoms following eating.

Data

Case	Sex	Age	R	H	V	W	D	N	C	Dd	Dy	M	Rd	1	2	3	4	5
						Symptoms								Foods Eaten				
1	M	25	26	20	N	x			x	x		x	x	x	x			x
2	F	20	14	15	Y	x			x	x	x	x	x	x	x	x		
3	M	40	15	17	Y	x			x	x	x	x	x	x	x		x	
4	M	55	14	17	Y	x			x		x	x	x	x	x	x		
5	F	72	15	16	N	x			x	x	x	x	x	x	x		x	
6	M	43	15	17	N	x					x	x		x	x	x	x	
7	F	37	16	17	Y	x			x	x	x	x	x	x	x			x
8	F	51	15	16	Y	x			x		x	x	x	x	x			x
9	F	25	14	16	N	x			x	x	x	x		x	x		x	x
10	M	40	16	—	—	x			x	x				x				x
11	F	35	14	—	—		x							x		x		
12	F	39	15	—	—		x							x	x		x	
13	M	54	15	18	N	x					x			x	x	x		x
14	F	34	15	18	Y	x		x	x		x	x	x	x	x	x		
15	M	45	14	16	Y	x			x		x	x	x	x	x		x	
16	M	27	16	—	—									x	x			x
17	F	37	14	15	Y	x			x	x	x	x	x	x	x		x	x
18	M	34	14	—	—									x			x	
19	M	30	15	—	—				x					x		x		
20	F	22	16	20	Y	x			x	x	x	x	x	x	x		x	
21	F	39	14	17	N	x			x	x	x	x		x	x			x
22	M	45	16	—	—	x								x	x			x
23	M	53	14	—	—				x					x	x		x	
24	F	41	15	20	N	x	x			x								x
25	F	42	14	16	N	x			x	x	x			x	x		x	
26	F	54	16	18	Y	x			x	x	x	x	x	x	x	x		
27	M	42	16	—	—	x			x					x	x		x	x
28	F	43	16	19	N	x		x		x	x	x				x		
29	M	42	15	—	—	x			x	x			x	x			x	
30	F	65	15	—	—	x			x					x	x	x		
31	F	33	16	21	N	x				x		x		x	x	x	x	
32	M	52	14	—	—			x	x					x		x		
33	F	26	14	—	—	x	x		x	x				x	x	x		
34	F	40	15	18	N	x			x	x		x					x	
35	F	22	15	19	Y	x			x		x	x	x	x	x	x		

Case	Sex	Age	R	H	V	Symptoms								Foods Eaten				
						W	D	N	C	Dd	Dy	M	Rd	1	2	3	4	5
36	M	63	16	20	N	x		x	x					x	x		x	x
37	M	35	15	—	—									x	x		x	x
38	M	56	15	17	Y	x		x	x			x	x	x	x			x
39	F	60	15	17	N	x		x	x					x	x	x		
40	M	37	15	—	—			x						x			x	
41	F	28	15	19	N	x			x					x	x			x
42	M	19	15	—	—									x	x	x		x
43	F	28	15	—	—			x						x			x	x
44	F	55	15	17	N	x					x						x	x
45	M	28	15	—	—									x			x	
46	F	45	15	18	N	x					x			x	x	x		

Legend:
R = Date at restaurant, H = Date hospitalized, V = Ventilated?
Symptoms: W = Weakness, lassitude, D = Diarrhea, N = Nausea, vomiting, C = Constipation, Dd = Diplopia, Dy = Dysphagia, dysphonia, M = Muscle weakness, Rd = Respiratory difficulty.
Food: 1–Patty Melt, 2–Sauteed Onions, 3–French-Fried Potatoes, 4–Potato Salad, 5–Lettuce and Tomato Salad.

The Solution

1. *Clostridium botulinum.*

2. Intoxication.

3. The onions were contaminated by *C. botulinum* from soil.

4. Of the 28 patients, 24 recalled eating the patty melt. All 24 patients, but only 10 of 18 controls, reported eating the sautéed onions. The original batch of sautéed onions was not available for culture or toxin testing, but type A botulinal toxin was detected in an extract made from washings of a discarded foil wrapper used by one of the patients to take a patty melt home. Type A botulinal spores were cultured from 5 of 75 skins of whole onions taken from the restaurant. No other ingredients of the sautéed onions contained toxin or spores.

23 Microbial Diseases of the Cardiovascular and Lymphatic Systems

LEARNING OBJECTIVES	CHECK YOUR UNDERSTANDING
23-1 Identify the role of the cardiovascular and lymphatic systems in spreading and eliminating infections.	Why is the lymphatic system so valuable for the working of the immune system?
23-2 List the signs and symptoms of sepsis, and explain the importance of infections that develop into septic shock.	What are two of the conditions that define the systemic inflammatory response syndrome of sepsis?
23-3 Differentiate gram-negative sepsis, gram-positive sepsis, and puerperal sepsis.	Are the endotoxins that cause sepsis from gram-positive or gram-negative bacteria?
23-4 Describe the epidemiologies of endocarditis and rheumatic fever.	What medical procedures are usually the cause of endocarditis?
23-5 Discuss the epidemiology of tularemia.	What animals are the most common reservoir for tularemia?
23-6 Discuss the epidemiology of brucellosis.	What ethnic group in the United States is most commonly affected by brucellosis, and why?
23-7 Discuss the epidemiology of anthrax.	How do animals such as cattle become victims of anthrax?
23-8 Discuss the epidemiology of gas gangrene.	Why are hyperbaric chambers effective in treating gas gangrene?
23-9 List three pathogens that are transmitted by animal bites and scratches.	*Bartonella henselae*, the pathogen of cat-scratch disease, is capable of growth in what insect?
23-10 Compare and contrast the causative agents, vectors, reservoirs, symptoms, treatments, and preventive measures for plague, Lyme disease and Rocky Mountain spotted fever.	Why is the plague-infected flea so eager to feed on a mammal?
23-11 Identify the vector, etiology, and symptoms of five diseases transmitted by ticks.	What animal does the infecting tick feed on just before it transmits Lyme disease to a human?
23-12 Describe the epidemiologies of epidemic typhus, endemic murine typhus, and spotted fevers.	Which disease is tickborne: epidemic typhus, endemic murine typhus, or Rocky Mountain spotted fever?
23-13 Describe the epidemiologies of Burkitt's lymphoma, infectious mononucleosis, and CMV inclusion disease.	Although not a disease with an insect vector, why is Burkitt's lymphoma most commonly a disease found in malarial areas?
23-14 Compare and contrast the causative agents, vectors, reservoirs, and symptoms of yellow fever, dengue, dengue hemorrhagic fever, and chikungunya fever.	Why is the mosquito *Aedes albopictus* a special concern to the population of temperate climates?

23-15 Compare and contrast the causative agents, reservoirs, and symptoms of Ebola hemorrhagic fever and *Hantavirus* pulmonary syndrome.	Which disease does Ebola hemorrhagic fever more closely resemble, Lassa fever or *Hantavirus* pulmonary syndrome?
23-16 Compare and contrast the causative agents, modes of transmission, reservoirs, symptoms, and treatments for Chagas' disease, toxoplasmosis, malaria, leishmaniasis, and babesiosis.	What tickborne disease in the United States is sometimes mistaken for malaria when blood smears are inspected?
23-17 Discuss the worldwide effects of these diseases on human health.	Eliminating which of these diseases, malaria or Chagas' disease, would have the greater effect on the well-being of the population of Africa?
23-18 Diagram the life cycle of *Schistosoma*, and show where the cycle can be interrupted to prevent human disease.	What freshwater creature is essential to the life cycle of the pathogen causing schistosomiasis?

NEW IN THIS EDITION

- Revised definitions of the similar terms *septicemia* and *sepsis*
- Rewritten discussions of brucellosis and rat-bite fever
- Revised discussion of ehrlichiosis, which includes the new terminology of anaplasmosis
- New discussion of chikungunya fever, included because of its current spread into temperate climates

CHAPTER SUMMARY

Introduction (p. 637)

1. The heart, blood, and blood vessels make up the cardiovascular system.
2. Lymph, lymph vessels, lymph nodes, and lymphoid organs constitute the lymphatic system.

Structure and Function of the Cardiovascular and Lymphatic Systems (p. 638)

1. The heart circulates substances to and from tissue cells.
2. Blood is a mixture of plasma and cells.
3. Plasma transports dissolved substances. Red blood cells carry oxygen. White blood cells are involved in the body's defense against infection.
4. Fluid that filters out of capillaries into spaces between tissue cells is called interstitial fluid.
5. Interstitial fluid enters lymph capillaries and is called lymph; vessels called lymphatics return lymph to the blood.
6. Lymph nodes contain fixed macrophages, B cells, and T cells.

Bacterial Diseases of the Cardiovascular and Lymphatic Systems (pp. 638–655)

Sepsis and Septic Shock (pp. 639–641)

1. Sepsis is an inflammatory response caused by the spread of bacteria or their toxin from a focus of infection. Septicemia is sepsis that involves proliferation of pathogens in the blood.
2. Gram-negative sepsis can lead to septic shock, characterized by decreased blood pressure. Endotoxin causes the symptoms.
3. Antibiotic-resistant enterococci and group B streptococci cause gram-positive sepsis.

4. Puerperal sepsis begins as an infection of the uterus following childbirth or abortion; it can progress to peritonitis or septicemia.

5. *Streptococcus pyogenes* is the most frequent cause of puerperal sepsis.

6. Oliver Wendell Holmes and Ignaz Semmelweiss demonstrated that puerperal sepsis was transmitted by the hands and instruments of midwives and physicians.

Bacterial Infections of the Heart (p. 641)

7. The inner layer of the heart is the endocardium.

8. Subacute bacterial endocarditis is usually caused by alpha-hemolytic streptococci, staphylococci, or enterococci.

9. The infection arises from a focus of infection, such as a tooth extraction.

10. Preexisting heart abnormalities are predisposing factors.

11. Signs include fever, anemia, and heart murmur.

12. Acute bacterial endocarditis is usually caused by *Staphylococcus aureus*.

13. The bacteria cause rapid destruction of heart valves.

Rheumatic Fever (pp. 641-642)

14. Rheumatic fever is an autoimmune complication of streptococcal infections.

15. Rheumatic fever is expressed as arthritis or inflammation of the heart. It can result in permanent heart damage.

16. Antibodies against group A beta-hemolytic streptococci react with streptococcal antigens deposited in joints or heart valves or cross-react with the heart muscle.

17. Rheumatic fever can follow a streptococcal infection, such as streptococcal sore throat. Streptococci might not be present at the time of rheumatic fever.

18. Prompt treatment of streptococcal infections can reduce the incidence of rheumatic fever.

19. Penicillin is administered as a preventive measure against subsequent streptococcal infections.

Tularemia (pp. 642-643)

20. Tularemia is caused by *Francisella tularensis*. The reservoir is small wild mammals, especially rabbits.

21. Signs include ulceration at the site of entry, followed by septicemia and pneumonia.

Brucellosis (Undulant Fever) (pp. 643-645)

22. Brucellosis can be caused by *Brucella abortus, B. melitensis,* and *B. suis.*

23. The bacteria enter through minute breaks in the mucosa or skin, reproduce in macrophages, and spread via lymphatics to liver, spleen, or bone marrow.

24. Signs include malaise and fever that spikes each evening (undulant fever).

25. Diagnosis is based on serological tests.

Anthrax (pp. 645-646)

26. *Bacillus anthracis* causes anthrax. In soil, endospores can survive for up to 60 years.

27. Grazing animals acquire an infection after ingesting the endospores.

28. Humans contract anthrax by handling hides from infected animals. The endospores enter through cuts in the skin, respiratory tract, or mouth.

29. Entry through the skin results in a pustule that can progress to sepsis. Entry through the respiratory tract can result in septic shock.

30. Diagnosis is based on isolating and identifying the bacteria.

Gangrene (p. 646)

31. Soft tissue death from ischemia (loss of blood supply) is called gangrene.

32. Microorganisms grow on nutrients released from gangrenous cells.

33. Gangrene is especially susceptible to the growth of anaerobic bacteria such as *Clostridium perfringens,* the causative agent of gas gangrene.

34. *C. perfringens* can invade the wall of the uterus during improperly performed abortions.

35. Surgical removal of necrotic tissue, hyperbaric chambers, and amputation are used to treat gas gangrene.

Systemic Diseases Caused by Bites and Scratches (pp. 647–648)

36. *Pasteurella multocida,* introduced by the bite of a dog or cat, can cause septicemia.

37. Anaerobic bacteria infect deep animal bites.

38. Cat-scratch disease is caused by *Bartonella henselae.*

39. Rat-bite fever is caused by *Streptobacillus moniliformis* and *Spirillum minus.*

Vector-Transmitted Diseases (pp. 648–655)

Plague (pp. 648–650)

40. Plague is caused by *Yersinia pestis.* The vector is usually the rat flea (*Xenopsylla cheopis*).

41. Reservoirs for bubonic plague include European rats and North American rodents.

42. Signs of bubonic plague include bruises on the skin and enlarged lymph nodes (buboes).

43. The bacteria can enter the lungs and cause pneumonic plague.

44. Laboratory diagnosis is based on isolating and identifying the bacteria.

45. Antibiotics are effective in treating plague, but they must be administered promptly after exposure to the disease.

Relapsing Fever (pp. 650–651)

46. Relapsing fever is caused by *Borrelia* species and transmitted by soft ticks.

47. The reservoir for the disease is rodents.

48. Signs include fever, jaundice, and rose-colored spots. Signs recur three or four times after apparent recovery.

49. Laboratory diagnosis is based on the presence of spirochetes in the patient's blood.

Lyme Disease (Lyme Borreliosis) (pp. 651–654)

50. Lyme disease is caused by *Borrelia burgdorferi* and is transmitted by a tick (*Ixodes*).

51. Field mice provide the animal reservoir.

52. Diagnosis is based on serological tests and clinical symptoms.

Ehrlichiosis and Anaplasmosis (p. 654)

53. Human ehrlichiosis and anaplasmosis are caused by *Ehrlichia* and *Anaplasma* and are transmitted by *Ixodes* ticks.

Typhus (pp. 654–655)

54. Typhus is caused by rickettsias, obligate intracellular parasites of eukaryotic cells.

Epidemic Typhus (p. 654)

55. The human body louse, *Pediculus humanus corporis,* transmits *Rickettsia prowazekii* in its feces, which are deposited while the louse is feeding.

56. Epidemic typhus is prevalent in crowded and unsanitary living conditions that allow the proliferation of lice.

57. The signs of typhus are rash, prolonged high fever, and stupor.

58. Tetracyclines and chloramphenicol are used in treatment.

Endemic Murine Typhus (p. 655)

59. Endemic murine typhus is a less severe disease caused by *Rickettsia typhi*. It is transmitted from rodents to humans by the rat flea.

Spotted Fevers (p. 655)

60. *Rickettsia rickettsii* is a parasite of ticks (*Dermacentor* spp.) in the southeastern United States, Appalachia, and the Rocky Mountain states.

61. The rickettsia may be transmitted to humans, in whom it causes tickborne typhus fever.

62. Chloramphenicol and tetracyclines effectively treat Rocky Mountain spotted fever, or tickborne typhus.

63. Serological tests are used for laboratory diagnosis.

Viral Diseases of the Cardiovascular and Lymphatic Systems (pp. 655–660)

Burkitt's Lymphoma (pp. 655–656)

1. Epstein-Barr virus (EB virus, HHV-4) causes Burkitt's lymphoma.

2. Burkitt's lymphoma tends to occur in patients whose immune system has been weakened; for example, by malaria or AIDS.

Infectious Mononucleosis (pp. 656–657)

3. Infectious mononucleosis is caused by EB virus.

4. The virus multiplies in the parotid glands and is present in saliva. It causes the proliferation of atypical lymphocytes.

5. The disease is transmitted by the ingestion of saliva from infected individuals.

6. Diagnosis is made by an indirect fluorescent-antibody technique.

7. EB virus may cause other diseases, including cancers and multiple sclerosis.

Cytomegalovirus Infections (p. 658)

8. CMV (HHV-5) causes intranuclear inclusion bodies and cytomegaly of host cells.

9. CMV is transmitted by saliva and other body fluids.

10. CMV inclusion disease can be asymptomatic, a mild disease, or progressive and fatal. Immunosuppressed patients may develop pneumonia.

11. If the virus crosses the placenta, it can cause congenital infection of the fetus, resulting in impaired mental development, neurological damage, and stillbirth.

Chikungunya Fever (p. 658)

12. The chikungunya virus, which causes fever and severe joint pain, is transmitted by *Aedes* mosquitoes.

Classic Viral Hemorrhagic Fevers (pp. 658–659)

13. Yellow fever is caused by the yellow fever virus. The vector is the *Aedes aegypti* mosquito.

14. Signs and symptoms include fever, chills, headache, nausea, and jaundice.

15. Diagnosis is based on the presence of virus-neutralizing antibodies in the host.

16. No treatment is available, but there is an attenuated, live viral vaccine.

17. Dengue is caused by the dengue fever virus and is transmitted by the *Aedes* mosquito.

18. Signs are fever, muscle and joint pain, and rash.

19. Mosquito abatement is necessary to control the disease.

20. Dengue hemorrhagic fever (DHF) can cause shock.

Emerging Viral Hemorrhagic Fevers (pp. 659–660)

21. Human diseases caused by Marburg, Ebola, and Lassa fever viruses were first noticed in the late 1960s.

22. Ebola virus is found in fruit bats; Lassa fever viruses are found in rodents.

23. Rodents are the reservoirs for Argentine and Bolivian hemorrhagic fevers.

24. *Hantavirus* pulmonary syndrome and hemorrhagic fever with renal syndrome are caused by hantavirus. The virus is contracted by inhalation of dried rodent urine and feces.

Protozoan Diseases of the Cardiovascular and Lymphatic Systems (pp. 660–666)

Chagas' Disease (American Trypanosomiasis) (p. 661)

1. *Trypanosoma cruzi* causes Chagas' disease. The reservoir includes many wild animals. The vector is a reduviid, the "kissing bug."

Toxoplasmosis (pp. 661–663)

2. Toxoplasmosis is caused by *Toxoplasma gondii*.

3. *T. gondii* undergoes sexual reproduction in the intestinal tract of domestic cats, and oocysts are eliminated in cat feces.

4. In the host cell, sporozoites reproduce to form either tissue-invading tachyzoites or bradyzoites.

5. Humans contract the infection by ingesting tachyzoites or tissue cysts in undercooked meat from an infected animal or contact with cat feces.

6. Congenital infections can occur. Signs and symptoms include severe brain damage or vision problems.

Malaria (pp. 663–665)

7. The signs and symptoms of malaria are chills, fever, vomiting, and headache, which occur at intervals of 2 to 3 days.

8. Malaria is transmitted by *Anopheles* mosquitoes. The causative agent is any one of four species of *Plasmodium*.

9. Sporozoites reproduce in the liver and release merozoites into the bloodstream, where they infect red blood cells and produce more merozoites.

10. New drugs are being developed as the protozoa develop resistance to drugs such as chloroquine.

Leishmaniasis (pp. 665–666)

11. *Leishmania* spp., which are transmitted by sandflies, cause leishmaniasis.

12. The protozoa reproduce in the liver, spleen, and kidneys.

13. Antimony compounds are used for treatment.

Babesiosis (p. 666)

14. Babesiosis is caused by the protozoan *Babesia microti* and is transmitted to humans by ticks.

Helminthic Diseases of the Cardiovascular and Lymphatic Systems (pp. 666–668)

Schistosomiasis (pp. 666–667)

1. Species of the blood fluke *Schistosoma* cause schistosomiasis.

2. Eggs eliminated with feces hatch into larvae that infect the intermediate host, a snail. Free-swimming cercariae are released from the snail and penetrate the skin of a human.

3. The adult flukes live in the veins of the liver or urinary bladder in humans.

4. Granulomas are from the host's defense to eggs that remain in the body.

5. Observation of eggs or flukes in feces, skin tests, or indirect serological tests may be used for diagnosis.

6. Chemotherapy is used to treat the disease; sanitation and snail eradication are used to prevent it.

Swimmer's Itch (p. 667)

7. Swimmer's itch is a cutaneous allergic reaction to cercariae that penetrate the skin. The definitive hosts for this fluke are wildfowl.

THE LOOP

For a taxonomic approach, pages can be assigned as follows:

Bacterial diseases	pp. 638–655
Viral diseases	pp. 655–660
Protozoan diseases	pp. 660–666
Helminthic infestations	pp. 666–667

ANSWERS

Diseases in Focus 23.1: Infections from Human Reservoirs

A 27-year-old woman had a fever and cough for 5 days. She was hospitalized when her blood pressure dropped. Despite aggressive treatment with fluids and massive doses of antibiotics, she died 5 hours after hospitalization. Catalase-negative, gram-positive cocci were isolated from her blood. The drop in blood pressure and presence of bacteria in her blood suggest septic shock, in this case caused by enterococci or streptococci.

Diseases in Focus 23.2: Infections from Animal Reservoirs

A 10-year-old girl was admitted to a local hospital after having fever (40°C) for 12 days and back pain for 8 days. Bacteria could not be cultured from tissues. She had a recent history of dog and cat scratches. She recovered without treatment. The absence of sepsis eliminates the systemic infections (due to animal bites and rat-bite fever), and the prolonged, rather than undulating fever, suggests cat-scratch disease.

Diseases in Focus 23.3: Infections Transmitted by Vectors

A 22-year-old soldier returning from a tour of duty in Iraq had three painless skin ulcers. She reported being bitten by insects every night. Ovoid, protozoa-like bodies were observed within her macrophages by examination with a light microscope. These diseases are all prevented by controlling exposure to insect and tick bites. Absence of fever or any systemic symptoms narrows the choices to Lyme disease and leishmaniasis. Her skin ulcers, the absence of a rash, and presence of protozoa indicate cutaneous leishmaniasis.

Diseases in Focus 23.4: Viral Hemorrhagic Fevers

Use the table below to identify the cause of a rash and severe joint pain in a 20-year-old woman. The absence of jaundice and bleeding eliminates yellow fever and emerging hemorrhagic fevers, respectively. Rash and joint pain are classic symptoms of dengue. Presence of the flavivirus provides definitive proof.

Review

1.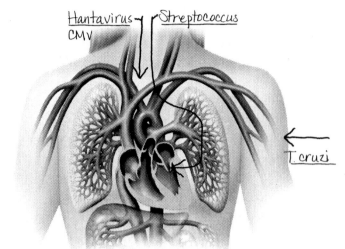

2.

Disease	Causative Agent	Predisposing Conditions
p.s.	*S. pyogenes*	Abortion or childbirth
s.b.e.	alpha-hemolytic strep.	Preexisting lesions
a.b.e.	*S. aureus*	Abnormal heart valves

Rheumatic fever is an autoimmune disease that is precipitated by streptococcal sore throat. It is treated with anti-inflammatory drugs to relieve the symptoms. It is prevented by early diagnosis and treatment of streptococcal sore throat.

3. All are vector-borne rickettsial diseases. They differ from each other in (1) etiologic agent, (2) vector, (3) severity and mortality, and (4) incidence (e.g., epidemic, sporadic).

4.

Causative Agent	Vector	Symptoms	Treatment
Plasmodium	*Anopheles*	Recurrent fever, chills	Quinine derivative
Flavivirus	*Aedes aegypti*	Fever, nausea, jaundice	None
Flavivirus	*Aedes aegypti*	Muscle and joint pain	None
Borrelia	Soft ticks	Recurrent fever	Tetracycline
Leishmania	Sandflies	Fever, chills	Antimony

5.

Causative Agent	Method of Transmission	Reservoir
Francisella tularensis	Animal reservoir, skin abrasions, ingestion, inhalation, bites	Rabbits
Brucella spp.	Animal reservoir, ingestion of milk, direct contact	Cattle
Bacillus anthracis	Skin abrasions, inhalation, ingestion	Soil, cattle
Borrelia burgdorferi	Tick bites	Deer, mice
Ehrlichia	Tick bites	Deer
HHV5	Saliva, blood	Humans
Yersinia pestis	Flea bites, inhalation	Rodents

6.

Causative Agent	Transmission	Reservoir	Endemic Area
Schistosoma spp.	Penetrate skin	Aquatic snail	Asia, South America
Toxoplasma gondii	Ingestion, inhalation	Cats	United States
Trypanosoma cruzi	"Kissing bug"	Rodents	Central America

7.

	Reservoir	Etiology	Transmission	Symptoms
Cat-scratch disease	Cats	*Bartonella henselae*	Scratch; touching eyes, fleas	Swollen lymph nodes, fever, malaise
Toxoplasmosis	Cats	*Toxoplasma gondii*	Ingestion	None, congenital infections, neurologic damage

8. Gangrenous tissue is anaerobic and has suitable nutrients for *C. perfringens.*

9. Infectious mononucleosis is caused by EB virus and transmitted in oral secretions.

Critical Thinking

1. Patient B has a rising antibody titer, which indicates an active infection. A therapeutic abortion could be recommended to this woman. Patient C has no immunity to *Toxoplasma* and should be advised to avoid contact with reservoirs. Patient A has antibodies against *Toxoplasma* that should provide long-lasting immunity.

2. Mosquito eradication.

3. The presence of antibodies is causing the more severe disease; this is called *antibody enhancement.* Antibodies and live viruses form immune complexes that attach to macrophages and other cells, thus increasing the number of viruses that infect a cell.

Clinical Applications

1. Tularemia. A slide agglutination test can be performed to identify the organism isolated from the lesions.

2. Incubation: March 27–29.

   Prodromal: March 30.

   Contacts were treated prophylactically, to prevent infection.

   Causative agent: *Yersinia pestis.*

   The bacterium can be identified by fluorescent-antibody tests and phage typing.

3. Symptoms: due to endotoxin; fever, weakness, shock.

   Gram-negative, oxidase-negative, lactose-positive, fish-eye colonies on EMB, IMViC (− − + +), glycerol-.

   The inside surface of the manometer was not sterile.

   Keep sterile systems closed, and sterilize internal surfaces of equipment.

4. Disease: Relapsing fever (transmitted by ticks in the cabin).

   Incubation period: A little less than 2 weeks.

   Lysis of the *Borrelia* by the immune response causes fever.

   Cell lysis releasing gram-negative cell wall fragments can cause septic shock.

5. *Bacillus anthracis.* Animals with anthrax should not be used in manufacturing.

CASE STUDY: A DELAYED DIAGNOSIS

Background

A 25-year-old New Mexico rancher was admitted to an El Paso Hospital on February 12 because of a 2-day history of headache, chills, and fever (40°C). The day before admission, he began vomiting. The day of admission, an orange-sized swelling in the left axilla was noted. A lymph-node aspirate and a smear of peripheral blood were reported to contain gram-positive cocci, often in pairs. Under the assumption that a gram-positive organism had caused the patient's illness, he was given cefoxitin. The man was acutely ill. Within a few hours of admission, he had a cardiopulmonary arrest. During resuscitation efforts, he vomited and aspirated his vomitus; a chest X-ray showed bilateral infiltrate. Additionally, the patient bled from several body sites. The patient died within 6 hours of admission. In the 2 weeks prior to becoming ill, the patient had trapped, killed, and skinned 3 kit foxes, 4 coyotes, and 1 bobcat. The patient had cut his left hand shortly before skinning the bobcat on February 7.

After his death, biochemical testing of a gram-negative rod isolated from blood cultures identified the etiology as *Enterobacter agglomerans*.

Questions

1. Identify the following periods: incubation, prodromal, illness, decline.
2. Identify the etiologic agent of this disease. Briefly explain how you arrived at your conclusion.
3. What microbiologic tests would you perform to verify the etiology?
4. How might the patient have been treated between February 7 and 12?
5. What special precautions needed to be taken by the hospital and mortuary personnel?

The Solution

1. Incubation period: February 7–10.

   Prodromal period: February 10.

   Period of illness: February 11–12.

   Period of decline: None; the patient died.

2. *Yersinia pestis*. The organisms may have been interpreted as being cocci or diplococci because of (1) the tendency of *Y. pestis* to assume a bipolar appearance when stained and (2) the rapid division of this coccobacillary organism, which might have given the impression that the dividing organisms were in pairs. *Y. pestis* and some strains of *E. agglomerans* are relatively inactive biochemically and may be difficult to differentiate. Other characteristics, such as colonial morphology, growth characteristics in broth, and motility, will aid in the differentiation of these organisms.

3. Culture and fluorescent-antibody stains.

4. With antibiotics.

5. The patient should have been placed in isolation, and special isolation procedures should have been used in handling his body fluids. Personnel should receive antibiotic prophylaxis.

24 Microbial Diseases of the Respiratory System

LEARNING OBJECTIVES	CHECK YOUR UNDERSTANDING
24-1 Describe how microorganisms are prevented from entering the respiratory system.	What is the function of hairs in the nasal passages?
24-2 Characterize the normal microbiota of the upper and lower respiratory system.	Normally, the lower respiratory tract is nearly sterile. What is the primary mechanism responsible?
24-3 Differentiate pharyngitis, laryngitis, tonsillitis, sinusitis, and epiglottitis.	Which one of the following is most likely to be associated with a headache: pharyngitis, largngitis, sinusitis, or epiglottitis?
24-4 List the causative agent, symptoms, prevention, preferred treatment, and laboratory identification tests for streptococcal pharyngitis, scarlet fever, diphtheria, cutaneous diphtheria, and otitis media.	Among streptococcal pharyngitis, scarlet fever, or diphtheria, which two diseases are usually caused by the same genus of bacteria?
24-5 List the causative agents and treatments for the common cold.	Which viruses, rhinoviruses or coronoviruses, cause about half of cases of the common cold?
24-6 List the causative agent, symptoms, prevention, preferred treatment, and laboratory identification tests for pertussis and tuberculosis.	Another name for pertussis is whooping cough. This symptom is caused by the pathogens' attack on which cells?
24-7 Compare and contrast the seven bacterial pneumonias discussed in this chapter.	What group of bacterial pathogens causes what is informally called "walking pneumonia"?
24-8 List the etiology, method of transmission, and symptoms of melioidosis.	The bacterium causing melioidosis in humans also causes a disease of horses known as what?
24-9 List the causative agent, symptoms, prevention, and preferred treatment for viral pneumonia, RSV, and influenza.	Is reassortment of the RNA segments of the influenza virus the cause of antigenic shift or antigenic drift?
24-10 List the causative agent, mode of transmission, preferred treatment, and laboratory identification tests for four fungal disease of the respiratory system.	The droppings of both blackbirds and bats support the growth of *Histoplasma capsulatum;* which of these two animal reservoirs is normally actually infected by the fungus?

NEW IN THIS EDITION

- Revised discussions of pertussis, tuberculosis, and influenza include recent changes
- Updated Applications of Microbiology box on biological weapons

CHAPTER SUMMARY
Introduction (p. 674)

1. Infections of the upper respiratory system are the most common type of infection.
2. Pathogens that enter the respiratory system can infect other parts of the body.

Structure and Function of the Respiratory System (p. 675)

1. The upper respiratory system consists of the nose, pharynx, and associated structures, such as the middle ear and auditory tubes.
2. Coarse hairs in the nose filter large particles from air entering the respiratory tract.
3. The ciliated mucous membranes of the nose and throat trap airborne particles and remove them from the body.
4. Lymphoid tissue, tonsils, and adenoids provide immunity to certain infections.
5. The lower respiratory system consists of the larynx, trachea, bronchial tubes, and alveoli.
6. The ciliary escalator of the lower respiratory system helps prevent microorganisms from reaching the lungs.
7. Microbes in the lungs can be phagocytized by alveolar macrophages.
8. Respiratory mucus contains IgA antibodies.

Normal Microbiota of the Respiratory System (pp. 675–676)

1. The normal microbiota of the nasal cavity and throat can include pathogenic microorganisms.
2. The lower respiratory system is usually sterile because of the action of the ciliary escalator.

MICROBIAL DISEASES OF THE UPPER RESPIRATORY SYSTEM (pp. 676–680)

1. Specific areas of the upper respiratory system can become infected to produce pharyngitis, laryngitis, tonsillitis, sinusitis, and epiglottitis.
2. These infections may be caused by several bacteria and viruses, often in combination.
3. Most respiratory tract infections are self-limiting.
4. *H. influenzae* type b can cause epiglottitis.

Bacterial Diseases of the Upper Respiratory System (pp. 677–679)

Streptococcal Pharyngitis (Strep Throat) (p. 677)

1. This infection is caused by group A beta-hemolytic streptococci, the group that consists of *Streptococcus pyogenes*.
2. Symptoms of this infection are inflammation of the mucous membrane and fever; tonsillitis and otitis media may also occur.
3. Rapid diagnosis is made by enzyme immunoassays.
4. Immunity to streptococcal infections is type-specific.

Scarlet Fever (p. 677)

5. Strep throat, caused by an erythrogenic toxin-producing *S. pyogenes*, results in scarlet fever.
6. *S. pyogenes* produces erythrogenic toxin when lysogenized by a phage.
7. Symptoms include a red rash, high fever, and a red, enlarged tongue.

Diphtheria (pp. 677–679)

8. Diphtheria is caused by exotoxin-producing *Corynebacterium diphtheriae.*

9. Exotoxin is produced when the bacteria are lysogenized by a phage.

10. A membrane, containing fibrin and dead human and bacterial cells, forms in the throat and can block the passage of air.

11. The exotoxin inhibits protein synthesis, and heart, kidney, or nerve damage may result.

12. Laboratory diagnosis is based on isolation of the bacteria and the appearance of growth on differential media.

13. Routine immunization in the United States includes diphtheria toxoid in the DTaP vaccine.

14. Slow-healing skin ulcerations are characteristic of cutaneous diphtheria.

15. There is minimal dissemination of the exotoxin in the bloodstream.

Otitis Media (p. 679)

16. Earache, or otitis media, can occur as a complication of nose and throat infections.

17. Pus accumulation causes pressure on the eardrum.

18. Bacterial causes include *Streptococcus pneumoniae,* nonencapsulated *Haemophilus influenzae, Moraxella catarrhalis, Streptococcus pyogenes,* and *Staphylococcus aureus.*

Viral Diseases of the Upper Respiratory System (pp. 679–680)

The Common Cold (pp. 679–680)

1. Any one of approximately 200 different viruses can cause the common cold; rhinoviruses cause about 50% of all colds.

2. Symptoms include sneezing, nasal secretions, and congestion.

3. Sinus infections, lower respiratory tract infections, laryngitis, and otitis media can occur as complications of a cold.

4. Rhinoviruses grow best slightly below body temperature.

5. The incidence of colds increases during cold weather, possibly because of increased interpersonal indoor contact or physiological changes.

6. Antibodies are produced against the specific viruses.

MICROBIAL DISEASES OF THE LOWER RESPIRATORY SYSTEM (pp. 680–699)

1. Many of the same microorganisms that infect the upper respiratory system also infect the lower respiratory system.

2. Diseases of the lower respiratory system include bronchitis and pneumonia.

Bacterial Diseases of the Lower Respiratory System (pp. 680–682)

Pertussis (Whooping Cough) (pp. 680–682)

1. Pertussis is caused by *Bordetella pertussis.*

2. The initial stage of pertussis resembles a cold and is called the catarrhal stage.

3. The accumulation of mucus in the trachea and bronchi causes deep coughs characteristic of the paroxysmal (second) stage.

4. The convalescence (third) stage can last for months.

5. Regular immunization for children has decreased the incidence of pertussis.

Tuberculosis (pp. 682–685)

6. Tuberculosis is caused by *Mycobacterium tuberculosis*.

7. Large amounts of lipids in the cell wall account for the bacterium's acid-fast characteristic as well as its resistance to drying and disinfectants.

8. *M. tuberculosis* may be ingested by alveolar macrophages; if not killed, the bacteria reproduce in the macrophages.

9. Lesions formed by *M. tuberculosis* are called tubercles; dead macrophages and bacteria form the caseous lesion that might calcify and appear in an X-ray image as a Ghon's complex.

10. Liquefaction of the caseous lesion results in a tuberculous cavity in which *M. tuberculosis* can grow.

11. New foci of infection can develop when a caseous lesion ruptures and releases bacteria into blood or lymph vessels; this is called miliary tuberculosis.

12. Miliary tuberculosis is characterized by weight loss, coughing, and loss of vigor.

13. Chemotherapy usually involves three or four drugs taken for at least 6 months; multidrug-resistant *M. tuberculosis* is becoming prevalent.

14. A positive tuberculin skin test can indicate either an active case of TB, prior infection, or vaccination and immunity to the disease.

15. *Mycobacterium bovis* causes bovine tuberculosis and can be transmitted to humans by unpasteurized milk.

16. *M. bovis* infections usually affect the bones or lymphatic system.

17. BCG vaccine for tuberculosis consists of a live, avirulent culture of *M. bovis*.

18. *M. avium-intracellulare* complex infects patients in the late stages of HIV infection.

Bacterial Pneumonias (pp. 685–692)

19. Typical pneumonia is caused by *S. pneumoniae*.

20. Atypical pneumonias are caused by other microorganisms.

Pneumococcal Pneumonia (pp. 685–688)

21. Pneumococcal pneumonia is caused by encapsulated *Streptococcus pneumoniae*.

22. Symptoms are fever, breathing difficulty, chest pain, and rust-colored sputum.

23. A vaccine consists of purified capsular material from 23 serotypes of *S. pneumoniae*.

Haemophilus influenzae *Pneumonia (p. 688)*

24. Alcoholism, poor nutrition, cancer, and diabetes are predisposing factors for *H. influenzae* pneumonia.

25. *H. influenzae* is a gram-negative coccobacillus.

Mycoplasmal Pneumonia (p. 688)

26. *Mycoplasma pneumoniae* causes mycoplasmal pneumonia; it is an endemic disease.

27. *M. pneumoniae* produces small "fried-egg" colonies after 2 weeks' incubation on enriched media containing horse serum and yeast extract.

Legionellosis (pp. 688–689)

28. The disease is caused by the aerobic gram-negative rod *Legionella pneumophila*.

29. The bacterium can grow in water, such as air-conditioning cooling towers, and then be disseminated in the air.

30. This pneumonia does not appear to be transmitted from person to person.

Psittacosis (Ornithosis) (p. 689)

31. *Chlamydophila psittaci* is transmitted by contact with contaminated droppings and exudates of fowl.

32. Elementary bodies allow the bacteria to survive outside a host.

33. Commercial bird handlers are most susceptible to this disease.

Chlamydial Pneumonia (p. 689)

34. *Chlamydophila pneumoniae* causes pneumonia; it is transmitted from person to person.

Q Fever (pp. 689–690)

35. Obligately parasitic, intracellular *Coxiella burnetii* causes Q fever.

36. The disease is usually transmitted to humans through unpasteurized milk or inhalation of aerosols in dairy barns.

Melioidosis (pp. 690–692)

37. Melioidosis, caused by *Burkholderia pseudomallei*, is transmitted by inhalation, ingestion, or through puncture wounds. Symptoms include pneumonia, sepsis, and encephalitis.

Viral Diseases of the Lower Respiratory System (pp. 692–695)

Viral Pneumonia (p. 692)

1. A number of viruses can cause pneumonia as a complication of infections such as influenza.

2. The etiologies are not usually identified in a clinical laboratory because of the difficulty in isolating and identifying viruses.

Respiratory Syncytial Virus (RSV) (p. 692)

3. RSV is the most common cause of pneumonia in infants.

Influenza (Flu) (pp. 692–695)

4. Influenza is caused by *Influenzavirus* and is characterized by chills, fever, headache, and general muscular aches.

5. Hemagglutinin (HA) and neuraminidase (NA) spikes project from the outer lipid bilayer of the virus.

6. Viral strains are identified by antigenic differences in the HA and NA spikes; they are also divided by antigenic differences in their protein coats (A, B, and C).

7. Viral isolates are identified by hemagglutination-inhibition tests and immunofluorescence testing with monoclonal antibodies.

8. Antigenic shifts that alter the antigenic nature of the HA and NA spikes make natural immunity and vaccination of questionable value. Minor antigenic changes are caused by antigenic drift.

9. Deaths during an influenza epidemic are usually from secondary bacterial infections.

10. Multivalent vaccines are available for older adults and other high-risk groups.

11. Amantadine and rimantadine are effective prophylactic and curative drugs against influenza A virus.

Fungal Diseases of the Lower Respiratory System (pp. 695–698)

1. Fungal spores are easily inhaled; they may germinate in the lower respiratory tract.

2. The incidence of fungal diseases has been increasing in recent years.

3. The mycoses in the following sections can be treated with amphotericin B.

Histoplasmosis (pp. 695–696)

4. *Histoplasma capsulatum* causes a subclinical respiratory infection that only occasionally progresses to a severe, generalized disease.

5. The disease is acquired by inhaling airborne conidia.

6. Isolating or identifying the fungus in tissue samples is necessary for diagnosis.

Coccidioidomycosis (pp. 696–697)

7. Inhaling the airborne arthroconidia of *Coccidioides immitis* can result in coccidioidomycosis.

8. Most cases are subclinical, but when there are predisposing factors such as fatigue and poor nutrition, a progressive disease resembling tuberculosis can result.

Pneumocystis Pneumonia (p. 697)

9. *Pneumocystis jirovecii* is found in healthy human lungs.

10. *P. jirovecii* causes disease in immunosuppressed patients.

Blastomycosis (North American Blastomycosis) (p. 697)

11. *Blastomyces dermatitidis* is the causative agent of blastomycosis.

12. The infection begins in the lungs and can spread to cause extensive abscesses.

Other Fungi Involved in Respiratory Disease (pp. 697–698)

13. Opportunistic fungi can cause respiratory disease in immunosuppressed hosts, especially when large numbers of spores are inhaled.

14. Among these fungi are *Aspergillus*, *Rhizopus*, and *Mucor*.

THE LOOP

For a taxonomic approach, pages can be assigned as follows:

Bacterial diseases of the respiratory system	pp. 676–679, 680–692
Viral diseases of the respiratory system	pp. 679–680, 642–659
Fungal diseases of the respiratory system	pp. 695–698

ANSWERS

Diseases in Focus 24.1: Microbial Diseases of the Upper Respiratory System

A patient presents with fever and a red, sore throat. Later a grayish membrane appears in the throat. All of these diseases except otitis media would be accompanied by fever and sore throat. The presence of the grayish membrane is diagnostic for diphtheria.

Diseases in Focus 24.2: Common Bacterial Pneumonias

A 27-year-old man with a history of asthma was hospitalized with a 4-day history of progressive cough and 2 days of spiking fevers. Gram-positive cocci in pairs were cultured from a blood sample. All pneumonias are accompanied by cough and fever. A culture is necessary to definitively identify the cause. In this case, *Streptococcus pneumoniae* was identified by the Gram reaction, morphology, and the optochin-inhibition test.

Diseases in Focus 24.3: Microbial Diseases of the Lower Respiratory System

Three weeks after working on the demolition of an abandoned building in Kentucky, a worker was hospitalized for acute respiratory illness. At the time of demolition, a colony of bats inhabited the building. An X-ray examination revealed a lung mass. A purified protein derivative test was negative; a cytological examination for cancer was also negative. The mass was surgically removed. Microscopic examination of the mass revealed ovoid yeast cells. The lung mass (not fluid infiltrates indicative of pneumonia) suggests cancer, tuberculosis, coccidioidomycosis, histoplasmosis, or blastomycosis. The tuberculin PPD and cancer tests were negative. The patient has one of the fungal infections because filamentous fungi were cultured and yeastlike fungi were observed. The patient's symptoms are more severe than those of coccidioidomycosis and, unlike blastomycosis, do not involve other tissues. The geographic location and presence of bats strongly suggests histoplasmosis.

Review

1.

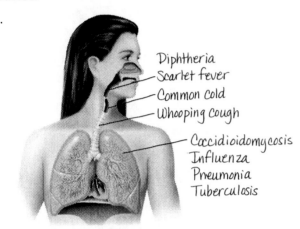

Diphtheria
Scarlet fever
Common cold
Whooping cough
Coccidioidomycosis
Influenza
Pneumonia
Tuberculosis

2. Mycoplasmal pneumonia is caused by *Mycoplasma pneumoniae* bacteria. Viral pneumonia can be caused by several different viruses. Mycoplasmal pneumonia can be treated with tetracyclines, whereas viral pneumonia cannot.

3. **Upper Respiratory System**

Common cold	Coronaviruses	Sneezing, excessive nasal secretions, congestion

Lower Respiratory System

Viral pneumonia	Several viruses	Fever, shortness of breath, chest pains
Influenza	*Influenzavirus*	Chills, fever, headache, muscular pains
RSV	Respiratory syncytial virus	Coughing, wheezing

Amantadine is used to treat influenza. Palivizumab, for life-threatening RSV.

4.

Disease	Symptoms
Streptococcal pharyngitis	Pharyngitis and tonsillitis
Scarlet fever	Rash and fever
Diphtheria	Membrane across throat
Whooping cough	Paroxysmal coughing
Tuberculosis	Tubercles and coughing
Pneumococcal pneumonia	Reddish lungs, fever
H. influenzae pneumonia	Similar to pneumococcal pneumonia
Chamydial pneumonia	Low fever, cough, and headache
Otitis media	Earache
Legionellosis	Fever and cough
Psittacosis	Fever and headache
Q fever	Chills and chest pain
Epiglottitis	Inflamed, abscessed epiglottis
Melioidosis	Delayed-onset pneumonia

5. Inhalation of large numbers of spores from *Aspergillus* or *Rhizopus* can cause infections in individuals with impaired immune systems, cancer, and diabetes.

6. No. Many different organisms (gram-positive bacteria, gram-negative bacteria, and viruses) can cause pneumonia. Each of these organisms is susceptible to different antimicrobial agents.

7. | **Disease** | **Endemic Areas in the United States** |
|---|---|
| Histoplasmosis | States adjoining the Mississippi and Ohio Rivers |
| Coccidioidomycosis | American Southwest |
| Blastomycosis | Mississippi |
| *Pneumocystis* | Ubiquitous |

Refer to Diseases in Focus 24.3.

8. In the tuberculin test, purified protein derivative (PPD) from *M. tuberculosis* is injected into the skin. Induration and reddening of the area around the injection site indicates an active infection or immunity to tuberculosis.

9.
   a. *Staphylococcus aureus*
   b. *Streptococcus pyogenes*
   c. *S. pneumoniae*
   d. *Corynebacterium diphtheriae*
   e. *Mycobacterium tuberculosis*
   f. *Moraxella catarrhalis*
   g. *Bordetella pertussis*
   h. *Burkholderia pseudomallei*
   i. *Legionella pneumophila*
   j. *Haemophilus influenzae*
   k. *Chlamydophila psittaci*
   l. *Coxiella burnetii*
   m. *Mycoplasma pneumoniae*

Critical Thinking

1.
   a. When *S. pyogenes* causing streptococcal sore throat produces an erythrogenic toxin, the infection is called scarlet fever.
   b. Diphtheroids are nonpathogenic species of corynebacteria. *C. diphtheriae*, like *S. pyogenes*, produces an exotoxin when it is lysogenized by a phage.

2. There are many strains of *Influenzavirus* because of antigenic drift and antigenic shift.

3. There are more than 200 viruses that cause colds. *Influenzavirus* changes its antigens every few months.

Clinical Applications

1. Coccidioidomycosis. Attempts to culture fungi after the initial diagnosis may have grown *C. immitis*.

2. AIDS patients were given pentamidine to prevent *Pneumocystis* pneumonia. Possible sources of infection: (1) the nurse diagnosed with tuberculosis, (2) aerosols created during pentamidine therapy, or (3) face-to-face exposure with TB patients.

3. The disease is psittacosis; transmitted by inhalation of particles from bird droppings.

CASE STUDY: PYTHONS IN THE UNITED STATES

Background

On May 25, the Suffolk County, New York Health Department was informed by a hospital infection control nurse that 2 days earlier, a 27-year-old man had been admitted with a 4-day history of fever (40°C), severe headache, chills, malaise, and vomiting. This patient had visited West Africa in April and was an employee of an exotic bird and reptile importing company. Within 1 week, three other employees of that company were admitted to the same hospital with similar symptoms. All were treated with oral tetracycline; recovery was rapid and complete.

All four persons had been involved in unpacking and deticking a shipment of 500 ball pythons that were imported on May 3 from Accra, Ghana. Examination of the hemolymph of five ticks removed from these snakes indicated that all contained numerous bacteria. Three types of ticks were identified: *Amblyomma nuttalli*, *Aponomma latum*, and *A. flavomaculatum*.

Questions

1. Identify the etiologic agent of this disease.
2. What was the probable mode of transmission? The probable reservoir?
3. What information do you need to verify your conclusions?
4. Briefly explain how you arrived at your conclusions.

The Solution

1. Q fever, caused by *Coxiella burnetii.*
2. Transmission could have been by aerosols or ticks.
3. A serologic test such as complement fixation or immunofluorescence.
4. Students will use clinical symptoms and association with exotic animals and ticks.

25

Microbial Diseases of the Digestive System

LEARNING OBJECTIVES

CHECK YOUR UNDERSTANDING

25-1 Name the structures of the digestive system that contact food.

There have been instances in which a surgeon was using spark-producing instruments in removing intestinal polyps and a small explosion occurred. What ignited?

25-2 Identify parts of the gastrointestinal tract that normally have microbiota.

How are normal microbiota confined to the mouth and large intestine?

25-3 Describe the events that lead to dental caries and periodontal disease.

Why are "sugarless" candies and gum, which actually contain sugar alcohols, not considered cariogenic (causing caries)?

25-4 List the causative agents, suspect foods, signs and symptoms, and treatments for staphylococcal food poisoning, shigellosis, salmonellosis, typhoid fever, cholera, gastroenteritis, and peptic ulcer disease.

Salmonellosis and typhoid fever are caused by closely related organisms. Why has typhoid fever been almost entirely eliminated in developed countries by modern sewage treatment whereas salmonellosis has not been?

25-5 List the causative agents, modes of transmission, sites of infection, and symptoms for mumps.

Why is mumps included with the diseases of the digestive system?

25-6 Differentiate among hepatitis A, hepatitis B, hepatitis C, hepatitis D, and hepatitis E.

Of the several hepatitis diseases, HAV, HBV, HCV, HDV, and HEV, which two now have effective vaccines to prevent them?

25-7 List the causative agents, mode of transmission, and symptoms of viral gastroenteritis.

Two very common causes of viral gastroenteritis are caused by rotaviruses and noroviruses. Which of these now can be prevented by a vaccine?

25-8 Identify the causes of ergot poisoning and aflatoxin poisoning.

What is the connection between the occasional hallucinogenic symptoms produced by ergot poisoning and a modern illicit drug?

25-9 List the causative agents, modes of transmission, symptoms, and treatments for giardiasis, cryptosporidiosis, Cyclospora diarrheal infection, and amoebic dysentery.

Is giardiasis caused by ingestion of a cyst or an oocyst?

25-10 List the causative agents, modes of transmission, symptoms, and treatments for tapeworms, hydatid disease, pinworms, hookworms, ascariasis, and trichinellosis.

What species of tapeworm is the cause of cysticercosis?

NEW IN THIS EDITION

- Revised discussion of traveler's diarrhea, to include the important pathogen, enteroaggregative *E. coli*
- Inclusion of some of the more recent therapeutic drugs for HBV in the discussion of this form of hepatitis
- Revised and updated discussion of noroviruses, with special attention to the decontamination methods available to deal with outbreaks

A FOODBORNE INFECTION

Answers to question in Clinical Focus (*MMWR*) box on a *Salmonella* outbreak associated with tomatoes, on p. 715.

Exposure	Relative risk
Chicken salad	1.71
Cole slaw	1.58
Fruit salad	1.17
Potato salad	1.18
Tomato salad	3.86

CHAPTER SUMMARY

Introduction (p. 705)

1. Diseases of the digestive system are the second most common illnesses in the United States.
2. Diseases of the digestive system usually result from ingesting microorganisms or their toxins in food and water.
3. The fecal–oral cycle of transmission can be broken by the proper disposal of sewage, the disinfection of drinking water, and proper food preparation and storage.

Structure and Function of the Digestive System (p. 706)

1. The gastrointestinal (GI) tract, or alimentary canal, consists of the mouth, pharynx, esophagus, stomach, small intestine, and large intestine.
2. In the GI tract, with mechanical and chemical help from the accessory structures, large food molecules are broken down into smaller molecules that can be transported by blood or lymph to cells.
3. Feces, the solids resulting from digestion, are eliminated through the anus.

Normal Microbiota of the Digestive System (pp. 706–707)

1. Large numbers of bacteria colonize the mouth.
2. The stomach and small intestine have few resident microorganisms.
3. Bacteria in the large intestine assist in degrading food and synthesizing vitamins.
4. Up to 40% of fecal mass is microbial cells.

Bacterial Diseases of the Mouth (pp. 707–710)

Dental Caries (Tooth Decay) (pp. 707–709)

1. Dental caries begin when tooth enamel and dentin are eroded and the pulp is exposed to bacterial infection.
2. *Streptococcus mutans,* found in the mouth, uses sucrose to form dextran from glucose and lactic acid from fructose.
3. Bacteria adhere to teeth by the sticky dextran, forming dental plaque.

4. Acid produced during carbohydrate fermentation destroys tooth enamel at the site of the plaque.

5. Gram-positive rods and filamentous bacteria can penetrate into dentin and pulp.

6. Carbohydrates such as starch, mannitol, sorbitol, and xylitol are not used by cariogenic bacteria to produce dextran and do not promote tooth decay.

7. Caries are prevented by restricting the ingestion of sucrose and by the physical removal of plaque.

Periodontal Disease (p. 709)

8. Caries of the cementum and gingivitis are caused by streptococci, actinomycetes, and anaerobic gram-negative bacteria.

9. Chronic gum disease (periodontitis) can cause bone destruction and tooth loss; periodontitis is due to an inflammatory response to a variety of bacteria growing on the gums.

10. Acute necrotizing ulcerative gingivitis is often caused by *Prevotella intermedia.*

Bacterial Diseases of the Lower Digestive System (pp. 710–721)

1. A gastrointestinal infection is caused by the growth of a pathogen in the intestines.

2. Incubation times range from 12 hours to 2 weeks. Symptoms of infection generally include a fever.

3. A bacterial intoxication results from ingesting preformed bacterial toxins.

4. Symptoms appear 1 to 48 hours after ingestion of the toxin. Fever is not usually a symptom of intoxication.

5. Infections and intoxications cause diarrhea, dysentery, or gastroenteritis.

6. These conditions are usually treated with fluid and electrolyte replacement.

Staphylococcal Food Poisoning (Staphylococcal Enterotoxicosis) (pp. 711–712)

7. Staphylococcal food poisoning is caused by the ingestion of an enterotoxin produced in improperly stored foods.

8. *S. aureus* is inoculated into foods during preparation. The bacteria grow and produce enterotoxin in food stored at room temperature.

9. Boiling for 30 minutes is not sufficient to denature the exotoxin.

10. Foods with high osmotic pressure and those not cooked immediately before consumption are most often the source of staphylococcal enterotoxicosis.

11. Laboratory identification of *S. aureus* isolated from foods is used to trace the source of contamination.

Shigellosis (Bacillary Dysentery) (p. 712)

12. Shigellosis is caused by any of four species of *Shigella.*

13. Symptoms include blood and mucus in stools, abdominal cramps, and fever. Infections by *S. dysenteriae* result in ulceration of the intestinal mucosa.

Salmonellosis (*Salmonella* Gastroenteritis) (pp. 712–714)

14. Salmonellosis, or *Salmonella* gastroenteritis, is caused by many *Salmonella enterica* serovars.

15. Symptoms include nausea, abdominal pain, and diarrhea and begin 12 to 36 hours after eating large numbers of *Salmonella*. Septic shock can occur in infants and in the elderly.

16. Mortality is lower than 1%, and recovery can result in a carrier state.

17. Cooking food will usually kill *Salmonella.*

Typhoid Fever (pp. 714–716)

18. *Salmonella typhi* causes typhoid fever; the bacteria are transmitted by contact with human feces.

19. Fever and malaise occur after a 2-week incubation period. Symptoms last 2 to 3 weeks.

20. *S. typhi* is harbored in the gallbladder of carriers.
21. Typhoid fever is treated with quinolones and cephalosporins; vaccines are available for high-risk people.

Cholera (pp. 716–717)

22. *Vibrio cholerae* O:1 and O:139 produce an exotoxin that alters the membrane permeability of the intestinal mucosa; the resulting vomiting and diarrhea cause a loss of body fluids.
23. The symptoms last for a few days. Untreated cholera has a 50% mortality rate.

Noncholera Vibrios (p. 717)

24. Ingestion of other *V. cholerae* serotypes can result in mild diarrhea.
25. *Vibrio* gastroenteritis can be caused by *V. parahaemolyticus* and *V. vulnificus*.
26. These diseases are contracted by eating contaminated crustaceans or contaminated mollusks.

Escherichia coli Gastroenteritis (pp. 717–718)

27. Traveler's diarrhea may be caused by enterotoxigenic or enteroinvasive strains of *E. coli*.
28. The disease is usually self-limiting and does not require chemotherapy.
29. Enterohemorrhagic *E. coli*, such as *E. coli* O157:H7, produces Shiga toxins that cause inflammation and bleeding of the colon, including hemorrhagic colitis and hemolytic uremic syndrome.
30. Shiga toxins can affect the kidneys to cause hemolytic uremic syndrome.

Campylobacter Gastroenteritis (p. 718)

31. *Campylobacter* is the second most common cause of diarrhea in the United States.
32. *Campylobacter* is transmitted in cow's milk.

Helicobacter Peptic Ulcer Disease (pp. 718–720)

33. *Helicobacter pylori* produces ammonia, which neutralizes stomach acid; the bacteria colonize the stomach mucosa and cause peptic ulcer disease.
34. Bismuth and several antibiotics may be useful in treating peptic ulcer disease.

Yersinia Gastroenteritis (p. 720)

35. *Y. enterocolitica* and *Y. pseudotuberculosis* are transmitted in meat and milk.
36. *Yersinia* can grow at refrigeration temperatures.

Clostridium perfringens Gastroenteritis (p. 720)

37. *C. perfringens* causes a self-limiting gastroenteritis.
38. Endospores survive heating and germinate when foods (usually meats) are stored at room temperature.
39. Exotoxin produced when the bacteria grow in the intestines is responsible for the symptoms.
40. Diagnosis is based on isolating and identifying the bacteria in stool samples.

Clostridium difficile–Associated Diarrhea (p. 720)

41. Growth of *C. difficile* following antibiotic therapy can result in mild diarrhea or colitis.
42. The condition is usually associated with hospitalized patients and nursing home residents.

Bacillus cereus Gastroenteritis (pp. 720–721)

43. Ingesting food contaminated with the soil saprophyte *Bacillus cereus* can result in diarrhea, nausea, and vomiting.

Viral Diseases of the Digestive System (pp. 721–729)

Mumps (p. 721)

1. Mumps virus enters and exits the body through the respiratory tract.

2. About 16 to 18 days after exposure, the virus causes inflammation of the parotid glands, fever, and pain during swallowing. About 4 to 7 days later, orchitis may occur.

3. After onset of the symptoms, the virus is found in the blood, saliva, and urine.

4. A measles, mumps, rubella (MMR) vaccine is available.

Hepatitis (pp. 721–728)

5. Inflammation of the liver is called hepatitis. Symptoms include loss of appetite, malaise, fever, and jaundice.

6. Viral causes of hepatitis include hepatitis viruses, Epstein-Barr virus (EBV), and cytomegalovirus (CMV).

Hepatitis A (pp. 721–723)

7. Hepatitis A virus (HAV) causes hepatitis A; at least 50% of all cases are subclinical.

8. HAV is ingested in contaminated food or water, grows in the cells of the intestinal mucosa, and spreads to the liver, kidneys, and spleen in the blood.

9. The virus is eliminated with feces.

10. The incubation period is 2 to 6 weeks; the period of disease is 2 to 21 days, and recovery is complete in 4 to 6 weeks.

11. A vaccine is available; passive immunization can provide temporary protection.

Hepatitis B (pp. 723–726)

12. Hepatitis B virus (HBV) causes hepatitis B, which is frequently serious.

13. HBV is transmitted by blood transfusions, contaminated syringes, saliva, sweat, breast milk, and semen.

14. Blood is tested for HB_sAg before being used in transfusions.

15. The average incubation period is 3 months; recovery is usually complete, but some patients develop a chronic infection or become carriers.

16. A vaccine against HB_sAg is available.

Hepatitis C (p. 726)

17. Hepatitis C virus (HCV) is transmitted via blood.

18. The incubation period is 2 to 22 weeks; the disease is usually mild, but some patients develop chronic hepatitis.

19. Blood is tested for HCV antibodies before being used in transfusions.

Hepatitis D (Delta Hepatitis) (pp. 726–727)

20. Hepatitis D virus (HDV) has a circular strand of RNA and uses HB_sAg as a coat.

Hepatitis E (pp. 727–728)

21. Hepatitis E virus (HEV) is spread by the fecal–oral route.

Other Types of Hepatitis (p. 728)

22. There is evidence of the existence of hepatitis types F and G.

Viral Gastroenteritis (pp. 728–729)

23. Viral gastroenteritis is most often caused by a rotavirus or norovirus.
24. The incubation period is 2 to 3 days; diarrhea lasts up to 1 week.

Fungal Diseases of the Digestive System (pp. 729–730)

1. Mycotoxins are toxins produced by some fungi.
2. Mycotoxins affect the blood, nervous system, kidneys, or liver.

Ergot Poisoning (pp. 729–730)

3. Ergot poisoning, or ergotism, is caused by the mycotoxin produced by *Claviceps purpurea.*
4. Cereal grains are the crop most often contaminated with the *Claviceps* mycotoxin.

Aflatoxin Poisoning (p. 730)

5. Aflatoxin is a mycotoxin produced by *Aspergillus flavus.*
6. Peanuts are the crop most often contaminated with aflatoxin.

Protozoan Diseases of the Digestive System (pp. 730–732)

Giardiasis (pp. 730–731)

1. *Giardia lamblia* grows in the intestines of humans and wild animals and is transmitted in contaminated water.
2. Symptoms of giardiasis are malaise, nausea, flatulence, weakness, and abdominal cramps that persist for weeks.

Cryptosporidiosis (p. 731)

3. *Crytosporidium hominis* causes diarrhea; in immunosuppressed patients, the disease is prolonged for months.
4. The pathogen is transmitted in contaminated water.

Cyclospora Diarrheal Infection (p. 731)

5. *C. cayetanensis* causes diarrhea; the protozoan was first identified in 1993.
6. It is transmitted in contaminated produce.

Amoebic Dysentery (Amoebiasis) (pp. 731–732)

7. Amoebic dysentery is caused by *Entamoeba histolytica* growing in the large intestine.
8. The amoeba feeds on red blood cells and GI tract tissues. Severe infections result in abscesses.

Helminthic Diseases of the Digestive System (pp. 732–737)

Tapeworms (pp. 732–733)

1. Tapeworms are contracted by the consumption of undercooked beef, pork, or fish containing encysted larvae (cysticerci).
2. The scolex attaches to the intestinal mucosa of humans (the definitive host) and matures into an adult tapeworm.
3. Eggs are shed in the feces and must be ingested by an intermediate host.

4. Adult tapeworms can be undiagnosed in a human.

5. Neurocysticercosis in humans occurs when the pork tapeworm larvae encyst in humans.

Hydatid Disease (pp. 733–734)

6. Humans infected with the tapeworm *Echinococcus granulosus* might have hydatid cysts in their lungs or other organs.

7. Dogs and wolves are usually the definitive hosts, and sheep or deer are the intermediate hosts for *E. granulosus.*

Nematodes (pp. 734–737)

Pinworms (pp. 734–735)

8. Humans are the definitive host for pinworms, *Enterobius vermicularis.*

9. The disease is acquired by ingesting *Enterobius* eggs.

Hookworms (pp. 735–736)

10. Hookworm larvae bore through skin and migrate to the intestine to mature into adults.

11. In the soil, hookworm larvae hatch from eggs shed in feces.

Ascariasis (p. 736)

12. *Ascaris lumbricoides* adults live in human intestines.

13. Ascariasis is acquired by ingesting Ascaris eggs.

Trichinellosis (pp. 736–737)

14. *Trichinella spiralis* larvae encyst in muscles of humans and other mammals to cause trichinellosis.

15. The roundworm is contracted by ingesting undercooked meat containing larvae.

16. Adult females mature in the intestine and lay eggs; the new larvae migrate to invade muscles.

17. Symptoms include fever, swelling around the eyes, and gastrointestinal upset.

THE LOOP   ⊶

For a taxonomic approach, pages can be assigned as follows:

Bacterial diseases	pp. 707–721
Viral diseases	pp. 721–729
Fungal diseases	pp. 729–730
Protozoan diseases	pp. 730–732
Helminthic infestations	pp. 732–737

The incidence of typhoid fever is shown in question 4 on page 426 of *Microbiology: An Introduction.* See also "The Role of Microorganisms in Water Quality" on pp. 778–782 of *Microbiology: An Introduction.*

ANSWERS

Diseases in Focus 25.1: Bacterial Diseases of the Mouth

Use the table below to identify infections that could cause persistent sore, swollen, red, or bleeding gums, as well as tooth pain or sensitivity and bad breath. The symptoms include periodontitis, but the pain and bad breath suggest progression to acute necrotizing ulcerative gingivitis.

Diseases in Focus 25.2: Bacterial Diseases of the Lower Digestive System

An 8-year-old boy had diarrhea, chills, fever (39.3°C), abdominal cramps, and vomiting for 3 days. The next month, his 12-year-old brother experienced the same symptoms. Two weeks before the first patient became ill, the family *had purchased a small (<10 cm) red-eared slider turtle at a flea market.* Staphylococcal food poisoning is not accompanied by a fever and the two boys did not have their symptoms at the same time; these facts eliminate an intoxication. The absence of serious diarrhea eliminates cholera and shigellosis; the absence of a high fever eliminates typhoid fever. Association with a reptile, especially a small turtle that is easily handled and is moist with water containing its feces, indicates salmonellosis.

Diseases in Focus 25.3: Characteristics of Viral Hepatitis

After eating at one restaurant, 355 people were diagnosed with the same hepatitis virus. Hepatitis A and hepatitis E are associated with food because they are transmitted by the fecal–oral route. Hepatitis A is most likely, although HEV is possible, especially in south and southeast Asia. To date, there have been no U.S. outbreaks of HEV.

Diseases in Focus 25.4: Viral Diseases of the Digestive System

An outbreak of diarrhea began in mid-June, peaked in mid-August, and tapered off in September. A clinical case was defined as diarrhea (three loose stools during a 24-hour period) in a person who was a member of a swim club. The outbreak is caused by either rotavirus or norovirus. It isn't possible to know for sure without genetic analysis of the isolated virus.

Diseases in Focus 25.5: Fungal, Protozoan, and Helminthic Diseases of the Lower Digestive System

Public health officials in Pennsylvania were notified of cases of watery diarrhea with frequent, sometimes explosive, bowel movements among persons associated with a residential facility (e.g., residents, staff, and volunteers). The disease was associated with eating snow peas. Based on symptoms alone, it isn't possible to differentiate the organisms in the table that cause diarrhea: *Giardia, Cryptosporidium, Cyclospora,* and *Entamoeba.* The presence of acid-fast protozoa is diagnostic for *Cryptosporidium* and *Cyclospora. Cyclospora* is larger than *Cryptosporidium.*

Review

1.

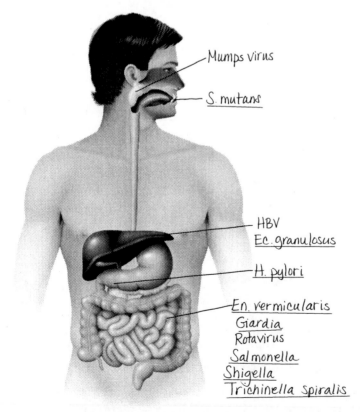

Mumps virus

S. mutans

HBV
Ec. granulosus

H. pylori

En. vermicularis
Giardia
Rotavirus
Salmonella
Shigella
Trichinella spiralis

2. | Disease | Suspect Foods | Symptoms |
|---|---|---|
| Staph | Not cooked prior to eating | Vomiting and diarrhea |
| Shigellosis | Contaminated water | Mucus and blood in stools |
| Salmonellosis | Poultry; contaminated water | Fever, vomiting, and diarrhea |
| Cholera | Contaminated water | Rice water stools |
| Traveler's | Contaminated water | Vomiting and diarrhea |

Refer to Diseases in Focus 25.2.

3. | Causative Agent | Suspect Foods | Prevention |
|---|---|---|
| *V. parahaemolyticus* | Oysters, shrimp | Cooking |
| *V. vulnificus* | Contact with coastal waters | |
| Enterotoxigenic *E. coli* | Water, vegetables | Cooking |
| Enteroinvasive *E. coli* | Water, vegetables | Cooking |
| Enterohemorrhagic *E. coli* | Alfalfa sprouts, tomatoes | Cooking |
| *C. jejuni* | Chicken | Cooking |
| *Y. enterocolitica* | Meat, milk | Cooking |
| *C. perfringens* | Meat | Refrigeration after cooking |
| *B. cereus* | Rice dishes | Refrigeration after cooking |

Refer to Diseases in Focus 25.2 to complete the table.

4. Certain strains of *E. coli* may produce an enterotoxin or invade the epithelium of the large intestine.

5. Toxins produced by fungi; see pp. 729–730.

6. All four are caused by protozoa. The infections are acquired by ingesting protozoa in contaminated water. Giardiasis is a prolonged diarrhea. Amoebic dysentery is the most severe dysentery, with blood and mucus in the stools. *Cryptosporidium* and *Cyclospora* produce severe diseases in persons with immune deficiencies.

7. **Food intoxication:** Microorganisms must be allowed to grow in food from the time of preparation to the time of ingestion. This usually occurs when foods are stored unrefrigerated or improperly canned. The etiologic agents (*Staphylococcus aureus* or *Clostridium botulinum*) must produce an exotoxin. Onset: 1 to 48 hours. Duration: A few days. Treatment: Antimicrobial agents are ineffective. The patient's symptoms may be treated.

   Food infection: Viable microorganisms must be ingested with food or water. The organisms could be present during preparation and survive cooking or be inoculated during later handling. The etiologic agents are usually gram-negative organisms (*Salmonella, Shigella, Vibrio,* and *Escherichia*) that produce endotoxins. *Clostridium perfringens* is a gram-positive bacterium that causes food infection. Onset: 12 hours to 2 weeks. Duration: Longer than intoxication because the microorganisms are growing in the patient. Treatment: Rehydration.

8. | Disease | Site | Symptoms |
|---|---|---|
| Mumps | Parotid glands | Inflammation of the parotid glands and fever |
| Infectious hepatitis | Liver | Anorexia, fever, diarrhea |
| Serum hepatitis | Liver | Anorexia, fever, joint pains, jaundice |
| Viral gastroenteritis | Lower GI tract | Nausea, diarrhea, vomiting |

Refer to Diseases in Focus 25.3 and 25.4 to complete this question.

9. Cook meat thoroughly. Eliminate the source of contamination to cattle and pigs.

Critical Thinking

1. Humans are not usually consumed by other animals. The larval stage of *Trichinella* is encysted in humans and must be ingested to mature in the intestines of a definitive host.

2.

Disease	Conditions	Diagnosis	Prevention
Staph	Lack of refrigeration	Symptoms, presence of *S. aureus* in food	Refrigeration
Salmonellosis	Fecal contamination, inadequate heating	Isolation of *Salmonella* from stools	Sanitation, thorough heating of foods
C. difficile diarrhea	Loss of normal microbiota	Cytotoxin assay	Handwashing

3. a. 3   c. 5   e. 1
   b. 4   d. 2   f. 6

4. The gram-negative bacterial infections, hepatitis A and E, viral gastroenteritis, and the protozoan diseases. The organisms are not likely to be salt-tolerant (except *Vibrio*), and an ocean swimmer swallows less water than a freshwater swimmer.

Clinical Applications

1. Source of infection: Crabs.

   Bacteria: *Vibrio cholerae.*

   Prevention: Proper cooking temperature.

2. Source of infection: Chickens and improper cooking procedures.

   Bacteria: *Salmonella heidelberg* and *S. stanley.*

   Prevention: Refrigeration overnight; higher cooking temperature.

3. Bacteria: *Shigella.*

   Transmitted: Fecal–oral route.

   Source: Sewage-contaminated well water.

4. Uncooked giblets are easily contaminated with *Salmonella* from the turkey's intestines. The length of the incubation period indicates this is an infection.

CASE STUDY: A CASE OF FOOD POISONING

Background

Twenty-eight kindergarten children and seven adults visited a raw milk bottling plant, where they were given ice cream and raw milk. Three to 6 days later, nine children and three adults developed gastroenteritis. The only foods eaten by all these children (ill and well) were in the school-provided lunches. No one else in the school became sick. Stool cultures showed one bacterium in common to nine of the ill children and not present in samples from nine well children. This bacterium is a curved gram-negative rod; it neither ferments nor oxidizes glucose.

Questions

1. Identify the etiologic agent of this outbreak of food poisoning.

2. Was it food infection or intoxication?

3. How did the food get contaminated, and what item was contaminated?

4.   What could be done to prevent this type of outbreak?

5.   Briefly explain how you arrived at your conclusions.

The Solution

Source of infection: Raw milk

Bacteria: *Campylobacter*

Prevention: Pasteurization

26 Microbial Diseases of the Urinary and Reproductive Systems

LEARNING OBJECTIVES

26-1 List the antimicrobial features of the urinary system.

26-2 Identify the portals of entry for microbes into the female and male reproductive systems.

26-3 Describe the normal microbiota of the upper urinary tract, the male urethra, and the female urethra and vagina.

26-4 Describe the modes of transmission for urinary and reproductive system infections.

26-5 List the microorganisms that cause cystitis, pyelonephritis, and leptospirosis, and name the predisposing factors for these diseases.

26-6 List the causative agents, symptoms, methods of diagnosis, and treatments for gonorrhea, nongonococcal urethritis (NGU), pelvic inflammatory disease (PID), syphilis, lymphogranuloma venereum (LGV), chancroid, and bacterial vaginosis.

26-7 Discuss the epidemiology of genital herpes and genital warts.

26-8 Discuss the epidemiology of candidiasis.

26-9 Discuss the epidemiology of trichomoniasis.

26-10 List reproductive system diseases that can cause congenital and neonatal infections, and explain how these infections can be prevented.

CHECK YOUR UNDERSTANDING

Does the pH of urine facilitate the growth of most bacteria?

Look at Figure 26.2. Is a microbe entering the female reproductive system (the uterus, etc.) necessarily also entering the bladder, causing cystitis?

What is the association between estrogens and the microbiota of the vagina?

Why is urethritis, an infection of the urethra, frequently preliminary to further infections of the urinary tract?

Why is *E. coli* the most common cause of cystitis, especially in females?

Why is the disease condition of the female reproductive system, principally featuring growth of *Gardernella vaginalis,* termed *vaginosis* rather than *vaginitis*?

Both genital herpes and genital warts are caused by viruses. Which one is the greater danger to a pregnancy?

What changes in the vaginal bacterial microbiota tend also to favor the growth of the yeast *Candida albicans*?

What are the symptoms of the presence of *Trichomonas vaginalis* in the male reproductive system?

What is the intent of the TORCH panel of tests?

NEW IN THIS EDITION

- Extensively revised discussion of vaginal microbiota
- Revised introductory discussion of syphilis, to include recent genetic analysis on its probable origin in the New World
- New discussion of the TORCH panel of tests

CHAPTER SUMMARY

Introduction (p. 743)

1. The urinary system regulates the chemical composition and volume of the blood and excretes nitrogenous waste and water.

2. The reproductive system produces gametes for reproduction and, in the female, supports the growing embryo.

3. Microbial diseases of these systems can result from infection from an outside source or from opportunistic infection by members of the normal microbiota.

Structure and Function of the Urinary System (p. 744)

1. Urine is transported from the kidneys through ureters to the urinary bladder and is eliminated through the urethra.

2. Valves prevent urine from flowing back to the urinary bladder and kidneys.

3. The flushing action of urine and the acidity of normal urine have some antimicrobial value.

Structure and Function of the Reproductive Systems (pp. 744–745)

1. The female reproductive system consists of two ovaries, two uterine tubes, the uterus, the cervix, the vagina, and the external genitals.

2. The male reproductive system consists of two testes, ducts, accessory glands, and the penis; seminal fluid leaves the male body through the urethra.

Normal Microbiota of the Urinary and Reproductive Systems (p. 745)

1. The urinary bladder and upper urinary tract are sterile under normal conditions.

2. Lactobacilli dominate the vaginal microbiota during the reproductive years.

3. The male urethra is normally sterile.

DISEASES OF THE URINARY SYSTEM (pp. 746–747)

Bacterial Diseases of the Urinary System (pp. 746–747)

1. Urethritis, cystitis, and ureteritis are terms describing inflammations of tissues of the lower urinary tract.

2. Pyelonephritis can result from lower urinary tract infections or from systemic bacterial infections.

3. Opportunistic gram-negative bacteria from the intestines often cause urinary tract infections.

4. Nosocomial infections following catheterization occur in the urinary system. *E. coli* causes more than half of these infections.

5. Treatment of urinary tract infections depends on the isolation and antibiotic sensitivity testing of the causative agents.

Cystitis (p. 746)

6. Inflammation of the urinary bladder, or cystitis, is common in females.

7. Microorganisms at the opening of the urethra and along the length of the urethra, careless personal hygiene, and sexual intercourse contribute to the high incidence of cystitis in females.

8. The most common etiologies are *E. coli* and *Staphylococcus saprophyticus*.

Pyelonephritis (p. 746)

9. Inflammation of the kidneys, or pyelonephritis, is usually a complication of lower urinary tract infections.
10. About 75% of pyelonephritis cases are caused by *E. coli.*

Leptospirosis (pp. 746–747)

11. The spirochete *Leptospira interrogans* is the cause of leptospirosis.
12. The disease is transmitted to humans by urine-contaminated water.
13. Leptospirosis is characterized by chills, fever, headache, and muscle aches.

DISEASES OF THE REPRODUCTIVE SYSTEMS (p. 747–756)

Bacterial Diseases of the Reproductive Systems (pp. 747–756)

1. Most diseases of the reproductive system are sexually transmitted diseases (STDs), now called sexually transmitted infections (STIs).
2. Most STIs can be prevented by the use of condoms and are treated with antibiotics.

Gonorrhea (pp. 747–750)

3. *Neisseria gonorrhoeae* causes gonorrhea.
4. Gonorrhea is a common reportable communicable disease in the United States.
5. *N. gonorrhoeae* attaches to mucosal cells of the oral-pharyngeal area, genitals, eyes, and rectum by means of fimbriae.
6. Symptoms in men are painful urination and pus discharge. Blockage of the urethra and sterility are complications of untreated cases.
7. Women might be asymptomatic unless the infection spreads to the uterus and uterine tubes (see pelvic inflammatory disease).
8. Gonorrheal endocarditis, gonorrheal meningitis, and gonorrheal arthritis are complications that can affect both sexes if gonorrheal infections are untreated.
9. Ophthalmia neonatorum is an eye infection acquired by infants during passage through the birth canal of an infected mother.
10. Gonorrhea is diagnosed by ELISA or nucleic acid amplification.

Nongonococcal Urethritis (NGU) (pp. 750–751)

11. Nongonococcal urethritis (NGU), or nonspecific urethritis (NSU), is any inflammation of the urethra not caused by *N. gonorrhoeae.*
12. Most cases of NGU are caused by *Chlamydia trachomatis.*
13. *C. trachomatis* infection is the most common STI.
14. Symptoms of NGU are often mild or lacking, although uterine tube inflammation and sterility may occur.
15. *C. trachomatis* can be transmitted to infants' eyes at birth.
16. Diagnosis is based on the detection of chlamydial DNA in urine.
17. *Ureaplasma urealyticum* and *Mycoplasma hominis* also cause NGU.

Pelvic Inflammatory Disease (PID) (pp. 751–752)

18. Extensive bacterial infection of the female pelvic organs, especially of the reproductive system, is called pelvic inflammatory disease (PID).

19. PID is caused by *N. gonorrhoeae, C. trachomatis,* and other bacteria that gain access to the uterine tubes. Infection of the uterine tubes is called salpingitis.

20. PID can result in blockage of the uterine tubes and sterility.

Syphilis (pp. 752–755)

21. Syphilis is caused by *Treponema pallidum,* a spirochete that has not been cultured in vitro. Laboratory cultures are grown in rabbits or cell cultures.

22. The primary lesion is a small, hard-based chancre at the site of infection. The bacteria then invade the blood and lymphatic system, and the chancre spontaneously heals.

23. The appearance of a widely disseminated rash on the skin and mucous membranes marks the secondary stage. Spirochetes are present in the lesions of the rash.

24. The patient enters a latent period after the secondary lesions spontaneously heal.

25. At least 10 years after the secondary lesion, tertiary lesions called gummas can appear on many organs.

26. Congenital syphilis, resulting from *T. pallidum* crossing the placenta during the latent period, can cause neurological damage in the newborn.

27. *T. pallidum* is identifiable through darkfield microscopy of fluid from primary and secondary lesions.

28. Many serological tests, such as VDRL, RPR, and FTA-ABS, can be used to detect the presence of antibodies against *T. pallidum* during any stage of the disease.

Lymphogranuloma Venereum (LGV) (p. 755)

29. *C. trachomatis* causes lymphogranuloma venereum (LGV), which is primarily a disease of tropical and subtropical regions.

30. The initial lesion appears on the genitals and heals without scarring.

31. The bacteria are spread in the lymph system and cause enlargement of the lymph nodes, obstruction of lymph vessels, and swelling of the external genitals.

32. The bacteria are isolated and identified from pus taken from infected lymph nodes.

Chancroid (Soft Chancre) (p. 756)

33. Chancroid, a swollen, painful ulcer on the mucous membranes of the genitals or mouth, is caused by *Haemophilus ducreyi.*

Bacterial Vaginosis (p. 756)

34. Bacterial vaginosis is an infection without inflammation caused by *Gardnerella vaginalis.*

35. Diagnosis of *G. vaginalis* is based on increased vaginal pH, fishy odor, and the presence of clue cells.

Viral Diseases of the Reproductive Systems (pp. 757–758)

Genital Herpes (pp. 757–758)

1. Herpes simplex viruses (HSV-1 and HSV-2) cause genital herpes.

2. Symptoms of the infection are painful urination, genital irritation, and fluid-filled vesicles.

3. The virus might enter a latent stage in nerve cells. Vesicles reappear following trauma and hormonal changes.

4. Neonatal herpes is contracted during fetal development or birth. It can result in neurological damage or infant fatalities.

Genital Warts (p. 758)

5. Human papillomaviruses cause warts.

6. Some human papillomaviruses that cause genital warts have been associated with cancer of the cervix.

AIDS (p. 758)

7. AIDS is a sexually transmitted disease of the immune system (see Chapter 19, pages 539–598).

Fungal Disease of the Reproductive Systems (pp. 758–759)

Candidiasis (pp. 758–759)

1. *Candida albicans* causes NGU in men and vulvovaginal candidiasis, or yeast infection, in women.

2. Vulvovaginal candidiasis is characterized by lesions that produce itching and irritation.

3. Predisposing factors are pregnancy, diabetes, tumors, and broad-spectrum antibacterial chemotherapy.

4. Diagnosis is based on observation of the fungus and its isolation from lesions.

Protozoan Disease of the Reproductive System (pp. 760–761)

Trichomoniasis (p. 760)

1. *Trichomonas vaginalis* causes trichomoniasis when the pH of the vagina increases.

2. Diagnosis is based on observation of the protozoa in purulent discharges from the site of infection.

The TORCH Panel of Tests (p. 760)

3. Antibodies against specific diseases that can infect a fetus are detected by the TORCH tests.

THE LOOP

For a taxonomic approach, pages can be assigned as follows:

Bacterial diseases	pp. 746–756
Viral diseases	pp. 757–758
Fungal diseases	pp. 758–759
Protozoan diseases	p. 760

AIDS is mentioned as a sexually transmitted disease, and the discussions on pp. 387, 389–390 (in Chapter 13) and pp. 539–548 (in Chapter 19) are cross-referenced.

ANSWERS

Diseases in Focus 26.1: Bacterial Diseases of the Urinary System

A 20-year-old woman felt a stinging sensation when urinating and felt an urgent need to urinate, even if very little urine was excreted. Absence of fever eliminates kidney infection; her symptoms are classic for cystitis.

Diseases in Focus 26.2: Characteristics of the Most Common Types of Vaginitis and Vaginosis

Use the table below to identify the infection caused by the organism in the figure, epithelial cells from a vaginal swab. The epithelial cells have small rods over the surface. These are clue cells, diagnostic for bacterial (*Gardnerella*) vaginosis.

Diseases in Focus 26.3: Microbial Diseases of the Reproductive System

A 26-year-old woman had abdominal pain, painful urination, and a fever. Cultures grown in a high-CO$_2$ environment revealed gram-negative diplococci. Absence of a focal sore eliminates warts, herpes, chancroid, and syphilis. Swollen lymph nodes usually accompany LGV. Fever and abdominal pain indicate a systemic infection, and the gram-negative diplococci are Neisseria gonorrhoeae. The patient has pelvic inflammatory disease.

Review

1.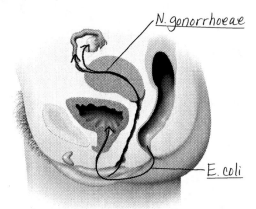

2. Urinary tract infections may be transmitted by improper personal hygiene and contamination during medical procedures. They are often caused by opportunistic pathogens.

3. The proximity of the anus to the urethra and the relatively short length of the urethra can allow contamination of the urinary bladder in females. Predisposing factors for cystitis in females are gastrointestinal infections and vaginal and urinary tract infections.

4. *Escherichia coli* causes about 75% of the cases. From lower urinary tract or systemic infections.

5.

Disease	Symptoms	Diagnosis
Gardnerella	Fishy odor	Odor, pH, clue cells
Gonorrhea	Painful urination	Isolation of *Neisseria*
Syphilis	Chancre	FTA–ABS
PID	Abdominal pain	Culture of pathogen
NGU	Urethritis	Absence of *Neisseria*
LGV	Lesion, lymph node enlargement	Observation of *Chlamydia* in cells
Chancroid	Swollen ulcer	Isolation of *Haemophilus*

6. Transmission—Water; enters via wounds.

    Activities—Water contact; contact with animals or rodent-infested places.

    Etiology—*Leptospira interrogans.*

7. Symptoms: Burning sensation, vesicles, painful urination.

    Etiology: Herpes simplex type 2 (sometimes type 1). When the lesions are not present, the virus is latent and noncommunicable.

8. *Candida albicans:* Severe itching; thick, yellow, cheesy discharge.

    Trichomonas vaginalis: Profuse yellow discharge with disagreeable odor.

9.

Disease	Prevention of Congenital Disease
Gonorrhea	Treatment of newborn's eyes
Syphilis	Prevention and treatment of mother's disease
NGU	Treatment of newborn's eyes
Genital herpes	Cesarean delivery during active infection

Critical Thinking

1. *T. pallidum pertenue* can survive on skin in the tropics because of the constant warm temperature and high humidity. In temperate regions, this type of infection (yaws) might not survive because of cooler, drier air. *T. pallidum pertenue* that successfully invades the body encounters warmth and moisture. Sexual contact is a method of transmission that provides constant protection for the microorganisms.

2. Eliminates normal microbiota. Changes (increases) pH.

3. Nystatin will inhibit yeast without affecting bacteria. Chocolate agar and increased CO_2 provide enriched conditions but are not selective.

4.

Aerobic	*Leptospira*
Anaerobic	*Treponema*
Coccus	*Neisseria*
Requires X factor	*Haemophilus*
Gram-positive wall	*Gardnerella*
Parasite	*Chlamydia*
Urease-positive	*Ureaplasma*
Urease-negative	*Mycoplasma*
Fungus	*Candida*
Protozoan	*Trichomonas*
No organism	Herpes simplex

Clinical Applications

1. Her disease appears to be meningitis; however, the gram-negative cocci in the cervical culture indicate this is disseminated gonococcal infection. The *N. gonorrhoeae* was sexually transmitted.

2. Pathogen: *Neisseria gonorrhoeae.*

   Treatment: Cefoxitin.

   The isolates all had the same antibiotic sensitivities.

3. The diagnosis of syphilis was made on November 8. Both the woman and the infant began syphilis therapy that day. Information on the baby's father was obtained in retrospect from a correctional facility. His condition was not diagnosed or treated until after his wife was diagnosed and interviewed for contacts.

   Darkfield examination of the lesion and STS were not done on June 6 or July 1. Copies of the positive RPR results should have been forwarded to the local STI control office to ensure treatment and epidemiologic case management. The regular laboratory clerk was on leave at the time, and her replacement inadvertently forwarded all copies of the laboratory reports to the hospital. Thus, the STI Control Program was unaware that the serologic results were reactive. The hospital's Infection Control Nurse, who was responsible for reviewing STS results, also was away on leave; both patients' results were filed without being brought to the attention of their attending physicians.

CASE STUDY: AN EPIDEMIC

Background

A pregnant 18-year-old woman came to the Ford County urgent-care clinic with a low-grade fever, malaise, and headache. She was sent home with a diagnosis of influenza. She again sought treatment 7 days later with a macular rash on her trunk, arms, hands, and feet. Further questioning of the patient when serology results were known revealed that 1 month previously, she had a painless ulcer on her vagina that healed spontaneously.

The same day, patient 2 sought medical treatment for a penile ulcer.

In a routine examination, patient 3, a pregnant woman, had positive serologic tests for this disease but was asymptomatic.

Patient 4 was tested because of her sexual contact with patient 2. She had no symptoms and a positive serologic test.

Patient 5, a contact of patients 3 and 6, was also serologically positive. He frequently traveled to a neighboring county, which reported a 290% increase in this disease over the preceding year.

Patient 6, a woman, had a rash and also tested positive. Patients 1 and 2 were in drug-abuse rehabilitation; these two were the only two who reported use of crack cocaine.

Questions

1. What bacterial diseases can cause rashes?

2. What serologic tests are used to diagnose these infections?

3. What is the disease? How did six residents of Ford County get this disease?

4. What are the consequences of not treating this infection?

The Solution

1. *Rickettsia rickettsii* (spotted fever), *Salmonella typhi, Borrelia burgdorferi, Staphylococcus aureus* (toxic shock syndrome), *Streptococcus pyogenes* (scarlet fever), and *Treponema pallidum.*

2. VDRL, rapid plasma reagin, and FTA-ABS for syphilis; agglutination tests for Lyme disease, *S. pyogenes*, and spotted fever. *S. aureus* is usually diagnosed from cultures (gram-positive, coagulase positive).

3. Syphilis. Patient 5 apparently brought the disease to Ford County and gave it to patients 3 and 6 during sexual intercourse; they could have given it to the others.

4. Tertiary syphilis may develop in the adults; the fetus can contract congenital syphilis.

27 Environmental Microbiology

LEARNING OBJECTIVES	CHECK YOUR UNDERSTANDING
27-1 Define *extremophile*, and identify two "extreme" habitats.	Can you identify two extreme habitats for extremophile organisms?
27-2 Define *symbiosis*.	What is the definition of *symbiosis*?
27-3 Define *mycorrhiza*, differentiate endomycorrhizae from ectomycorrhizae, and give an example of each.	Is a truffle an example of an endomycorrhiza or an ectomycorrhiza?
27-4 Define *biogeochemical cycle*.	What biogeochemical cycle is much publicized as contributing to global warming?
27-5 Outline the carbon cycle, and explain the roles of microorganisms in this cycle.	What is the main source of the carbon in the cellulose forming the mass of a forest?
27-6 Outline the nitrogen cycle, and explain the roles of microorganisms in this cycle.	What is the common name for the group of microbes that oxidize soil nitrogen into a form that is mobile in soil and likely to be used as nutrition by plants?
27-7 Define a*mmonification, nitrification, denitrification,* and *nitrogen fixation*.	Bacteria of the genus *Pseudomonas*, in the absence of oxygen, will use fully oxidized nitrogen as an electron acceptor, a process in the nitrogen cycle that is given what name?
27-8 Outline the sulfur cycle, and explain the roles of microorganisms in this cycle.	Certain nonphotosynthetic bacteria accumulated granules of sulfur within the cell; were the bacteria using hydrogen sulfide or sulfates as an energy source?
27-9 Describe how the ecological community can exist without light energy.	What chemical usually serves as an energy source for organisms that survive in darkness?
27-10 Compare and contrast the carbon cycle and the phosphorus cycle.	Why does phosphorus tend to accumulate in the seas?
27-11 Give two examples of the use of bacteria to remove pollutants.	Why are petroleum products naturally resistant to metabolism by most bacteria?
27-12 Define *bioremediation*.	What is the definition of the term *bioremediation*?
27-13 Describe the freshwater and seawater habitats of microorganisms.	Purple and green sulfur bacteria are photosynthetic organisms, but they are generally found deep in freshwater rather than at the surface. Why?
27-14 Explain how wastewater pollution is a public health problem and an ecological problem.	Which disease is more likely to be transmitted by polluted water, cholera or influenza?

27-15 Discuss the causes and effects of eutrophication.	Name a microorganism that will grow in water even if there is no source of organic matter for energy or a nitrogen source—but does require small inputs of phosphorus.
27-16 Explain how water is tested for bacteriological quality.	Coliforms are the most common bacterial indicator of health-threatening water pollution in the United States. Why is it usually necessary to specify the term *fecal coliform*?
27-17 Describe how pathogens are removed from drinking water.	How do flocculants such as alum remove colloidal impurities, including microorganisms, from water?
27-18 Compare primary, secondary, and tertiary sewage treatment.	Which type of sewage treatment is designed to remove almost all phosphorus from sewage?
27-19 List some of the biochemical activities that take place in an anaerobic sludge digester.	What metabolic group of anaerobic bacteria is especially encouraged by operation of a sludge digestion system?
27-20 Define *biochemical oxygen demand (BOD), activated sludge system, trickling filter, septic tank,* and *oxidation pond.*	What is the relationship between BOD and the welfare of fish?

NEW IN THIS EDITION

- Revised and updated discussion of biodegradable plastics

CHAPTER SUMMARY

Microbial Diversity and Habitats (p. 767)

1. Microorganisms live in a wide variety of habitats because of their metabolic diversity and their ability to use a variety of carbon and energy sources and to grow under different physical conditions.
2. Extremophiles live in extreme conditions of temperature, acidity, alkalinity, or salinity.

Symbiosis (p. 767)

3. Symbiosis is a relationship between two different organisms or populations.
4. Symbiotic fungi called mycorrhizae live in and on plant roots; they increase the surface area and nutrient absorption of the plant.

Soil Microbiology and Biogeochemical Cycles (pp. 768–776)

1. In biogeochemical cycles, certain chemical elements are recycled.
2. Microorganisms in the soil decompose organic matter and transform carbon-, nitrogen-, and sulfur-containing compounds into usable forms.
3. Microbes are essential to the continuation of biogeochemical cycles.
4. Elements are oxidized and reduced by microorganisms during these cycles.

The Carbon Cycle (pp. 768–770)

5. Carbon dioxide is incorporated, or fixed, into organic compounds by photoautotrophs and chemoautotrophs.
6. These organic compounds provide nutrients for chemoheterotrophs.

7. Chemoheterotrophs release CO_2 that is then used by photoautotrophs.

8. Carbon is removed from the cycle when it is in $CaCO_3$ and fossil fuels.

The Nitrogen Cycle (pp. 770–772)

9. Microorganisms decompose proteins from dead cells and release amino acids.

10. Ammonia is liberated by microbial ammonification of the amino acids.

11. The nitrogen in ammonia is oxidized to produce nitrates for energy by nitrifying bacteria.

12. Denitrifying bacteria reduce the nitrogen in nitrates to molecular nitrogen (N_2).

13. N_2 is converted into ammonia by nitrogen-fixing bacteria.

14. Nitrogen-fixing bacteria include free-living genera such as *Azotobacter*, cyanobacteria, and the symbiotic bacteria *Rhizobium* and *Frankia*.

15. Ammonium and nitrate are used by bacteria and plants to synthesize amino acids that are assembled into proteins.

The Sulfur Cycle (pp. 772–773)

16. Hydrogen sulfide (H_2S) is used by autotrophic bacteria; the sulfur is oxidized to form S^0 or SO_4^{2-}.

17. Plants and other microorganisms can reduce SO_4^{2-} to make certain amino acids. These amino acids are in turn used by animals.

18. H_2S is released by decay or dissimilation of these amino acids.

Life without Sunshine (pp. 773–774)

19. Chemoautotrophs are the primary producers in deep-sea vents and within deep rocks.

The Phosphorus Cycle (p. 774)

20. Phosphorus (as PO_4^{3-}) is found in rocks and bird guano.

21. When solubilized by microbial acids, the PO_4^{3-} is available for plants and microorganisms.

22. Endolithic bacteria live in solid rock; these autotrophic bacteria use hydrogen as an energy source.

The Degradation of Synthetic Chemicals in Soil and Water (pp. 775–776)

23. Many synthetic chemicals, such as pesticides, are resistant to degradation by microbes.

24. The use of microorganisms to remove pollutants is called bioremediation.

25. The growth of oil-degrading bacteria can be enhanced by the addition of nitrogen and phosphorus fertilizer.

26. Municipal landfills prevent decomposition of solid wastes because they are dry and anaerobic.

27. In some landfills, methane produced by methanogens can be recovered for an energy source.

28. Composting can be used to promote biodegradation of organic matter.

Aquatic Microbiology and Sewage Treatment (pp. 776–789)

Aquatic Microorganisms (pp. 776–778)

1. The study of microorganisms and their activities in natural waters is called aquatic microbiology.

2. Natural waters include lakes, ponds, streams, rivers, estuaries, and the oceans.

3. The concentration of bacteria in water is proportional to the amount of organic material in the water.

4. Most aquatic bacteria tend to grow on surfaces rather than in a free-floating state.

5. The number and location of freshwater microbiota depend on the availability of oxygen and light.

6. Photosynthetic algae are the primary producers of a lake; they are found in the limnetic zone.

7. Pseudomonads, *Cytophaga, Caulobacter,* and *Hyphomicrobium* are found in the limnetic zone, where oxygen is abundant.

8. Microbes in stagnant water use available oxygen and can cause odors and the death of fish.

9. Wave action increases the amount of dissolved oxygen.

10. Purple and green sulfur bacteria are found in the profundal zone, which contains light and H_2S but no oxygen.

11. *Desulfovibrio* reduces SO_4^{2-} to H_2S in benthic mud.

12. Methane-producing bacteria are also found in the benthic zone.

13. Phytoplankton are the primary producers of the open ocean.

14. *Pelagibacter ubique* is a decomposer in ocean waters.

15. Archaea predominate below 100 m.

16. Some algae and bacteria are bioluminescent. They possess the enzyme luciferase, which can emit light.

The Role of Microorganisms in Water Quality (pp. 778–782)

17. Microorganisms are filtered from water that percolates into groundwater supplies.

18. Some pathogenic microorganisms are transmitted to humans in drinking and recreational waters.

19. Resistant chemical pollutants may be concentrated in animals in an aquatic food chain.

20. Mercury is metabolized by certain bacteria into a soluble compound that is concentrated in animals.

21. Nutrients such as phosphates cause algal blooms, which can lead to eutrophication of aquatic ecosystems.

22. Eutrophication is the result of the addition of pollutants or natural nutrients.

23. *Thiobacillus ferrooxidans* produces sulfuric acid at coal-mining sites.

24. Tests for the bacteriological quality of water are based on the presence of indicator organisms, the most common of which are coliforms.

25. Coliforms are aerobic or facultatively anaerobic, gram-negative, non–endospore-forming rods that ferment lactose with the production of acid and gas within 48 hours of being placed in a medium at 35°C.

26. Fecal coliforms, predominantly *E. coli,* are used to indicate the presence of human feces.

Water Treatment (p. 782)

27. Drinking water is held in a holding reservoir long enough that suspended matter settles.

28. Flocculation treatment uses a chemical such as alum to coalesce and then settle colloidal material.

29. Filtration removes protozoan cysts and other microorganisms.

30. Drinking water is disinfected with chlorine to kill remaining pathogenic bacteria.

Sewage (Wastewater) Treatment (pp. 783–789)

31. Domestic wastewater is called sewage; it includes household water, toilet wastes, and rainwater.

32. Primary sewage treatment is the removal of solid matter called sludge.

33. Biological activity is not very important in primary treatment.

34. Biochemical oxygen demand (BOD) is a measure of the biologically degradable organic matter in water.

35. Primary treatment removes about 25–35% of the BOD of sewage.

36. BOD is determined by measuring the amount of oxygen bacteria require to degrade the organic matter.

37. Secondary sewage treatment is the biological degradation of organic matter after primary treatment.

38. Activated sludge systems, trickling filters, and rotating biological contactors are methods of secondary treatment.

39. Microorganisms degrade the organic matter aerobically.

40. Secondary treatment removes up to 95% of the BOD.

41. Treated sewage is disinfected, usually by chlorination, before discharge onto land or into water.

42. Sludge is placed in an anaerobic sludge digester; bacteria degrade organic matter and produce simpler organic compounds, methane, and CO_2.

43. The methane produced in the digester is used to heat the digester and operate other equipment.

44. Excess sludge is periodically removed from the digester, dried, and disposed of (as landfill or soil conditioner) or incinerated.

45. Septic tanks can be used in rural areas to provide primary treatment of sewage.

46. Small communities can use oxidation ponds for secondary treatment.

47. These require a large area in which to build an artificial lake.

48. Tertiary sewage treatment uses physical filtration and chemical precipitation to remove all the BOD, nitrogen, and phosphorus from water.

49. Tertiary treatment provides drinkable water, whereas secondary treatment provides water usable only for irrigation.

THE LOOP

Bioremediation, "Bacterial Banqueters Attend Oil Spill"   p. 33
Symbiosis   pp. 107, 307, 401–403

ANSWERS

Review

1. The koala should have an organ housing a large population of cellulose-degrading microorganisms.

2. *Penicillium* might make penicillin to reduce competition from faster-growing bacteria.

3. a. Amino acids   b. SO_4^{2-} c. plants and bacteria   d. H_2S e. carbohydrates   f. S^0

4. Phosphorus must be available for all organisms.

5.

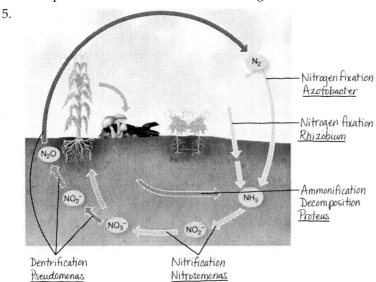

6. Cyanobacteria: With fungi, cyanobacteria act as the photoautotrophic partner in a lichen; they may also fix nitrogen in the lichen. With *Azolla*, they fix nitrogen.

   Mycorrhizae: Fungi that grow in and on the roots of higher plants; increase absorption of nutrients.

   Rhizobium: In root nodules of legumes; fix nitrogen.

   Frankia: In root nodules of alders, roses, and other plants; fix nitrogen.

7. Settling; flocculation treatment; sand filtration (or activated charcoal filtration); chlorination; the amount of treatment prior to chlorination depends on the amount of inorganic and organic matter in the water.

8. a. 2   b. 1   c. 2   d. 2   e. 3   f. 2   g. 3

9. Biodegradation of sewage, herbicides, oil, or PCBs.

Critical Thinking

1. The straight chain is readily degraded by beta oxidation (refer to "Lipid Catabolism," pp. 136–137).

2.

	BOD	**Rate of Eutrophication**	**Dissolved Oxygen**
Untreated	3+	3+	+
Primary	2+	2+	2+
Secondary	+	+	3+

   Accumulation of BOD and loss of dissolved oxygen would be much less in a fast-moving river. Continual aeration caused by the river's movement would result in rapid oxidation of organic matter.

Clinical Applications

1. Sewage infiltrated the municipal water supply via a pipe that was damaged by the flooding. Flow through the damaged pipe must be stopped; drinking water must be hyperchlorinated; infected individuals must be treated. A fecal coliform count of the water would show the contamination and indicate when the problem was remedied.

2. Nitrates, phosphates, oxygen, or water may not be present in sufficient amounts for bacterial growth. The naturally occurring bacteria may be able to degrade the hydrocarbons.

CASE STUDY: AN EPIDEMIC OF FOOD POISONING

Background

An outbreak of food poisoning occurred the last week of June, affecting two-thirds of the 1700 persons who attended a dinner in Port Allen, Louisiana. A questionnaire to obtain information concerning the illness was administered to 122 persons. Of this sample, 82 (67.2%) reported illness. Physicians treated 32 patients (26.2%); 9 (7.4%) required hospitalization.

Laboratory analysis yielded positive cultures of the etiological agents from the leftover shrimp, potatoes, corn, and hogshead cheese, and from 7 of 15 stool samples from patients. The person who collected the food stored all of it in one container.

Potatoes were purchased from a farmer. They had been stored in a root cellar and were transported loose in a pickup truck. The morning of the dinner, the potatoes were washed, peeled, and boiled until tender. The pots were covered with aluminum foil and transported unrefrigerated 50 miles to the dinner.

Corn was purchased from a produce market. The night before the dinner, the corn was shucked and kept in the wooden boxes in which it had been purchased. The day of the dinner, the corn was boiled. For transport, it was wrapped in aluminum foil.

Hogshead cheese was purchased the morning of the dinner along with the salt meat. The headcheese and salt meat were kept refrigerated by the delicatessen. After purchase, they were stored unrefrigerated until dinner. (Read labels in the deli section of your grocery store to ascertain the ingredients in headcheese.)

Raw shrimp was purchased at one location and shipped to a second location in standard wooden seafood boxes. It was boiled on the morning of the dinner and placed back into the boxes. After being covered with aluminum foil, it was transported 40 miles in an unrefrigerated truck to the dinner. An inspection of the wholesale seafood establishment was undertaken 6 days later. The investigation revealed that the shrimp had been boiled in 300-1b. batches in the following manner: A batch was placed in a container until the water came to a rolling boil; then the gas was turned off, and the shrimp kept in the hot water for 15 minutes.

Questions

1. On one page, identify the etiologic agent of this outbreak of food poisoning.
2. Was it food infection or intoxication?
3. How did the food get contaminated, and which item was contaminated?
4. Briefly explain how you arrived at your conclusions. Why did you eliminate the other major causes of food poisoning?

Data

Case	Age	Sex	Symptoms								Foods Eaten							Onset		Duration (Days)
			D	C	W	N	C	H	F	V	1	2	3	4	5	6	7	Day	Hour	
1	13	F	+	+	+	+	+	+	+	+	+	+	+	+	+	+	+	S	11p	1
2	21	F	+	+	+	+	+	+	+	+		+				+	+	M	12n	4
3	64	F	+	+	+	+	+		+		+	+	+	+	+	+	+	M	1p	3
4	32	M	+	+	+	+	+	+	+	+	+	+	+	+			+	M	5p	2
5	41	F	+	+	+	+	+	+		+	+	+	+		+		+	T	8a	4
6	42	M	+	+	+	+	+	+	+	+	+	+	+	+			+	M	8a	6
7	30	M	+	+	+	+				+		+	+			+	+	S	12m	7
8	50	M				+						+	+		+	+	+	W	8a	
9	55	M	+	+	+	+		+	+		+	+	+		+		+	S	11p	1
10	60	F	+							+	+	+	+	+	+		+	T	7p	3
11	61	M	+		+		+	+	+		+	+	+	+			+	M	12n	4
12	19	M	+	+			+	+	+		+	+				+	+	S	10p	4
13	22	F										+	+		+	+	+			
14	70	F	+	+	+			+	+	+	+	+	+	+	+		+	M	1p	6
15	69	F	+	+	+			+	+	+	+	+	+	+	+		+	M	9a	6
16	68	M	+	+	+		+					+	+	+	+	+	+	M	12n	5
17	34	F	+	+	+		+				+	+			+		+	M	1p	5
18	40	F			+	+	+					+	+		+	+	+	M	pm	7
19	41	F	+	+	+	+	+	+	+		+	+		+	+	+	+	S	pm	5
20	59	M										+			+	+	+			

Case	Age	Sex	Symptoms								Foods Eaten							Onset		Duration (Days)
			D	C	W	N	C	H	F	V	1	2	3	4	5	6	7	Day	Hour	
21	78	M	+	+	+	+	+	+	+		+			+		+	+	T	am	5
22	73	F	+	+	+		+				+		+	+			+	M	3p	4
23	46	F	+	+	+		+				+		+		+			M	4a	3
24	57	M	+	+	+						+	+	+	+	+		+	M	9a	2
25	34	M	+	+	+	+					+		+			+	+	M	9p	8
26	72	M	+	+	+						+		+	+		+		T	1a	8+
27	32	M	+	+	+	+	+	+	+	+	+		+				+	T	am	7
28	61	F	+	+	+	+	+	+	+	+	+		+		+			S	12m	1
29	36	F	+	+	+	+	+	+	+	+	+		+	+		+		M	1a	2
30	59	M	+	+	+	+	+	+	+		+		+		+		+	M	pm	2
31	74	M	+	+	+	+	+	+	+		+		+		+		+	M	10a	4
32	50	M										+	+	+		+	+			
33	54	M	+	+		+						+	+		+	+	+	M	am	5
34	?	M	+	+	+	+					+		+	+		+		T	am	6
35	39	M	+	+	+	+					+	+	+		+		+	S	pm	8
36	40	M	+	+	+	+		+			+		+	+		+		M	10a	1
37	78	F	+	+	+	+						+	+	+	+		+	M	9a	8
38	57	F	+		+	+						+	+	+		+	+	M	8a	7
39	14	M	+		+	+						+	+		+	+	+	M	pm	4
40	15	M		+	+	+						+	+		+	+		M	10a	2
41	60	F	+	+	+	+	+	+	+		+		+	+		+	+	M	11a	4
42	63	M	+	+	+	+	+	+	+		+		+		+	+		S	11p	5
43	81	F	+	+	+	+	+	+	+		+		+	+	+	+	+	T	11a	6
44	57	F	+	+	+	+	+	+	+		+		+			+	+	T	12n	7
45	32	M	+	+	+	+	+	+	+		+		+	+				M	12n	6
46	?	F	+	+	+	+	+	+	+		+			+	+	+	+	M	8a	7
47	20	F	+	+	+	+	+	+	+		+			+	+		+	M	9a	2
48	25	M	+	+	+	+						+				+		S	10p	2
49	32	F	+	+	+	+					+	+		+		+	+	S	12n	3

Case	Age	Sex	Symptoms								Foods Eaten							Onset		Duration (Days)
			D	C	W	N	C	H	F	V	1	2	3	4	5	6	7	Day	Hour	
50	38	M	+	+	+	+					+	+			+	+		M	10a	4
51	40	F	+	+	+	+					+	+	+	+		+	+	M	12n	5
52	45	M	+	+	+	+					+		+		+		+	T	12n	5
53	18	F	+	+	+	+					+		+	+		+	+	M	12n	3
54	10	M	+	+	+	+	+	+	+		+		+	+	+	+	+	M	11a	2
55	20	F	+	+	+	+	+	+	+		+		+	+				T	1a	2
56	60	F	+	+	+	+	+	+	+		+		+		+	+	+	M	11a	3
57	63	M	+	+	+	+						+			+	+	+	T	11a	4
58	57	M	+	+	+							+		+		+		S	pm	4
59	46	F										+		+	+		+			
60	45	M	+	+	+							+		+		+	+	M	am	3
61	60	M	+	+	+		+	+	+		+	+		+	+	+	+	M	8a	1
62	14	M	+	+	+						+	+	+		+	+	+	M	6p	5
63	39	M	+	+	+								+	+	+	+	+	M	5a	3
64	48	M	+	+	+						+	+	+		+	+	+	T	1a	2
65	33	F	+	+	+	+	+	+	+	+	+	+	+	+		+	+	T	11p	3
66	50	F	+	+	+						+	+	+		+	+		M	3p	7
67	17	F	+	+	+	+	+	+	+	+	+	+	+	+	+		+	M	2a	3
68	59	M	+	+	+	+	+	+	+	+	+		+		+		+	M	11a	5
69	46	F	+	+	+	+	+	+	+	+	+		+	+		+	+	S	10p	6
70	34	F	+	+	+						+		+	+	+		+	T	3a	1
71	35	M	+	+	+						+		+		+		+	T	4a	2
72	50	F	+	+	+								+	+		+	+	M	9a	8
73	56	M	+	+	+	+					+		+			+		M	9p	8
74	45	M	+	+	+	+					+		+		+		+	M	1a	5
75	?	F	+	+	+	+	+	+	+	+	+		+					T	2a	7
76	63	M	+	+	+	+	+	+	+	+	+				+	+	+	S	12m	3
77	54	F	+	+	+								+	+	+		+	S	11p	4
78	35	F	+	+	+	+	+	+	+		+		+		+		+	M	12n	4

Case	Age	Sex	Symptoms								Foods Eaten							Onset		Duration (Days)
			D	C	W	N	C	H	F	V	1	2	3	4	5	6	7	Day	Hour	
79	38	M	+	+	+	+	+	+	+		+			+			+	M	4a	5
80	33	M											+	+		+				
81	32	F									+	+		+		+				
82	47	F	+	+	+	+	+	+	+		+		+	+		+	+	M	4a	7
83	49	M						+			+		+		+		+	S	9p	
84	38	F	+	+	+	+	+	+	+		+		+	+			+	M	3p	1
85	42	F	+	+	+	+	+	+	+		+	+			+		+	M	5a	5
86	45	M	+	+	+	+	+	+	+		+			+			+	M	2a	5
87	49	M	+	+	+	+	+	+	+		+			+	+	+		T	3a	6
88	71	F	+	+	+	+	+	+	+	+	+				+	+	+	M	10a	3
89	75	F	+	+	+	+	+	+	+		+				+		+	M	2p	8
90	39	M	+	+	+	+	+	+	+		+			+			+	S	11p	2
91	70	F	+	+	+										+	+	+	M	5a	4
92	48	F	+	+	+	+	+	+	+		+			+		+	+	M	6p	6
93	21	F	+	+		+					+	+		+	+		+	M	2a	5
94	24	F	+			+					+	+	+	+	+	+	+	M	11p	7
95	25	M	+		+	+					+			+				M	9a	5
96	40	M	+	+	+	+	+	+			+	+		+			+	M	8a	2
97	36	F		+	+	+	+					+					+	T	2a	4
98	58	M	+	+	+						+	+	+	+	+	+	+	S	10p	1
99	?	F	+	+	+	+	+	+	+		+	+		+		+	+	T	1a	7
100	41	F	+	+	+	+	+	+	+		+	+	+	+			+	M	3p	5
101	55	F	+	+	+	+	+	+	+		+	+	+		+		+	S	9p	3
102	42	M	+	+	+	+	+	+	+		+	+	+			+	+	T	2p	4
103	27	M	+	+	+	+	+	+	+		+		+	+		+		M	3a	3
104	25	F	+	+	+	+	+	+	+		+			+			+	M	11a	6
105	20	M											+		+	+	+			
106	18	F									+		+	+		+				
107	43	M	+	+	+	+							+		+		+	M	2a	5

Case	Age	Sex	Symptoms								Foods Eaten							Onset		Duration (Days)
			D	C	W	N	C	H	F	V	1	2	3	4	5	6	7	Day	Hour	
108	33	F	+	+							+		+		+	+	+	M	5p	6
109	65	M									+		+			+				
110	14	F	+	+	+	+	+	+	+		+	+				+	+	M	6a	1
111	13	M	+	+	+	+						+			+	+		M	3p	7
112	50	F	+	+	+	+	+	+	+		+	+	+	+		+	+	S	1p	7
113	?	F	+	+	+	+						+		+			+	M	2a	5
114	12	F	+	+	+	+	+	+	+		+			+		+	+	T	3a	4
115	18	M	+	+	+	+						+	+	+				S	10p	6
116	70	M	+	+	+	+	+	+	+	+	+			+		+		T	1a	3
117	33	M	+	+	+	+						+		+	+			M	11p	2
118	60	F	+	+	+	+	+				+	+	+			+	+	M	6a	5
119	50	M	+	+	+	+	+				+			+			+	T	2a	5
120	48	F	+	+	+	+	+		+		+				+	+	+	M	3p	7
121	13	F	+	+	+	+	+									+		M	4a	4
122	19	F	+	+	+	+	+		+		+	+		+		+	+	S	10p	6

Legend: Symptoms: D = Diarrhea, C = Cramps, W = Weakness, N = Nausea, C = Chills, H = Headache, F = Fever, V = Vomiting.

       Foods Eaten: 1-Boiled shrimp, 2-Headcheese, 3-Boiled potatoes, 4-Boiled corn, 5-Boiled salt meat, 6-Bread and butter, 7-Watermelon.

Dinner was at 6 PM Sunday.

Hints

1. Make a summary table of the persons not ill.
2. Make a table of the onset of symptoms following the dinner.

The Solution

1. *Vibrio parahaemolyticus.*
2. Infection.
3. The shrimp became contaminated while feeding in polluted coastal waters.
4. Students should find a correlation between eating the shrimp and illness. Unrefrigerated transport of the shrimp allowed bacterial growth, and low-temperature cooking did not kill the bacteria.

28

Applied and Industrial Microbiology

LEARNING OBJECTIVES

28-1 Describe thermophilic anaerobic spoilage and flat sour spoilage by mesophilic bacteria.

28-2 Compare and contrast food preservation by industrial food canning, aseptic packaging, radiation, and high pressure.

28-3 Name four beneficial activities of microorganisms.

28-4 Define *industrial fermentation* and *bioreactor*.

28-5 Differentiate primary from secondary metabolites.

28-6 Describe the role of microorganisms in the production of industrial chemicals and pharmaceuticals.

28-7 Define *bioconversion*, and list its advantages.

28-8 List biofuels that can be made by microorganisms.

CHECK YOUR UNDERSTANDING

Is botulism a greater danger in spoilage of canned goods under thermophilic or under mesophilic conditions?

Canned foods are usually in metal cans. What sorts of containers are used for aseptically packaged foods?

Roquefort and blue cheeses are characterized by blue-green clumps. What are these?

Are bioreactors designed to operate aerobically or anaerobically?

Penicillin is produced in its greatest quantities after the trophophase of fermentation. Does that make it a primary or secondary metabolite?

At one time, citric acid was extracted on an industrial scale from lemons and other citrus fruits. What organism is used to produce it today?

Landfills are the site of a major form of bioconversion—what is the product?

How can microbes provide fuels for cars and electricity?

NEW IN THIS EDITION

- An expanded discussion of biofuels

CHAPTER SUMMARY

Food Microbiology (pp. 794–800)

1. The earliest methods of preserving foods were drying, the addition of salt or sugar, and fermentation.

Foods and Disease (p. 794)

2. Food safety is monitored by the FDA and USDA and also by use of the HACCP system.

Industrial Food Canning (pp. 794–795)

3. Commercial sterilization of food is accomplished by steam under pressure in a retort.

4. Commercial sterilization heats canned foods to the minimum temperature necessary to destroy *Clostridium botulinum* endospores while minimizing alteration of the food.

5. The commercial sterilization process uses sufficient heat to reduce a population of *C. botulinum* by 12 logarithmic cycles (12D treatment).

6. Endospores of thermophiles can survive commercial sterilization.

7. Canned foods stored above 45°C can be spoiled by thermophilic anaerobes.

8. Thermophilic anaerobic spoilage is sometimes accompanied by gas production; if no gas is formed, the spoilage is called flat sour spoilage.

9. Spoilage by mesophilic bacteria is usually from improper heating procedures or leakage.

10. Acidic foods can be preserved by heat of 100°C because microorganisms that survive are not capable of growth in a low pH.

11. *Byssochlamys, Aspergillus,* and *Bacillus coagulans* are acid-tolerant and heat-resistant microbes that can spoil acidic foods.

Aseptic Packaging (pp. 795–796)

12. Presterilized materials are assembled into packages and aseptically filled with heat-sterilized liquid foods.

Radiation and Industrial Food Preservation (pp. 796–797)

13. Gamma and X-ray radiation can be used to sterilize food, kill insects and parasitic worms, and prevent the sprouting of fruits and vegetables.

High-Pressure Food Preservation (p. 797)

14. Pressurized water is used to kill bacteria in fruit and meat.

The Role of Microorganisms in Food Production (pp. 797–800)

Cheese (pp. 798–799)

15. The milk protein casein curdles because of the action by lactic acid bacteria or the enzyme rennin.

16. Cheese is the curd separated from the liquid portion of milk, called whey.

17. Hard cheeses are produced by lactic acid bacteria growing in the interior of the curd.

18. The growth of microbes in cheese is called ripening.

19. Semisoft cheeses are ripened by bacteria growing on the surface; soft cheeses are ripened by *Penicillium* growing on the surface.

Other Dairy Products (p. 799)

20. Old-fashioned buttermilk was produced by lactic acid bacteria growing during the butter-making process.

21. Commercial buttermilk is made by letting lactic acid bacteria grow in skim milk for 12 hours.

22. Sour cream, yogurt, kefir, and kumiss are produced by lactobacilli, streptococci, or yeasts growing in low-fat milk.

Nondairy Fermentations (pp. 799–800)

23. Sugars in bread dough are fermented by yeast to ethanol and CO_2; the CO_2 causes the bread to rise.

24. Sauerkraut, pickles, olives, soy sauce, and even cocoa and coffee, are products of microbial fermentations.

Alcoholic Beverages and Vinegar (p. 800)

25. Carbohydrates obtained from grains, potatoes, or molasses are fermented by yeasts to produce ethanol in the production of beer, ale, sake, and distilled spirits.

26. The sugars in fruits such as grapes are fermented by yeasts to produce wines.

27. In winemaking, lactic acid bacteria convert malic acid into lactic acid in malolactic fermentation.
28. *Acetobacter* and *Gluconobacter* oxidize ethanol in wine to acetic acid (vinegar).

Industrial Microbiology (pp. 800–808)

1. Microorganisms produce alcohols and acetone that are used in industrial processes.
2. Industrial microbiology has been revolutionized by the ability of genetically modified cells to make many new products.
3. Biotechnology is a way of making commercial products by using living organisms.

Fermentation Technology (pp. 801–804)

4. The growth of cells on a large scale is called industrial fermentation.
5. Industrial fermentation is carried on in bioreactors, which control aeration, pH, and temperature.
6. Primary metabolites such as ethanol are formed as the cells grow (during the trophophase).
7. Secondary metabolites such as penicillin are produced during the stationary phase (idiophase).
8. Mutant strains that produce a desired product can be selected.

Immobilized Enzymes and Microorganisms (pp. 803–804)

9. Enzymes or whole cells can be bound to solid spheres or fibers. When substrate passes over the surface, enzymatic reactions change the substrate to the desired product.
10. They are used to make paper, textiles, and leather and are environmentally safe.

Industrial Products (pp. 804–806)

11. Most amino acids used in foods and medicine are produced by bacteria.
12. Microbial production of amino acids can be used to produce L-isomers; chemical production results in both D- and L-isomers.
13. Lysine and glutamic acid are produced by *Corynebacterium glutamicum*.
14. Citric acid, used in foods, is produced by *Aspergillus niger*.
15. Enzymes used in manufacturing foods, medicines, and other goods are produced by microbes.
16. Some vitamins used as food supplements are made by microorganisms.
17. Vaccines, antibiotics, and steroids are products of microbial growth.
18. The metabolic activities of *Thiobacillus ferrooxidans* can be used to recover uranium and copper ores.
19. Yeasts are grown for wine- and breadmaking; other microbes (*Rhizobium, Bradyrhizobium,* and *Bacillus thuringiensis*) are grown for agricultural use.

Alternative Energy Sources Using Microorganisms (pp. 806–807)

20. Organic waste, called biomass, can be converted by microorganisms into the alternative fuel methane, a process called bioconversion.
21. Fuels produced by microbial fermentation are methane, ethanol, and hydrogen.

Biofuels (pp. 807–808)

22. Biofuels include alcohols and hydrogen (from microbial fermentation) and oils (from algae).

Industrial Microbiology and the Future (p. 808)

23. Recombinant DNA technology will continue to enhance the ability of industrial microbiology to produce medicines and other useful products.

THE LOOP

The topics in Chapter 28 can be studied along with general principles discussed in earlier chapters. These topics are cross-referenced to the principles in *Microbiology: An Introduction*.

ANSWERS

Review

1. Industrial microbiology is the science of using microorganisms to produce products or accomplish a process. Industrial microbiology provides (1) chemicals such as antibiotics that would not otherwise be available, (2) processes to remove or detoxify pollutants, (3) fermented foods that have desirable flavors or enhanced shelf life, and (4) enzymes for manufacturing a variety of goods.

2. The goal of commercial sterilization is to eliminate spoilage and disease-causing organisms. The goal of hospital sterilization is complete sterilization.

3. The acid in the berries will prevent the growth of some microbes.

4. Milk $\xrightarrow{\text{Lactic acid bacteria}}$ Curd + Whey
   $\qquad\qquad\qquad\qquad\quad\downarrow\qquad\downarrow$
   $\qquad\qquad\qquad\qquad$ Cheese   Waste

   Hard cheese is ripened by lactic acid bacteria growing anaerobically in the interior of the curd. Soft cheese is ripened by molds growing aerobically on the outside of the curd.

5. Nutrients must be dissolved in water; water is also needed for hydrolysis. Malt is the carbon and energy source that the yeast will ferment to make alcohol. Malt contains glucose and maltose from the action of amylases on starch in seeds (barley).

6. A bioreactor provides the following advantages over simple flask containers:
   - Larger culture volumes can be grown.
   - Process instrumentation for monitoring and controlling critical environmental conditions such as pH, temperature, dissolved oxygen, and aeration can be used.
   - Sterilization and cleaning systems are designed in place.
   - Aseptic sampling and harvest systems for in-process sampling exist.
   - Improved aeration and mixing characteristics result in improved cell growth and high final cell densities.
   - A high degree of automation is possible.
   - Process reproducibility is improved.

7. (1) Enzymes don't produce hazardous wastes. (2) Enzymes work under reasonable conditions; e.g., they don't require high temperatures or acidity. (3) Enzymes eliminate the need to use petroleum in chemical syntheses of solvents such as alcohol and acetone. (4) Enzymes are biodegradable. (5) Enzymes are not toxic.

8. The production of ethanol from corn; or methane from sewage. Alcohols and hydrogen are produced by fermentation; methane is produced by anaerobic respiration.

9. A primary metabolite is produced during trophophase; a secondary metabolite, during idiophase.

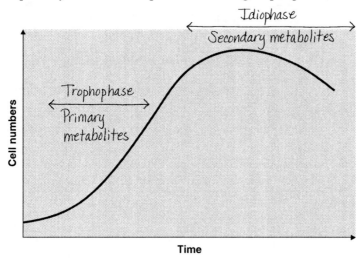

Critical Thinking

1. Lactic acid bacteria. Lactic acid bacteria are found in milk and are responsible for fermenting it. Lactic acid bacteria, likewise, could contaminate any food made with milk and cause fermentation (e.g., sourdough bread). Some lactic acid bacteria are found on plants and are responsible for their fermentation (e.g., sauerkraut and the malolactic fermentation of wine).

2. See page 148. Amination of α-ketoglutaric acid will make glutamic acid.

3. Cellulases hydrolyze the fibers to soften the fabric. The cellulases are extracted from the fungus, *Trichoderma*. See page 3.

Clinical Applications

1. a. New medium added will neutralize pH. Some old medium must flow out as new medium is added, so some acid will leave.
    b. During stationary phase
    c. During log phase

2. The *E. coli* grew well in the cider at room temperature (25°C). Refrigeration and sorbate both slowed the growth but did not completely stop it or kill the bacteria. None of these treatments is sufficient to prevent transmission of *E. coli* by cider.

3. Production is best after logarithmic growth stops; lipids and oxygen are necessary. It is a secondary metabolite.

CASE STUDY: MAKING A PRODUCT

Background

You have isolated a bacterium that produces a bacteriocin against *Salmonella*. The bacterium grows well in Medium 1 but doesn't produce its bacteriocin. Testing one component at a time, you determine that iron interferes with bacteriocin production. When you try Medium 1 without iron, the bacteria don't grow. Bacteriocin production is best in Medium 2.

Medium 1		Medium 2	
Glucose	0.5%	Glycerol	3.5%
Citric acid	0.1%	Glucose	0.5%
20 amino acids, each	0.04%	Citric acid	0.1%
K_2HPO_4	0.15%	20 amino acids, each	0.04%
$MgSO_4$	0.12%	K_2HPO_4	0.15%
$FeSO_4$	$1.52 \times 10^{-5}\%$	$MgSO_4$	0.12%

Data

Medium	Generation time (min)	Bacteriocin (mg/1)
1	27	0.02
2	300	0.20

Questions

1. Design a procedure to maximize the biomass (total cells) and the yield of the bacteriocin.
2. What are bacteriocins?
3. How might a bacteriocin against *Salmonella* be used?

The Solution

1. Use a two-stage production. Grow the cells in Medium 1 until stationary phase, and then transfer them to Medium 2 to maximize bacteriocin production.
2. Bacteriocins are toxins produced by bacteria that kill other bacteria.
3. Bacteriocins against *Salmonella* could be useful in food production or storage to prevent *Salmonella* infections.

Answers to Multiple-Choice Questions

Chapter 1	Chapter 2	Chapter 3	Chapter 4	Chapter 5	Chapter 6	Chapter 7
1. a	1. c	1. e	1. e	1. a	1. c	1. d
2. c	2. b	2. d	2. d	2. d	2. a	2. b
3. d	3. b	3. b	3. b	3. b	3. c	3. d
4. c	4. e	4. a	4. a	4. c	4. a	4. d
5. b	5. b	5. a	5. d	5. c	5. c	5. b
6. e	6. c	6. e	6. e	6. b	6. d	6. b
7. c	7. a	7. d	7. b	7. b	7. e	7. b
8. a	8. a	8. b	8. e	8. a	8. c	8. a
9. c	9. b	9. a	9. a	9. c	9. b	9. a
10. a	10. c	10. c	10. b	10. b	10. b	10. b

Chapter 8	Chapter 9	Chapter 10	Chapter 11	Chapter 12	Chapter 13	Chapter 14
1. c	1. b	1. b	1. d	1. c	1. e	1. a
2. d	2. b	2. e	2. b	2. b	2. c	2. b
3. c	3. b	3. d	3. e	3. b	3. b	3. a
4. d	4. b	4. b	4. a	4. a	4. c	4. d
5. c	5. c	5. e	5. b	5. d	5. b	5. a
6. b	6. d	6. a	6. c	6. b	6. e	6. b
7. a	7. c	7. a	7. e	7. a	7. c	7. c
8. c	8. b	8. e	8. b	8. c	8. d	8. a
9. d	9. e	9. a	9. b	9. a	9. d	9. c
10. a	10. a	10. b	10. a	10. d	10. c	10. d

Chapter 15	Chapter 16	Chapter 17	Chapter 18	Chapter 19	Chapter 20	Chapter 21
1. e	1. a	1. d	1. c	1. b	1. b	1. c
2. c	2. d	2. e	2. d	2. b	2. a	2. d
3. d	3. c	3. b	3. b	3. b	3. a	3. b
4. d	4. d	4. c	4. a	4. a	4. b	4. c
5. c	5. b	5. d	5. a	5. d	5. a	5. d
6. a	6. a	6. e	6. b	6. e	6. d	6. d
7. b	7. c	7. c	7. c	7. a	7. e	7. e
8. a	8. b	8. d	8. a	8. d	8. b	8. d
9. d	9. d	9. c	9. b	9. c	9. c	9. a
10. c	10. e	10. d	10. c	10. b	10. d	10. d

Chapter 22	Chapter 23	Chapter 24	Chapter 25	Chapter 26	Chapter 27	Chapter 28
1. a	1. e	1. a	1. d	1. b	1. a	1. c
2. c	2. b	2. c	2. e	2. e	2. b	2. b
3. a	3. d	3. e	3. e	3. a	3. b	3. e
4. b	4. c	4. a	4. c	4. c	4. b	4. c
5. a	5. a	5. c	5. e	5. d	5. c	5. b
6. c	6. e	6. b	6. b	6. c	6. c	6. c
7. b	7. a	7. a	7. b	7. c	7. b	7. e
8. a	8. c	8. e	8. e	8. e	8. b	8. a
9. c	9. c	9. b	9. a	9. b	9. e	9. b
10. a	10. c	10. d	10. d	10. a	10. c	10. a

Test Bank

There are 45 objective questions for each chapter. Below each question are the answer and degree of difficulty. Degrees of difficulty are categorized as follows:

Recall	Requires memorization
Analysis	Requires selecting an answer from similar-appearing choices
Understanding	Requires interpretation of newly learned material

The questions are taken from material presented in *Microbiology: An Introduction,* Tenth Edition. You may want to add your own questions on additional material covered in class. The tests can be photocopied and used directly from this guide. However, note that the answers appear below each question. The following are suggested ways to use the chapter tests:

1. Use 10 to 15 questions as a chapter test or weekly quiz, and incorporate other questions into the midterm or final examination.

2. Or, prepare alternative post-tests in a class designed for mastery learning.

Tests are learning instruments, and these questions were designed to provide accurate information for the students. Test questions that ask the students to identify the *incorrect* item provide more factual information than questions incorporating only one correct answer. Asking a student to identify an incorrect item is more apt to encourage critical thinking. A series of matching items also requires that the student have more information at hand than a single list.

Objective questions that ask the student to identify the incorrect statement can replace some essay questions. The student must analyze information just as in an essay, but these questions are more easily and objectively scored.

Suggested essay questions are provided for each chapter. These questions require the students to assimilate and organize their newly acquired information. Essay questions follow the objective questions for each chapter.

Test Bank Contents

Chapter 1 The Microbial World and You

Objective Questions

1) Which of the following pairs is mismatched?
    A) Ehrlich — chemotherapy
    B) Koch — aseptic surgery
    C) Pasteur — proof of biogenesis
    D) Jenner — vaccination

    Answer: B
    Skill: Recall

2) Which of the following is a scientific name?
    A) IGAS
    B) Flesh-eating bacteria
    C) Group A streptococcus
    D) *Streptococcus pyogenes*
    E) Streptococci

    Answer: D
    Skill: Analysis

3) Which of the following is *NOT* a domain in the three-domain system?
    A) Animalia
    B) Archaea
    C) Bacteria
    D) Eukarya

    Answer: A
    Skill: Recall

4) Which of the following statements about fungi is true?
    A) All are prokaryotic.
    B) All are multicellular.
    C) All require organic material for growth.
    D) All grow using sunlight and carbon dioxide.
    E) All are plants.

    Answer: C
    Skill: Recall

5) Which of the following statements about protozoa is false?
    A) They have rigid cell walls.
    B) They are classified by their method of locomotion.
    C) All are unicellular.
    D) All have complex cells.
    E) All are eukaryotic.

    Answer: A
    Skill: Recall

6) Which of the following statements about viruses is false?
    A) They lack cells.
    B) They cannot metabolize nutrients.
    C) They cannot reproduce themselves.
    D) They have both DNA and RNA.
    E) They are parasites.

Answer: D
Skill: Recall

7) Regarding the experiments that "proved" spontaneous generation, which of the following statements is probably true?
    A) Air was lacking.
    B) Too much heat was applied.
    C) The food source could not support life.
    D) Microorganisms were already present.
    E) Excess carbon dioxide was present.

Answer: D
Skill: Analysis

8) Regarding Pasteur's experiments with the S–neck flask, which of the following statements is true?
    A) There was air involved.
    B) There was a food source involved.
    C) Any possibility of contamination was removed.
    D) All microorganisms were killed before beginning.
    E) All of the above.

Answer: E
Skill: Understanding

9) Which of the following statements about insect control by microorganisms is true?
    A) The insects develop resistance to the microorganisms.
    B) The microorganisms are permanent in the environment.
    C) The microorganisms are specific for the insect pest.
    D) The microorganisms may cause disease in other animals.
    E) This technique is just as dangerous as the use of chemical pesticides.

Answer: C
Skill: Analysis

10) Which of the following pairs is mismatched?
    A) Hooke — cell theory
    B) Jenner — vaccines
    C) van Leeuwenhoek — germ theory
    D) Lister — aseptic surgery
    E) Pasteur — fermentation

Answer: C
Skill: Recall

11) Who disproved the theory of spontaneous generation?
   A) Hooke
   B) Koch
   C) van Leeuwenhoek
   D) Pasteur
   E) Virchow

Answer: D
Skill: Recall

12) Who observed cells in plant material?
   A) Hooke
   B) Koch
   C) van Leeuwenhoek
   D) Lister
   E) Pasteur

Answer: A
Skill: Recall

13) Who was the first to observe microorganisms with a microscope?
   A) Hooke
   B) Koch
   C) van Leeuwenhoek
   D) Pasteur
   E) Weizmann

Answer: C
Skill: Recall

14) Who proved that microorganisms cause disease?
   A) Fleming
   B) Koch
   C) van Leeuwenhoek
   D) Pasteur
   E) Semmelweis

Answer: B
Skill: Recall

15) Which of the following is a scientific name?
   A) *Mycobacterium leprae*
   B) Hansen's bacillus
   C) Leprosy bacterium
   D) Acid–fast bacteria

Answer: A
Skill: Recall

16) Classification of organisms in the three domains is based on
   A) Cell wall.
   B) Number of cells.
   C) Type of cell.
   D) Nutritional type.
   E) Nucleus.

Answer: C
Skill: Recall

17) Which of the following statements is false?
   A) All bacteria lack nuclear membranes.
   B) All fungi are multicellular.
   C) All protozoa are unicellular.
   D) All viruses are parasites.
   E) All fungi have nuclear membranes.

Answer: B
Skill: Analysis

18) Which of the following statements is true?
   A) Viruses cannot reproduce outside a host cell.
   B) Bacteria cannot move.
   C) Fungi are plants.
   D) Protozoa have rigid cell walls.
   E) Algae are parasites.

Answer: A
Skill: Recall

19) Which of the following findings was essential for Jenner's vaccination process?
   A) A weakened microorganism may produce immunity.
   B) A weakened microorganism will not cause disease.
   C) Someone who recovers from a disease will not acquire that disease again.
   D) Disease is caused by viruses.
   E) Vaccination provides immunity.

Answer: A
Skill: Analysis

20) Which of the following requirements was *NOT* necessary for Pasteur to disprove spontaneous generation?
   A) Providing a food source that would support growth
   B) Supplying air
   C) Keeping microorganisms out
   D) Removing microorganisms that were initially present
   E) Identifying bacteria

Answer: E
Skill: Analysis

21) Which of the following pairs is mismatched?
   A) Immunologist — studies ecology of *Legionella pneumophila*
   B) Virologist — studies human immunodeficiency virus
   C) Microbial ecologist — studies bacteria that degrade oil
   D) Microbial physiologist — studies fermentation of sourdough bread
   E) Molecular biologist — studies recombinant DNA

Answer: A
Skill: Analysis

22) Which of the following pairs is mismatched?
   A) Chemotherapy — treatment of disease
   B) Pathogen — disease causing
   C) Vaccine — a preparation of microorganisms
   D) Penicillin — antibiotic
   E) Normal microbiota — harmful

Answer: E
Skill: Recall

23) Which one of the following does *NOT* belong with the others?
   A) Archaea
   B) Bacteria
   C) Eukarya
   D) Fungi

Answer: D
Skill: Understanding

24) Which of the following is *NOT* an example of biotechnology?
   A) Bacterial production of French bread
   B) Bacterial degradation of a dead animal
   C) Bacterial production of yogurt
   D) Bacterial production of vinegar
   E) Bacterial production of human insulin

Answer: B
Skill: Analysis

25) Which of the following *CANNOT* be made by using recombinant DNA technology?
   A) Vaccines
   B) Human hormones
   C) Pharmaceutical drugs
   D) Life
   E) Pest-resistant crops

Answer: D
Skill: Understanding

26) Which of the following is the best definition of *biotechnology*?
    A) The development of recombinant DNA technology
    B) The use of living organisms to make desired products
    C) The curing of diseases
    D) The use of microorganisms in sewage treatment
    E) Bacterial production of foods

Answer: B
Skill: Analysis

27) You are observing a cell through a microscope and note that it has no apparent nucleus. You conclude that it most likely
    A) Has a peptidoglycan cell wall.
    B) Has a cellulose cell wall.
    C) Moves by pseudopods.
    D) Is part of a multicellular animal.
    E) Is a plant cell.

Answer: A
Skill: Analysis

28) A nucleated, green cell that moves by means of flagella is a(n)
    A) Alga.
    B) Bacterium.
    C) Fungus.
    D) Helminth.
    E) Virus.

Answer: A
Skill: Recall

29) An agent that reproduces in cells but is *NOT* composed of cells and contains RNA as its genetic material is a(n)
    A) Alga.
    B) Bacterium.
    C) Fungus.
    D) Helminth.
    E) Virus.

Answer: E
Skill: Recall

30) A multicellular organism that has chitin cell walls and absorbs organic material is a(n)
    A) Alga.
    B) Bacterium.
    C) Fungus.
    D) Helminth.
    E) Virus.

Answer: C
Skill: Recall

31) A multicellular organism that has a mouth and lives in an animal host is a(n)
    A) Alga.
    B) Bacterium.
    C) Fungus.
    D) Helminth.
    E) Virus.

Answer: D
Skill: Recall

32) In the name *Escherichia coli, coli* is the
    A) Domain.
    B) Kingdom.
    C) Genus.
    D) Specific epithet.
    E) Discoverer.

Answer: D
Skill: Analysis

33) Which of the following pairs is mismatched?
    A) Lancefield — immunology
    B) Weizmann — virology
    C) Jenner — immunology
    D) Jacob and Monod — microbial genetics
    E) Winogradsky — microbial ecology

Answer: B
Skill: Recall

34) You are looking at a white cottony growth on a culture medium. Microscopic examination reveals it is multicellular. Which of the following conclusions about this organism is false?
    A) It has cell walls.
    B) It has DNA enclosed in a nucleus.
    C) It is eukaryotic.
    D) It is a bacterium.
    E) It absorbs organic nutrients.

Answer: D
Skill: Analysis

35) Which of the following groups include members that lack DNA?
    A) Bacteria
    B) Fungi
    C) Helminths
    D) Protozoa
    E) Viruses

Answer: E
Skill: Recall

36) Which one of the following does *NOT* belong with the others?
   A) Cellulose
   B) Chitin
   C) Nucleus
   D) Peptidoglycan
   Answer: C
   Skill: Understanding

37) Which of the following organisms lack cell walls?
   A) Animalia
   B) Bacteria
   C) Fungi
   D) Plantae
   Answer: A
   Skill: Recall

38) Which of the following does *NOT* belong with the others?
   A) Animalia
   B) Fungi
   C) Helminthes
   D) Plantae
   E) Protista
   Answer: E
   Skill: Understanding

39) Fungi differ from bacteria in that fungi
   A) Have cell walls.
   B) Have DNA.
   C) Have a nucleus.
   D) Spoil food.
   E) Are cellular.
   Answer: C
   Skill: Analysis

40) Archaea differ from bacteria in that archaea
   A) Lack peptidoglycan.
   B) Lack nuclei.
   C) Use organic compounds for food.
   D) Reproduce by binary fission.
   E) Are prokaryotic.
   Answer: A
   Skill: Analysis

41) Bacteria differ from viruses in that bacteria
   A) Have DNA and RNA.
   B) Are composed of cells.
   C) Can live without a host.
   D) All of the above.
   Answer: D
   Skill: Analysis

42) Which of the following lack a nucleus?
    A) Animalia
    B) Bacteria
    C) Fungi
    D) Protozoa
    E) None of the above

Answer: B
Skill: Recall

43) Regular use of antibacterial cleaning products
    A) Prevents occurrence of infections.
    B) Is necessary for good health.
    C) Promotes survival of bacteria that are resistant.
    D) Prevents bacteria from growing.
    E) A, B, and D

Answer: C
Skill: Recall

44) Which of the following statements about biofilms is false?
    A) Compared to free–living bacteria, biofilms are more sensitive to antibiotics.
    B) Biofilms in pipes block the flow of water.
    C) Biofilms in your body protect mucous membranes from harmful microbes.
    D) Biofilms on medical implants cause infections.
    E) Biofilms on rocks provide food for animals.

Answer: A
Skill: Recall

45) Which of the following processes in making blue jeans is incorrectly matched?
    A) Blue dye — *E. coli* indigo
    B) Cotton — fungal hyphae
    C) Debleaching — bacterial enzyme
    D) Plastic — bacterial PHA
    E) Stone–washed — fungal enzyme

Answer: B
Skill: Recall

Essay Questions

1) In 1835 Bassi showed that a fungus caused a silkworm disease, and in 1865 Pasteur discovered that a protozoan caused another silkworm disease. Why do we use Koch's postulates instead of "Bassi's" or "Pasteur's" postulates?

2) List two examples of biotechnology that involve recombinant DNA technology and two examples that do not.

3) Paul Berg received the Nobel Prize for developing the procedure for incorporating fragments of animal DNA into bacteria. List some reasons why his work was a major contribution to science.

Chapter 2   Chemical Principles

Objective Questions

1) Which of the following statements about the atom $^{12}_{6}C$ is false?

   A) It has 6 protons in its nucleus.
   B) It has 12 neutrons in its nucleus.
   C) It has 6 electrons orbiting the nucleus.
   D) Its atomic number is 6.
   E) Its atomic weight is 12.

   Answer: B
   Skill: Understanding

Table 2.1

$$^{16}_{8}O \quad ^{12}_{6}C \quad ^{1}_{1}H$$

2) Using the information in Table 2.1, calculate the molecular weight of ethanol, C_2H_5OH.

   A) 96
   B) 46
   C) 34
   D) 33
   E) Can't tell

   Answer: B
   Skill: Analysis

3) Antacids neutralize acid by the following reaction. Identify the salt.
   $Mg(OH)_2 + 2HCl \rightarrow MgCl_2 + H_2O$

   A) $Mg(OH)_2$
   B) HCl
   C) $MgCl_2$
   D) H_2O
   E) None of the above

   Answer: C
   Skill: Analysis

4) Which of the following statements is false?
   A) Salts readily dissolve in water.
   B) Water molecules are formed by hydrolysis.
   C) Water freezes from the top down.
   D) Water is a part of a dehydration reaction.
   E) Water is a polar molecule.

   Answer: B
   Skill: Recall

5) Which of the following is the type of bond holding K^+ and I^- ions in KI?
    A) Ionic bond
    B) Covalent bond
    C) Hydrogen bond

Answer: A
Skill: Analysis

6) Which of the following is the type of bond between molecules of water in a beaker of water?
    A) Ionic bond
    B) Covalent bond
    C) Hydrogen bond

Answer: C
Skill: Analysis

7) What is the type of bond holding hydrogen and oxygen atoms in the H_2O molecule?
    A) Ionic bond
    B) Covalent bond
    C) Hydrogen bond

Answer: B
Skill: Analysis

8) Identify the following reaction: Glucose + Fructose → Sucrose + Water
    A) Dehydration synthesis reaction
    B) Hydrolysis reaction
    C) Exchange reaction
    D) Reversible reaction
    E) Ionic reaction

Answer: A
Skill: Analysis

9) Identify the following reaction: Lactose + H_2O → Glucose + Galactose
    A) Dehydration synthesis reaction
    B) Hydrolysis reaction
    C) Exchange reaction
    D) Reversible reaction
    E) Ionic reaction

Answer: B
Skill: Analysis

10) Identify the following reaction: HCl + $NaHCO_3$ → NaCl + H_2CO_3
    A) Dehydration synthesis reaction
    B) Hydrolysis reaction
    C) Exchange reaction
    D) Reversible reaction
    E) Ionic reaction

Answer: C
Skill: Analysis

11) Identify the following reaction: $NH_4OH \rightleftharpoons NH_3 + H_2O$
  A) Dehydration synthesis reaction
  B) Hydrolysis reaction
  C) Exchange reaction
  D) Reversible reaction
  E) Ionic reaction

Answer: D
Skill: Analysis

12) Which type of molecule contains the alcohol glycerol?
  A) Carbohydrate
  B) Lipid
  C) Nucleic acid
  D) Protein

Answer: B
Skill: Recall

13) Which type of molecule is composed of (CH_2O) units?
  A) Carbohydrate
  B) Lipid
  C) Nucleic acid
  D) Protein

Answer: A
Skill: Recall

14) Which type of molecule contains $-NH_2$ groups?
  A) Carbohydrate
  B) Lipid
  C) Nucleic acid
  D) Protein

Answer: D
Skill: Recall

15) Which type of molecule *NEVER* contains a phosphate group?
  A) Carbohydrate
  B) Lipid
  C) Nucleic acid
  D) Protein

Answer: A
Skill: Recall

16) Which of the following statements about the atom $^{16}_{8}O$ is false?

  A) It has 8 protons in its nucleus.
  B) It has 8 electrons in its nucleus.
  C) It has 8 neutrons in its nucleus.
  D) Its atomic number is 8.
  E) Its atomic weight is 16.

Answer: B
Skill: Understanding

Table 2.1

$$\begin{matrix} 16 \\ 8 \end{matrix} O \qquad \begin{matrix} 12 \\ 6 \end{matrix} C \qquad \begin{matrix} 1 \\ 1 \end{matrix} H$$

17) Using the information in Table 2.1, calculate the number of moles in 92 grams of ethanol, C_2H_5OH.

    A) 1
    B) 2
    C) 3
    D) 4
    E) Can't tell

Answer: B
Skill: Analysis

18) The following chemical reaction is used to remove chlorine from water. What type of reaction is it?

$HClO + Na_2SO_3 \rightarrow Na_2SO_4 + HCl$

    A) Dehydration synthesis reaction
    B) Hydrolysis synthesis reaction
    C) Exchange synthesis reaction
    D) Reversible synthesis reaction
    E) Ionic synthesis reaction

Answer: C
Skill: Analysis

19) Which of the following pairs is mismatched?

    A) $NaOH \rightleftharpoons Na^+ + OH^- -$ base
    B) $HF \rightleftharpoons H^+ + F^- -$ acid
    C) $MgSO_4 \rightleftharpoons Mg^{2+} + SO_4^{2-} -$ salt
    D) $KH_2PO_4 \rightleftharpoons K^+ + H_2PO_4^- -$ acid
    E) $H_2SO_4 \rightleftharpoons 2H^+ + SO_4^{2-} -$ acid

Answer: D
Skill: Analysis

Table 2.2
Refer to these reactions to answer the question below.

$$NaOH \rightleftharpoons Na^+ + OH^- - base$$
$$HF \rightleftharpoons H^+ + F^- - acid$$
$$MgSO_4 \rightleftharpoons Mg^{2+} + SO_4^{2-} - salt$$
$$KH_2PO_4 \rightleftharpoons K^+ H_2PO_4^- - acid$$
$$H_2SO_4 \rightleftharpoons 2H^+ + SO_4^{2-} - salt$$

20) Which of the following statements about the reactions in Table 2.2 is false?
    A) They are exchange reactions.
    B) They are ionization reactions.
    C) They occur when the reactants are dissolved in water.
    D) They are dissociation reactions.
    E) They are reversible reactions.

    Answer: A
    Skill: Understanding

21) What is the type of bond between the hydrogen of one molecule and the nitrogen of another molecule?
    A) Ionic bond
    B) Covalent bond
    C) Hydrogen bond
    D) Disulfide bond
    E) Hydrophobic bond

    Answer: C
    Skill: Recall

22) What is the type of bond between carbon, hydrogen, and oxygen atoms in organic molecules?
    A) Ionic bond
    B) Covalent bond
    C) Hydrogen bond

    Answer: B
    Skill: Recall

23) What is the type of bond between ions in salt?
    A) Ionic bond
    B) Covalent bond
    C) Hydrogen bond

    Answer: A
    Skill: Recall

24) Identify the following reaction: $H_2O + CO_2 \rightleftharpoons H_2CO_3$
    A) Dehydration synthesis reaction
    B) Hydrolysis reaction
    C) Exchange reaction
    D) Reversible reaction
    E) Covalent reaction
Answer: C
Skill: Analysis

25) Identify the following reaction: Glycine + Lysine $\rightarrow$ Dipeptide + H_2O
    A) Dehydration synthesis reaction
    B) Hydrolysis reaction
    C) Exchange reaction
    D) Reversible reaction
    E) Covalent reaction
Answer: E
Skill: Analysis

26) Identify the following reaction: Sucrose + H_2O $\rightarrow$ Glucose + Fructose
    A) Dehydration synthesis reaction
    B) Hydrolysis reaction
    C) Exchange reaction
    D) Reversible reaction
    E) Covalent reaction
Answer: B
Skill: Analysis

27) Structurally, ATP is most like which type of molecule?
    A) Carbohydrate
    B) Lipid
    C) Protein
    D) Nucleic acid
Answer: D
Skill: Recall

28) What do genes consist of?
    A) Carbohydrates
    B) Lipids
    C) Proteins
    D) Nucleic acids
Answer: D
Skill: Recall

29) Which molecule is composed of a chain of amino acids?
    A) Carbohydrate
    B) Lipid
    C) Protein
    D) Nucleic acid
Answer: C
Skill: Recall

30) Which are the primary molecules making up plasma membranes in cells?
    A) Carbohydrates
    B) Lipids
    C) Proteins
    D) Nucleic acids

Answer: B
Skill: Recall

31) The antimicrobial drug imidazole inhibits sterol synthesis. This would most likely interfere with
    A) Bacterial cell walls.
    B) Fungal cell walls.
    C) Eukaryotic plasma membranes.
    D) Prokaryotic plasma membranes.
    E) Genes.

Answer: C
Skill: Analysis

Figure 2.1

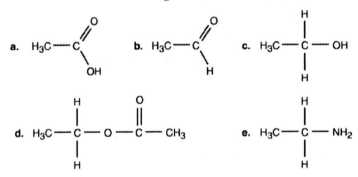

32) In Figure 2.1, which is an alcohol?
    A) a
    B) b
    C) c
    D) d
    E) e

Answer: C
Skill: Analysis

33) Which compound in Figure 2.1 is an ester?
    A) a
    B) b
    C) c
    D) d
    E) e

Answer: D
Skill: Analysis

34) Which compound in Figure 2.1 is an organic acid?
   A) a
   B) b
   C) c
   D) d
   E) e
Answer: A
Skill: Analysis

Figure 2.2

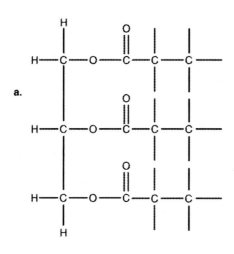

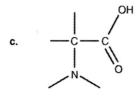

35) Use Figure 2.2 to answer the following question. Archaea differ from bacteria in the
   composition of the cell membrane lipids. Archaea have ether–bonded lipids, shown in part
   _____ of Figure 2.2, and bacteria have ester–bonded lipids, shown in part _____ of
   Figure 2.2.
   A) b; a
   B) b; c
   C) a; d
   D) c; d
   E) d; c
Answer: A
Skill: Analysis

Figure 2.3

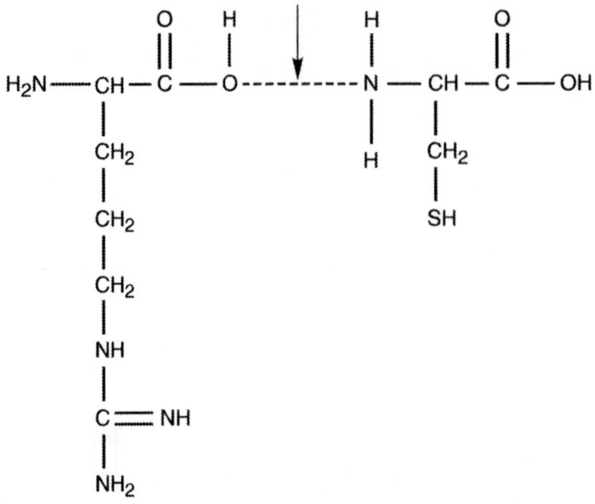

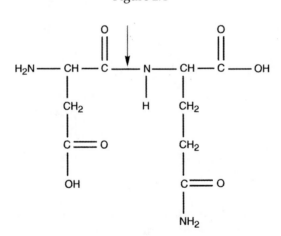

36) What kind of bond is at the arrow in Figure 2.3?
    A) Ionic bond
    B) Hydrogen bond
    C) Peptide bond
    D) Single covalent bond
    E) Double covalent bond

Answer: B
Skill: Analysis

Figure 2.4

37) What kind of bond is at the arrow in Figure 2.4?
    A) Disulfide bridge
    B) Double covalent bond
    C) Hydrogen bond
    D) Ionic bond
    E) Peptide bond

Answer: E
Skill: Analysis

38) An *E. coli* culture that has been growing at 37°C is moved to 25°C. Which of the following changes must be made in its plasma membrane?
    A) The number of phosphate groups must increase.
    B) The viscosity must increase.
    C) The number of saturated chains must increase.
    D) The number of unsaturated chains must increase.
    E) No changes are necessary.
Answer: D
Skill: Understanding

39) Assume *Saccharomyces cerevisiae* is grown in a nutrient medium containing the radioisotope ^{35}S. After a 48-hour incubation, the ^{35}S would most likely be found in the *S. cerevisiae*'s
    A) Carbohydrates.
    B) Nucleic acids.
    C) Water.
    D) Lipids.
    E) Proteins.
Answer: E
Skill: Understanding

40) Assume *Saccharomyces cerevisiae* is grown in a nutrient medium containing the radioisotope ^{32}P. After a 48-hour incubation, the ^{32}P would most likely be found in the *S. cerevisiae*'s
    A) Plasma membrane.
    B) Cell wall.
    C) Water.
    D) Proteins.
    E) Carbohydrates.
Answer: A
Skill: Understanding

41) Starch, dextran, glycogen, and cellulose are polymers of
    A) Amino acids.
    B) Glucose.
    C) Fatty acids.
    D) Nucleic acids.
    E) Acids.
Answer: B
Skill: Recall

42) Which of the following is a base?
    A) $C_2H_5OCOOH \rightarrow H^+ + C_2H_5OCOO^-$
    B) C_2H_5OH
    C) $NaOH \rightarrow Na^+ + OH^-$
    D) $H_2O \rightarrow H^+ + OH^-$
    E) H_2CO
Answer: C
Skill: Analysis

43) Two glucose molecules are combined to make a maltose molecule. What is the chemical formula for maltose?
  A) $C_3H_6O_3$
  B) $C_6H_{12}O_6$
  C) $C_{12}H_{24}O_{12}$
  D) $C_{12}H_{22}O_{11}$
  E) $C_{12}H_{23}O_{10}$

Answer: D
Skill: Analysis

44) *Desulfovibrio* bacteria can perform the following reaction: $S^{6-} \rightarrow S^{2-}$. These bacteria are
  A) Synthesizing sulfur.
  B) Reducing sulfur.
  C) Hydrolyzing sulfur.
  D) Oxidizing sulfur.

Answer: D
Skill: Understanding

45) Oil–degrading bacteria are naturally present in the environment but cannot degrade an oil spill fast enough to avoid ecological damage. How can the actions of these bacteria be sped up?
  A) Provide oil for them.
  B) Provide sugar as a carbon source.
  C) Provide nitrogen and phosphorus.
  D) Add water.
  E) Add NaCl.

Answer: C
Skill: Recall

Essay Questions

1) Describe how the properties of phospholipids make these molecules well suited for plasma membranes.

Figure 2.5

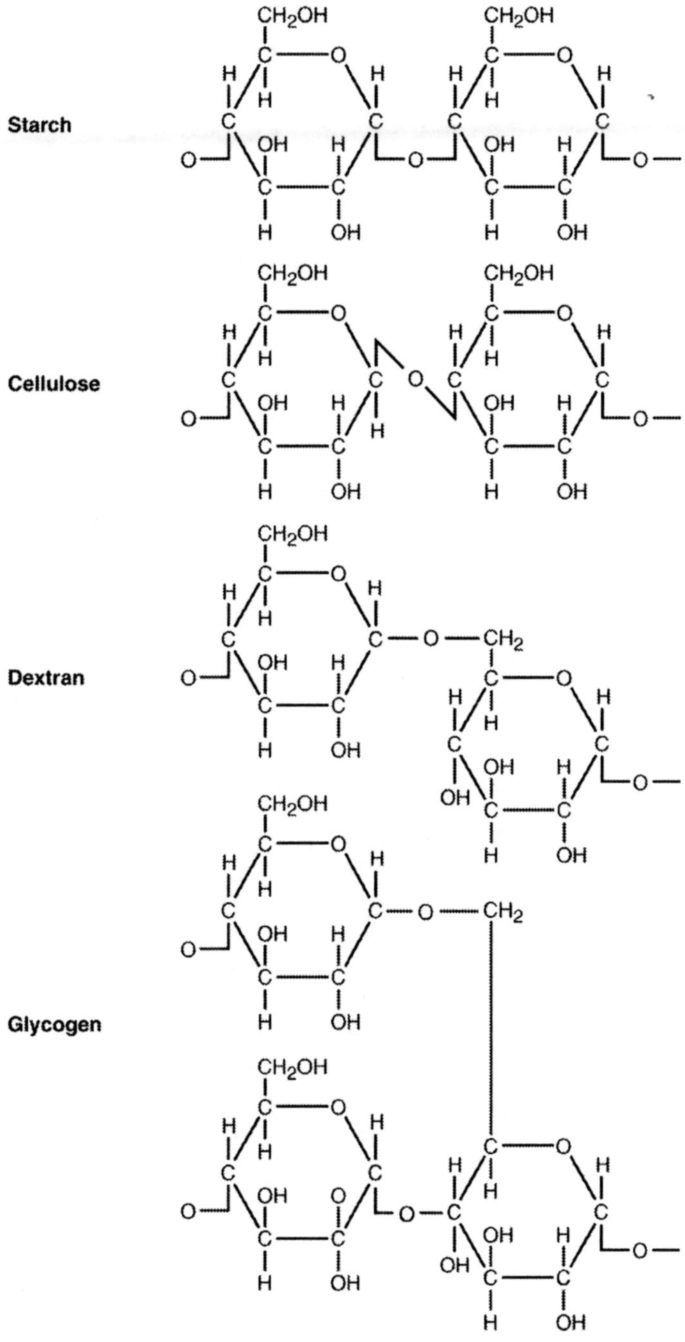

2) Use Figure 2.5 to answer the following question. Starch, cellulose, dextran, and glycogen are polysaccharides. How are they similar? To what are their different properties due? Why can't an enzyme that hydrolyzes starch degrade cellulose?

Chapter 3 Observing Microorganisms Through a Microscope

Objective Questions

1) Which of the following is *NOT* equal to 1 m?
   A) 10^6 μm
   B) 10^9 nm
   C) 10 dm
   D) 100 mm
   E) 0.001 km
   Answer: D
   Skill: Analysis

2) What structure does light pass through after leaving the condenser in a compound light microscope?
   A) Ocular lens
   B) Objective lens
   C) Specimen
   D) Illuminator
   Answer: C
   Skill: Analysis

3) Which of the following pairs is mismatched?
   A) Gram–negative bacteria — negative stain
   B) Iodine — mordant
   C) Alcohol–acetone — decolorizer
   D) Acid–alcohol — decolorizer
   E) Crystal violet — simple stain
   Answer: A
   Skill: Recall

4) Place the steps of the Gram stain in the correct order:
   1–Alcohol–acetone; 2–Crystal violet; 3–Safranin; 4–Iodine.
   A) 1–2–3–4
   B) 2–1–4–3
   C) 2–4–1–3
   D) 4–3–2–1
   E) 1–3–2–4
   Answer: C
   Skill: Recall

5) Which of the following pairs is mismatched?
   A) Alcohol–acetone — decolorizer
   B) Crystal violet — basic dye
   C) Safranin — acid dye
   D) Iodine — mordant
   E) Carbolfuchsin — basic dye

Answer: C
Skill: Recall

6) The counterstain in the acid–fast stain is
   A) A basic dye.
   B) An acid dye.
   C) A negative stain.
   D) A mordant.
   E) Necessary to determine acid–fast cells.

Answer: A
Skill: Recall

7) The purpose of a mordant in the Gram stain is
   A) To remove the simple stain.
   B) To make the bacterial cells larger.
   C) To make the flagella visible.
   D) To prevent the crystal violet from leaving the cells.
   E) To make gram–negative cells visible.

Answer: D
Skill: Recall

8) Place the following steps in the correct sequence:
   1–Staining; 2–Making a smear; 3–Fixing.
   A) 1–2–3
   B) 3–2–1
   C) 2–3–1
   D) 1–3–2
   E) The order doesn't matter

Answer: C
Skill: Recall

9) The best use of a negative stain is
   A) To determine cell size.
   B) To determine cell shape.
   C) To determine Gram reaction.
   D) To see endospores.
   E) A and B

Answer: E
Skill: Recall

10) Simple staining is often necessary to improve contrast in this microscope.
   A) Compound light microscope
   B) Phase–contrast microscope
   C) Darkfield microscope
   D) Fluorescence microscope
   E) Electron microscope

   Answer: A
   Skill: Recall

11) Which microscope is used to see internal structures of cells in a natural state?
   A) Compound light microscope
   B) Phase–contrast microscope
   C) Darkfield microscope
   D) Fluorescence microscope
   E) Electron microscope

   Answer: B
   Skill: Recall

12) Which of the following microscopes uses visible light?
   A) Confocal microscope
   B) DIC
   C) Fluorescence microscope
   D) Scanning acoustic microscope
   E) Scanning electron microscope

   Answer: B
   Skill: Analysis

13) Which microscope achieves the highest magnification and greatest resolution?
   A) Compound light microscope
   B) Phase–contrast microscope
   C) Darkfield microscope
   D) Fluorescence microscope
   E) Electron microscope

   Answer: E
   Skill: Recall

14) In this microscope, the observer does *NOT* look at an image through a lens.
   A) Compound light microscope
   B) Phase–contrast microscope
   C) Darkfield microscope
   D) Fluorescence microscope
   E) Electron microscope

   Answer: E
   Skill: Recall

15) This microscope produces an image of a light cell against a dark background; internal structures are *NOT* visible.
    A) Compound light microscope
    B) Phase–contrast microscope
    C) Darkfield microscope
    D) Fluorescence microscope
    E) Electron microscope
Answer: C
Skill: Recall

16) Which of the following is *NOT* correct?
    A) $1 \ \mu m = 10^{-6} \ m$
    B) $1 \ nm = 10^{-9} \ m$
    C) $1 \ \mu m = 10^{3} \ nm$
    D) $1 \ \mu m = 10^{-3} \ mm$
    E) $1 \ nm = 10^{-6} \ \mu m$
Answer: E
Skill: Analysis

17) The counterstain in the Gram stain is
    A) A negative stain.
    B) A mordant.
    C) A basic dye.
    D) An acid dye.
    E) Necessary to determine the Gram reaction.
Answer: C
Skill: Understanding

Figure 3.1

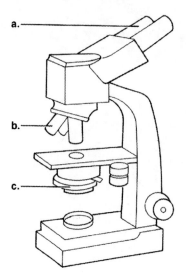

18) In Figure 3.1, line "a." points to the microscope's
    A) Illuminator.
    B) Condenser.
    C) Ocular lens.
    D) Objective lens.

   Answer: C
   Skill: Recall

19) In Figure 3.1, line "b." points to the microscope's
    A) Illuminator.
    B) Condenser.
    C) Ocular lens.
    D) Objective lens.

   Answer: D
   Skill: Recall

20) In Figure 3.1, line "c." points to the microscope's
    A) Illuminator.
    B) Condenser.
    C) Ocular lens.
    D) Objective lens.

   Answer: B
   Skill: Recall

21) Which microscope can be used to visualize DNA or botulinum toxin?
    A) Compound light microscope
    B) Phase–contrast microscope
    C) Scanning tunneling microscope
    D) Confocal microscope
    E) Scanning electron microscope

   Answer: C
   Skill: Recall

22) Which microscope is used to observe a specimen that emits light when illuminated with an ultraviolet light?
    A) Compound light microscope
    B) Phase–contrast microscope
    C) Darkfield microscope
    D) Fluorescence microscope
    E) Electron microscope

Answer: D
Skill: Recall

23) Which microscope is most useful for visualizing a biofilm?
    A) Compound light microscope
    B) Phase–contrast microscope
    C) Atomic force microscope
    D) Scanning acoustic microscope
    E) Transmission electron microscope

Answer: D
Skill: Recall

24) Which microscope takes advantage of differences in the refractive indexes of cell structures?
    A) Compound light microscope
    B) Phase–contrast microscope
    C) Darkfield microscope
    D) Fluorescence microscope
    E) Electron microscope

Answer: B
Skill: Recall

25) The appearance of gram–positive bacteria after addition of the first dye in the Gram stain.
    A) Purple
    B) Red
    C) Colorless
    D) Brown

Answer: A
Skill: Analysis

26) The appearance of gram–negative bacteria after addition of the mordant in the Gram stain.
    A) Purple
    B) Red
    C) Colorless
    D) Brown

Answer: A
Skill: Analysis

27) The appearance of gram–negative bacteria after addition of the decolorizing agent in the Gram stain.
   A) Purple
   B) Red
   C) Colorless
   D) Brown

   Answer: C
   Skill: Analysis

28) The appearance of gram–positive bacteria after adding the counterstain in the Gram stain.
   A) Purple
   B) Red
   C) Colorless
   D) Brown

   Answer: A
   Skill: Analysis

29) The appearance of gram–negative bacteria after completing the Gram stain.
   A) Purple
   B) Red
   C) Colorless
   D) Brown

   Answer: B
   Skill: Analysis

30) Which of the following pairs is mismatched?
   A) Confocal microscope – produces a three-dimensional image
   B) Darkfield microscope – uses visible light
   C) Fluorescence microscope – uses a fluorescent light
   D) Scanning electron microscope – produces a three-dimensional image
   E) Scanning tunneling microscope – allows visualization of atoms

   Answer: C
   Skill: Analysis

31) What is the total magnification of a chloroplast viewed with a 10x ocular lens and a 45x objective lens?
   A) 4.5x
   B) 10x
   C) 45x
   D) 100x
   E) 450x

   Answer: E
   Skill: Analysis

32) You suspect a 100-nm structure is present in a cell. Which of the following provides the lowest magnification that you can use to see this structure?
   A) Brightfield microscope
   B) Darkfield microscope
   C) Transmission electron microscope
   D) Phase-contrast microscope
   E) Scanning electron microscope

Answer: E
Skill: Analysis

33) Which microscope uses two beams of light to produce a three-dimensional, color image?
   A) Fluorescence microscope
   B) Phase-contrast microscope
   C) Darkfield microscope
   D) DIC microscope
   E) Electron microscope

Answer: D
Skill: Recall

34) Which microscope is used to see intracellular detail in a living cell?
   A) Fluorescence microscope
   B) Two-photon microscope
   C) Atomic force microscope
   D) Transmission electron microscope
   E) Brightfield microscope

Answer: B
Skill: Recall

35) In which microscope does the image look like a negative stain?
   A) Fluorescence microscope
   B) Phase-contrast microscope
   C) Darkfield microscope
   D) Two-photon microscope
   E) Scanning acoustic microscope

Answer: C
Skill: Recall

36) Which microscope is used to see detail of a 300-nm virus?
   A) Fluorescence microscope
   B) Phase-contrast microscope
   C) Darkfield microscope
   D) DIC microscope
   E) Electron microscope

Answer: E
Skill: Recall

37) Assume you stain *Bacillus* by applying malachite green with heat and then counterstaining with safranin. Through the microscope, the green structures are
   A) Cell walls.
   B) Capsules.
   C) Endospores.
   D) Flagella.
   E) Can't tell.

Answer: C
Skill: Analysis

38) Cells are differentiated after which step in the Gram stain?
   A) Safranin
   B) Alcohol-acetone
   C) Iodine
   D) Crystal violet

Answer: B
Skill: Understanding

39) You find colorless areas in cells in a Gram-stained smear. What should you do next?
   A) An acid-fast stain
   B) A flagella stain
   C) A capsule stain
   D) An endospore stain
   E) A simple stain

Answer: D
Skill: Analysis

40) What Gram reaction do you expect from acid-fast bacteria?
   A) Gram-positive
   B) Gram-negative
   C) Both gram-positive and gram-negative
   D) Can't tell

Answer: A
Skill: Analysis

41) Bacterial smears are fixed before staining to
   A) Kill the bacteria.
   B) Affix the cells to the slide.
   C) Make their walls permeable.
   D) A and B.
   E) Accept stain.

Answer: D
Skill: Recall

42) The resolution of a microscope can be improved by changing the
     A) Condenser.
     B) Fine adjustment.
     C) Wavelength of light.
     D) Diaphragm.
     E) Coarse adjustment.

Answer: C
Skill: Recall

43) Van Leeuwenhoek's microscope magnified up to 300x. This was a(n)
     A) Electron microscope.
     B) Phase–contrast microscope.
     C) Simple microscope.
     D) Confocal microscope.
     E) Compound microscope.

Answer: C
Skill: Recall

44) The purpose of the ocular lens is to
     A) Improve resolution.
     B) Magnify the image from the objective lens.
     C) Decrease the refractive index.
     D) Increase the light.
     E) Decrease the light.

Answer: B
Skill: Recall

45) The signal molecule produced in quorum sensing is
     A) A counterstain.
     B) An inducer.
     C) Light.
     D) A simple stain.
     E) An endospore.

Answer: B
Skill: Recall

Essay Questions

1) In 1877, Robert Koch thought preparing permanently stained slides would be valuable. Why was his assessment correct?

2) In 1884, Hans Christian Gram described a method of staining bacterial cells while not staining surrounding animal tissues. However, he thought that the staining method he developed was faulty because not all bacteria stained. In a letter to the editor of the journal in which Gram published his findings, write your response to Gram's concern.

Chapter 4 Functional Anatomy of Prokaryotic and Eukaryotic Cells

Objective Questions

1) Which of the following is *NOT* a distinguishing characteristic of prokaryotic cells?
   A) Their DNA is not enclosed within a membrane.
   B) They lack membrane–enclosed organelles.
   C) They have cell walls containing peptidoglycan.
   D) Their DNA is not associated with histones.
   E) They lack a plasma membrane.

   Answer: E
   Skill: Recall

2) Which of the following statements about a gram–positive cell wall is false?
   A) It maintains the shape of the cell.
   B) It is sensitive to lysozyme.
   C) It protects the cell in a hypertonic environment.
   D) It contains teichoic acids.
   E) It is sensitive to penicillin.

   Answer: C
   Skill: Analysis

3) Which of the following statements best describes what happens when a bacterial cell is placed in a solution containing 5% NaCl?
   A) Sucrose will move into the cell from a higher to a lower concentration.
   B) The cell will undergo osmotic lysis.
   C) Water will move out of the cell.
   D) Water will move into the cell.
   E) No change will result; the solution is isotonic.

   Answer: C
   Skill: Understanding

4) The best definition of *osmotic pressure* is
   A) The movement of solute molecules from a higher to a lower concentration.
   B) The force with which a solvent moves across a semipermeable membrane from a higher to a lower concentration.
   C) The movement of a substance across a semipermeable membrane from a higher to a lower concentration.
   D) The active transport of a substance out of a cell to maintain equilibrium.
   E) The movement of solute molecules from a lower to a higher concentration across a semipermeable membrane.

   Answer: B
   Skill: Understanding

5) By which of the following mechanisms can a cell transport a substance from a lower to a higher concentration?
    A) Simple diffusion
    B) Facilitated diffusion
    C) Active transport
    D) Extracellular enzymes
    E) Aquaporins
Answer: C
Skill: Analysis

6) Which of the following is *NOT* a characteristic of the plasma membrane?
    A) Maintains cell shape
    B) Is composed of a phospholipid bilayer
    C) Contains proteins
    D) Is the site of cell wall formation
    E) Is selectively permeable
Answer: A
Skill: Analysis

7) Which of the following have a cell wall?
    A) Protoplasts
    B) Fungi
    C) L forms
    D) Mycoplasmas
    E) Animal cells
Answer: B
Skill: Recall

8) Which of the following statements is true?
    A) Endospores are for reproduction.
    B) Endospores allow a cell to survive environmental changes.
    C) Endospores are easily stained in a Gram stain.
    D) A cell produces one endospore and keeps growing.
    E) A cell can produce many endospores.
Answer: B
Skill: Recall

9) Which of the following pairs is mismatched?
    A) Endoplasmic reticulum — internal transport
    B) Golgi complex — secretion
    C) Mitochondria — ATP production
    D) Centrosome — food storage
    E) Lysosome — digestive enzymes
Answer: D
Skill: Recall

10) Which of the following organelles most closely resembles a prokaryotic cell?
   A) Nucleus
   B) Mitochondrion
   C) Golgi complex
   D) Vacuole
   E) Cell wall

   Answer: B
   Skill: Analysis

Figure 4.1

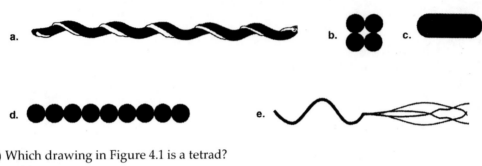

11) Which drawing in Figure 4.1 is a tetrad?
   A) a
   B) b
   C) c
   D) d
   E) e

   Answer: B
   Skill: Recall

12) Which drawing in Figure 4.1 possesses an axial filament?
   A) a
   B) b
   C) c
   D) d
   E) e

   Answer: A
   Skill: Recall

13) Which drawing in Figure 4.1 is streptococci?
   A) a
   B) b
   C) c
   D) d
   E) e

   Answer: D
   Skill: Recall

14) Which drawing in Figure 4.1 is a bacillius?
   A) a
   B) b
   C) c
   D) d
   E) e

Answer: C
Skill: Recall

15) Which of the following statements about prokaryotic cells is generally false?
   A) They have a semirigid cell wall.
   B) They are motile by means of flagella.
   C) They possess 80S ribosomes.
   D) They reproduce by binary fission.
   E) They lack membrane–bound nuclei.

Answer: C
Skill: Recall

16) Which of the following statements about gram–negative cell walls is false?
   A) They protect the cell in a hypotonic environment.
   B) They have an extra outer layer composed of lipoproteins, lipopolysaccharides, and phospholipids.
   C) They are toxic to humans.
   D) They are sensitive to penicillin.
   E) Their Gram reaction is due to the outer membrane.

Answer: D
Skill: Analysis

17) Which of the following structures is *NOT* found in prokaryotic cells?
   A) Flagellum
   B) Axial filament
   C) Cilium
   D) Pilus
   E) Peritrichous flagella

Answer: C
Skill: Recall

18) Which of the following statements about the glycocalyx is false?
   A) It may be composed of polysaccharide.
   B) It may be composed of polypeptide.
   C) It may be responsible for virulence.
   D) It is used to adhere to surfaces.
   E) It protects from osmotic lysis.

Answer: E
Skill: Analysis

19) Which of the following is *NOT* a chemical component of a bacterial cell wall?
   A) Cellulose
   B) Peptidoglycan
   C) Teichoic acids
   D) Peptide chains
   E) N–acetylmuramic acid

Answer: A
Skill: Analysis

20) Which of the following is *NOT* part of the active transport process?
   A) Plasma membrane
   B) Transporter proteins
   C) ATP
   D) Cell wall
   E) None of the above

Answer: D
Skill: Analysis

Figure 4.2

21) Which of the following terms best describes the cell in Figure 4.2?
   A) Peritrichous flagella
   B) Amphitrichous flagella
   C) Lophotrichous flagella
   D) Monotrichous flagella
   E) Axial filament

Answer: C
Skill: Recall

22) In bacteria, photosynthetic pigments are found in
   A) Chloroplasts.
   B) Cytoplasm.
   C) Chromatophores.
   D) Mesosomes.
   E) Ribosomes.

Answer: C
Skill: Recall

23) The difference between simple diffusion and facilitated diffusion is that facilitated diffusion
   A) Can move materials from a higher to a lower concentration.
   B) Can move materials from a lower to a higher concentration.
   C) Requires ATP.
   D) Requires transporter proteins.
   E) Doesn't require ATP.

Answer: D
Skill: Analysis

24) Which of the following is *NOT* a possible function of magnetosomes?
    A) Get cells to the North Pole
    B) Protect cells from hydrogen peroxide accumulation
    C) Store iron
    D) Locate suitable environments
Answer: A
Skill: Recall

25) You have isolated a motile, gram–positive cell with no visible nucleus. You can safely assume that the cell
    A) Has 9 pairs + 2 flagella.
    B) Has a mitochondrion.
    C) Has a cell wall.
    D) Lives in an extreme environment.
    E) Has a nucleus.
Answer: C
Skill: Analysis

26) Fimbriae and pili differ in that pili
    A) Are composed of pilin.
    B) Are composed of flagellin.
    C) Are used to transfer DNA.
    D) Are used for motility.
    E) Are used for attachment.
Answer: D
Skill: Recall

Figure 4.3

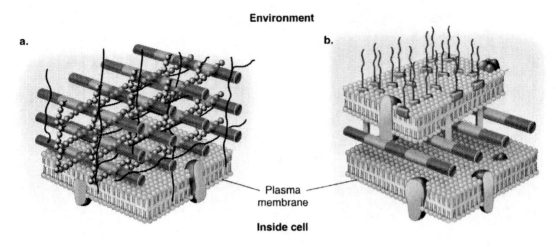

27) In Figure 4.3, which diagram of a cell wall is a gram–negative cell wall?
  A) a
  B) b
  C) Both a and b
  D) Neither a nor b
  E) Can't tell

Answer: B
Skill: Analysis

28) In Figure 4.3, which diagram of a cell wall is a toxic cell wall?
  A) a
  B) b
  C) Both a and b
  D) Neither a nor b
  E) Can't tell

Answer: B
Skill: Analysis

29) In Figure 4.3, which diagram of a cell wall has a wall that protects against osmotic lysis?
  A) a
  B) b
  C) Both a and b
  D) Neither a nor b
  E) Can't tell

Answer: C
Skill: Analysis

30) In Figure 4.3, which diagram of a cell wall is decolorized by acetone–alcohol?
   A) a
   B) b
   C) Both a and b
   D) Neither a nor b
   E) Can't tell

Answer: B
Skill: Analysis

31) In Figure 4.3, which diagram of a cell wall is resistant to many antibiotics (e.g., penicillin)?
   A) a
   B) b
   C) Both a and b
   D) Neither a nor b
   E) Can't tell

Answer: B
Skill: Analysis

32) In Figure 4.3, which diagram of a cell wall contains teichoic acids?
   A) a
   B) b
   C) Both a and b
   D) Neither a nor b
   E) Can't tell

Answer: A
Skill: Analysis

33) In Figure 4.3, which diagram of a cell wall contains porins?
   A) a
   B) b
   C) Both a and b
   D) Neither a nor b
   E) Can't tell

Answer: B
Skill: Analysis

34) Where are phospholipids most likely found in a prokaryotic cell?
   A) Flagella
   B) Around organelles
   C) Plasma membrane
   D) Ribosomes
   E) B and C

Answer: C
Skill: Understanding

35) Where are phospholipids most likely found in a eukaryotic cell?
   A) Flagella
   B) Around organelles
   C) Plasma membrane
   D) Ribosomes
   E) B and C

Answer: E
Skill: Understanding

36) Which of the following is *NOT* found in mitochondria and prokaryotes?
   A) Circular chromosome
   B) 70S ribosomes
   C) Cell wall
   D) Binary fission
   E) ATP–generating mechanism

Answer: C
Skill: Analysis

Figure 4.4

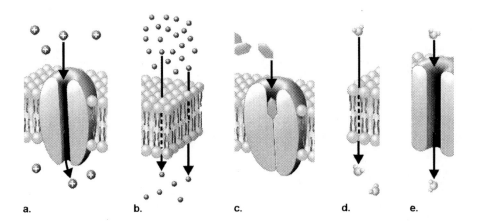

a.   b.   c.   d.   e.

37) Figure 4.4 shows movement across a plasma membrane. Which figure best represents a specific transporter protein?
   A) a
   B) b
   C) c
   D) d
   E) e

Answer: C
Skill: Understanding

38) Figure 4.4 shows movement across a plasma membrane. Which figure best represents simple diffusion?
    A) a
    B) b
    C) c
    D) d
    E) e

Answer: B
Skill: Understanding

39) Figure 4.4 shows movement across a plasma membrane. Which figure best represents an aquaporin?
    A) a
    B) b
    C) c
    D) d
    E) e

Answer: E
Skill: Understanding

40) What will happen if a bacterial cell is placed in distilled water with lysozyme?
    A) The cell will plasmolyze.
    B) The cell will undergo osmotic lysis.
    C) Water will leave the cell.
    D) Lysozyme will diffuse into the cell.
    E) No change will result; the solution is isotonic.

Answer: B
Skill: Analysis

41) What will happen if a bacterial cell is placed in 10% NaCl with penicillin?
    A) The cell will plasmolyze.
    B) The cell will undergo osmotic lysis.
    C) Water will enter the cell.
    D) Penicillin will diffuse into the cell.
    E) No change will result; the solution is isotonic.

Answer: A
Skill: Analysis

42) Which one of the following pairs is mismatched?
    A) Metachromatic granules — phosphate storage
    B) Lipid inclusions — energy reserve
    C) Ribosomes — protein storage
    D) Sulfur granules — energy reserve
    E) Gas vacuoles — flotation

Answer: C
Skill: Analysis

43) Which of the following are *NOT* energy reserves?
    A) Carboxysomes.
    B) Polysaccharide granules.
    C) Lipid inclusions.
    D) Sulfur granules.
    E) Metachromatic granules.

Answer: A
Skill: Recall

44) Which of the following pairs is *NOT* a functionally analogous pair?
    A) Nucleus — nuclear region
    B) Mitochondria — prokaryotic plasma membrane
    C) Chloroplasts — thylakoids
    D) Cilia — pili
    E) 9+2 flagella — bacterial flagella

Answer: D
Skill: Understanding

45) The bacteria on the outside of termite protozoa
    A) Digest cellulose.
    B) Steer the protozoan to food.
    C) Are transient microbiota.
    D) Propel the protozoan.
    E) None of the above.

Answer: D
Skill: Recall

Essay Questions

1) What is the importance of a phospholipid bilayer to living cells? Where is it in prokaryotic cells?

2) Provide evidence to substantiate the hypothesis that eukaryotic cells evolved from prokaryotic cells.

3) Compare and contrast gram–positive and gram–negative cell walls with regard to (a) sensitivity to antimicrobial agents, (b) resistance to phagocytosis, (c) chemical composition, and (d) decolorization by alcohol.

4) Group A beta–hemolytic streptococci ("the flesh–eating bacteria") rapidly spread through the human body by digesting the hyaluronic acid between cells. Label the bacterial plasma membrane shown below to illustrate digestion of the polysaccharide, hyaluronic acid.

Add these labels to the diagram in the appropriate places:
hyaluronic acid (a polysaccharide); GluUA–GlcNAc (a disaccharide);
glucose (a monosaccharide); hyaluronidase (an exoenzyme);
hyaluronic acid transporter protein.

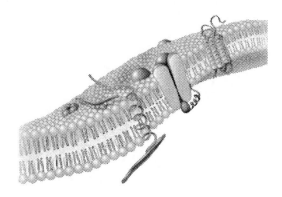

Chapter 5 Microbial Metabolism

Objective Questions

1) Which of the following compounds is *NOT* an enzyme?
    A) Dehydrogenase
    B) Cellulase
    C) Coenzyme A
    D) β–galactosidase
    E) Sucrase

Answer: C
Skill: Recall

Figure 5.1

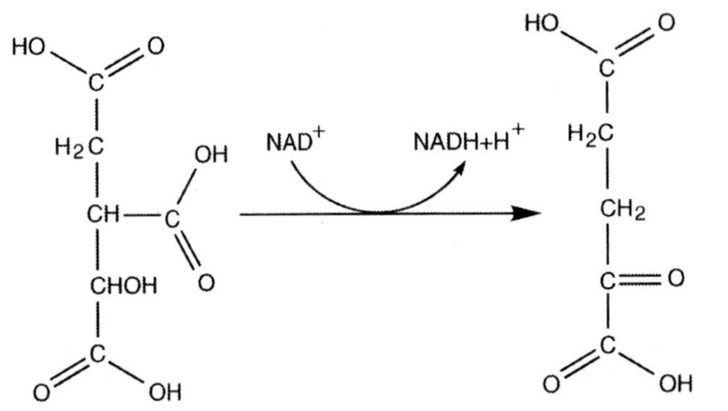

Isocitric acid ... **α-ketoglutaric acid**

2) Which compound is being reduced in the reaction shown in Figure 5.1?
    A) Isocitric acid and α–ketoglutaric acid
    B) α–ketoglutaric acid and NAD^+
    C) NAD^+
    D) NADH
    E) NADH and isocitric acid

Answer: C
Skill: Analysis

3) Which organism is *NOT* correctly matched to its energy source?
    A) Photoheterotroph — light
    B) Photoautotroph — CO_2
    C) Chemoautotroph — Fe^{2+}
    D) Chemoheterotroph — glucose
    E) Chemoautotroph — NH_3

Answer: B
Skill: Recall

4) Which of the following statements about anaerobic respiration is false?
 A) It involves glycolysis only.
 B) It involves the Krebs cycle.
 C) It involves the reduction of nitrate.
 D) It generates ATP.
 E) It requires cytochromes.

Answer: A
Skill: Recall

Figure 5.2

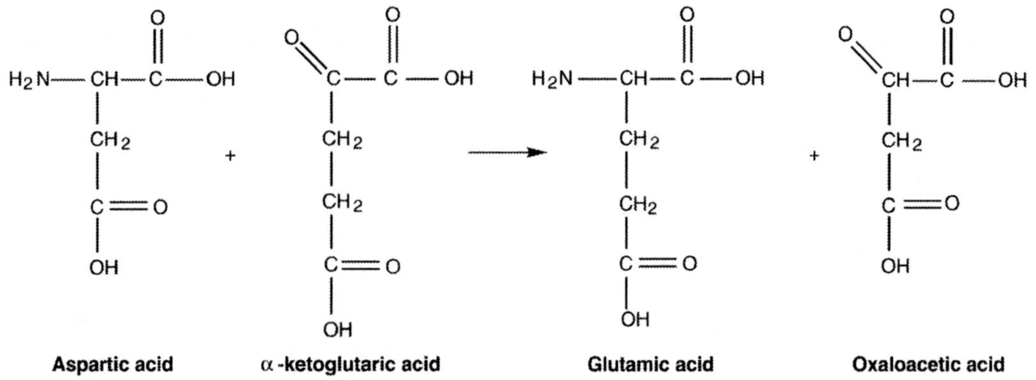

| Aspartic acid | α -ketoglutaric acid | Glutamic acid | Oxaloacetic acid |

5) What type of reaction is in Figure 5.2?
 A) Decarboxylation
 B) Transamination
 C) Dehydrogenation
 D) Oxidation
 E) Reduction

Answer: B
Skill: Analysis

6) What is the fate of pyruvic acid in an organism that uses aerobic respiration?
 A) It is reduced to lactic acid.
 B) It is oxidized in the Krebs cycle.
 C) It is oxidized in the electron transport chain.
 D) It is catabolized in glycolysis.
 E) It is reduced in the Krebs cycle.

Answer: B
Skill: Understanding

Figure 5.3

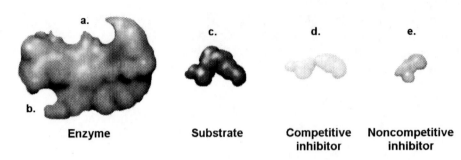

7) How would a noncompetitive inhibitor interfere with a reaction involving the enzyme shown in Figure 5.3?
   A) It would bind to a.
   B) It would bind to b.
   C) It would bind to c.
   D) It would bind to d.
   E) Can't tell.

Answer: B
Skill: Analysis

Figure 5.4

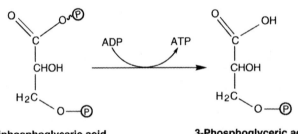

8) How is ATP generated in the reaction shown in Figure 5.4?
   A) Glycolysis
   B) Fermentation
   C) Photophosphorylation
   D) Oxidative phosphorylation
   E) Substrate-level phosphorylation

Answer: E
Skill: Analysis

9) Fatty acids are catabolized in
   A) The Krebs cycle.
   B) The electron transport chain.
   C) Glycolysis.
   D) The pentose phosphate pathway.
   E) The Entner Doudoroff pathway.

Answer: A
Skill: Recall

Figure 5.5

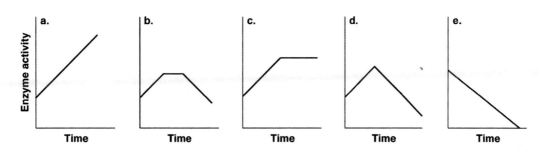

10) Which of the graphs in Figure 5.5 best illustrates the activity of an enzyme that is saturated with substrate?

    A) a

    B) b

    C) c

    D) d

    E) e

Answer: C

Skill: Analysis

11) Which of the following is the best definition of *oxidative phosphorylation?*

    A) Electrons are passed through a series of carriers to O_2.

    B) The energy released as carrier molecules are oxidized is used to generate ATP.

    C) The energy released in the reduction of carrier molecules is used to generate ATP.

    D) The transfer of a high–energy phosphate group to ADP.

Answer: B

Skill: Analysis

12) Which of the following statements about substrate–level phosphorylation is false?

    A) It involves the direct transfer of a high–energy phosphate group from an intermediate metabolic compound to ADP.

    B) No final electron acceptor is required.

    C) It occurs in glycolysis.

    D) The oxidation of intermediate metabolic compounds releases energy that is used to generate ATP.

    E) It occurs in the Krebs cycle.

Answer: D

Skill: Analysis

13) Which of the following statements about photophosphorylation is false?

    A) Light liberates an electron from chlorophyll.

    B) The oxidation of carrier molecules releases energy.

    C) Energy from oxidation reactions is used to generate ATP from ADP.

    D) It requires CO_2.

    E) It occurs in photosynthesizing cells.

Answer: D

Skill: Analysis

14) A strictly fermentative bacterium produces energy
    A) By glycolysis only.
    B) By aerobic respiration only.
    C) By fermentation or aerobic respiration.
    D) Only in the absence of oxygen.
    E) Only in the presence of oxygen.

Answer: A
Skill: Understanding

15) The advantage of the pentose phosphate pathway is that it produces all of the following
EXCEPT
    A) Precursors for nucleic acids.
    B) Precursors for the synthesis of glucose.
    C) Three ATPs.
    D) NADPH.
    E) Precursors for the synthesis of amino acids.

Answer: C
Skill: Recall

16) Which of the following statements about beta oxidation is false?
    A) It is a method of catabolizing fatty acids.
    B) It involves the formation of 2-carbon units.
    C) It involves the formation of acetyl-CoA.
    D) It is a step in glycolysis.
    E) It is used in petroleum degradation.

Answer: D
Skill: Analysis

17) In noncyclic photophosphorylation, O_2 is produced from
    A) CO_2.
    B) H_2O.
    C) $C_6H_{12}O_6$.
    D) Sunlight.
    E) Chlorophyll.

Answer: B
Skill: Understanding

18) Which of the following is the best definition of *fermentation*?
    A) The reduction of glucose to pyruvic acid
    B) The oxidation of glucose with organic molecules serving as electron acceptors
    C) The complete catabolism of glucose to CO_2 and H_2O
    D) The production of energy by substrate-level phosphorylation
    E) The production of ethanol from glucose

Answer: B
Skill: Analysis

19) Which of the following is *NOT* necessary for respiration?
   A) Cytochromes
   B) Flavoproteins
   C) A source of electrons
   D) Oxygen
   E) Quinones

Answer: D
Skill: Understanding

20) Which one of the following would you predict is an allosteric inhibitor of the Krebs cycle enzyme, α–ketoglutarate dehydrogenase?
   A) Citric acid
   B) α–ketoglutaric acid
   C) NAD^+
   D) NADH
   E) ADP

Answer: D
Skill: Understanding

21) In green and purple bacteria, electrons to reduce CO_2 come from
   A) CO_2.
   B) H_2O.
   C) $C_6H_{12}O_6$.
   D) Sunlight.
   E) Chlorophyll.

Answer: A
Skill: Understanding

22) Assume you are growing bacteria on a lipid medium that started at pH 7. The action of bacterial lipases should cause the pH of the medium to
   A) Increase.
   B) Decrease.
   C) Stay the same.

Answer: B
Skill: Understanding

23) Which of the following uses CO_2 for carbon and H_2 for energy?
   A) Chemoautotroph
   B) Chemoheterotroph
   C) Photoautotroph
   D) Photoheterotroph

Answer: A
Skill: Analysis

24) Which of the following uses glucose for carbon and energy?
    A) Chemoautotroph
    B) Chemoheterotroph
    C) Photoautotroph
    D) Photoheterotroph

Answer: B
Skill: Analysis

25) Which of the following has bacteriochlorophylls and uses alcohols for carbon?
    A) Chemoautotroph
    B) Chemoheterotroph
    C) Photoautotroph
    D) Photoheterotroph

Answer: D
Skill: Analysis

26) Cyanobacteria are a type of
    A) Chemoautotroph.
    B) Chemoheterotroph.
    C) Photoautotroph.
    D) Photoheterotroph.

Answer: C
Skill: Analysis

27) Which statements are true?
    1—Electron carriers are located at ribosomes.
    2—ATP is a common intermediate between catabolic and anabolic pathways.
    3—ATP is used for the long-term storage of energy and so is often found in storage granules.
    4—Anaerobic organisms are capable of respiration.
    5—ATP is generated by the flow of protons across the cell membrane.

    A) 2, 4, 5
    B) 1, 3, 4
    C) 2, 3, 5
    D) 1, 2, 3
    E) All

Answer: A
Skill: Analysis

28) $C_2H_5OH \xrightarrow{\text{Acetobacter}} C_2H_3OOH$
    Ethanol   Acetic acid
    Which of the following is true about this reaction?
    A) This process requires O_2.
    B) This process occurs anaerobically.

Answer: A
Skill: Understanding

29) $C_6H_{12}O_6$ $\xrightarrow{\textit{Saccharomyces}}$ $2C_2H_5OH + 2CO_2$
   Glucose   Ethanol
   Which of the following is true about this reaction?
   A) This process requires O_2.
   B) This process occurs anaerobically.

Answer: B
Skill: Understanding

30) $NO_3^- + 2H^+$ $\xrightarrow{\textit{Pseudomonas}}$ $NO_2^- + H_2O$
   Nitrate ion   Nitrite ion
   Which of the following is true about this reaction?
   A) This process requires O_2.
   B) This process occurs anaerobically.

Answer: B
Skill: Understanding

31) $2H^+$ $\xrightarrow{\textit{E. coli}}$ H_2O
   Hydrogen ions   Water
   Which of the following is true about this reaction?
   A) This process requires O_2.
   B) This process occurs anaerobically.

Answer: A
Skill: Understanding

32) Assume you are working for a chemical company and are responsible for growing a yeast
   culture that produces ethanol. The yeasts are growing well on the maltose medium but are not
   producing alcohol. What is the most likely explanation?
   A) The maltose is toxic.
   B) O_2 is in the medium.
   C) Not enough protein is provided.
   D) The temperature is too low.
   E) The temperature is too high.

Answer: B
Skill: Understanding

Figure 5.6

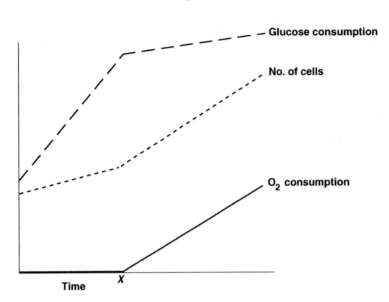

33) The rates of O_2 and glucose consumption by a bacterial culture are shown in Figure 5.6. Assume a bacterial culture was grown in a glucose medium without O_2. Then O_2 was added at the time marked X. The data indicate that
    A) These bacteria don't use O_2.
    B) These bacteria get more energy anaerobically.
    C) Aerobic metabolism is more efficient than fermentation.
    D) These bacteria can't grow anaerobically.

Answer: C
Skill: Analysis

34) An enzyme, citrate synthase, in the Krebs cycle is inhibited by ATP. This is an example of all of the following *EXCEPT*
    A) Allosteric inhibition.
    B) Competitive inhibition.
    C) Feedback inhibition.
    D) Noncompetitive inhibition.
    E) Beta oxidation.

Answer: B
Skill: Understanding

35) A shipping company employee notices that the inside of ships' hulls where ballast water is stored are deteriorating. The hull paint contained cyanide to prevent microbial growth. Bacteria were growing on the hulls. You can therefore conclude that the
    A) Bacteria were using aerobic respiration.
    B) Bacteria were using anaerobic respiration.
    C) Bacteria were growing by fermentation.
    D) Bacteria were using cytochromes.
    E) Bacteria were photosynthetic.

Answer: C
Skill: Analysis

36) *Beggiatoa* bacteria get energy by oxidizing S^{2-} to S^{6+}. This means they take _____ for their
_____.

    A) electrons; electron transport chain
    B) electrons; fermentation
    C) protons; NAD^+
    D) sulfur; photophosphorylation
    E) glucose; glycolysis

Answer: A
Skill: Analysis

Figure 5.7

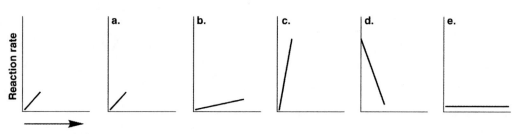

37) The graph at the left in Figure 5.7 shows the reaction rate for an enzyme at its optimum
temperature. Which graph shows enzyme activity at a higher temperature?
    A) a
    B) b
    C) c
    D) d
    E) e

Answer: B
Skill: Analysis

38) A bacterial culture grown in a glucose–peptide medium causes the pH to increase. The
bacteria are most likely
    A) Fermenting the glucose.
    B) Oxidizing the glucose.
    C) Using the peptides.
    D) Not growing.

Answer: C
Skill: Analysis

39) *Gallionella* bacteria can get energy from the reaction $Fe^{2+} \rightarrow Fe^{3+}$. This reaction is an example of
    A) Oxidation.
    B) Reduction.
    C) Fermentation.
    D) Photophosphorylation.
    E) The Calvin–Benson cycle.

Answer: A
Skill: Analysis

Figure 5.8

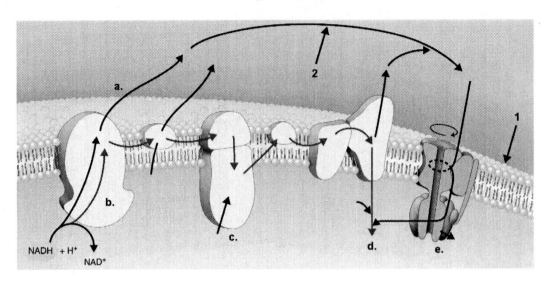

40) In Figure 5.8, where is ATP produced?
   A) a
   B) b
   C) c
   D) d
   E) e

Answer: E
Skill: Recall

41) Refer to Figure 5.8. In aerobic respiration, where is water formed?
   A) a
   B) b
   C) c
   D) d
   E) e

Answer: D
Skill: Recall

42) In Figure 5.8, the structure labeled (1) is
   A) NAD⁺.
   B) ATP synthase.
   C) Plasma membrane.
   D) Cell wall.
   E) Cytoplasm.

Answer: C
Skill: Recall

43) In Figure 5.8, the path labeled (2) is the flow of
    A) Electrons.
    B) Protons.
    C) Energy.
    D) Water.
    E) Glucose.

Answer: B
Skill: Recall

44) What is the most acidic place in Figure 5.8?
    A) a
    B) b
    C) c
    D) d
    E) e

Answer: A
Skill: Analysis

45) A urease test is used to identify *Myobacterium tuberculosis* because
    A) Urease is a sign of tuberculosis.
    B) *M. tuberculosis* produces urease.
    C) Urea accumulates during tuberculosis.
    D) Some bacteria reduce nitrate ion.
    E) *M. bovis* can cause tuberculosis.

Answer: B
Skill: Understanding

Essay Questions

1) Compare and contrast photophosphorylation and oxidative phosphorylation.

2) *Rhodopseudomonas* is an anaerobic photoautotroph that uses organic compounds as an electron donor. It is also capable of chemoheterotrophic metabolism. Diagram the metabolic pathways of this bacterium.

3) Identify the catabolic pathways used by the following bacteria:
   Pseudomonas   Oxidizes glucose
   Lactobacillus   Ferments glucose
   Alcaligenes   Neither oxidizes nor ferments glucose
   Escherichia   Oxidizes and ferments glucose

4) Differentiate the following two laboratory tests: starch hydrolysis and starch fermentation.

5) *Streptococcus* lacks an electron transport chain. How does this bacterium reoxidize NADH? Where is the NADH formed?

6) You look in the refrigerator and find some orange drink you had forgotten was there. The drink now has an off taste and bubbles. What is the most likely explanation for the changes in the drink?

7) Why is *Clostridium perfringens* likely to grow in gangrenous wounds?

Chapter 6   Microbial Growth

Objective Questions

Figure 6.1

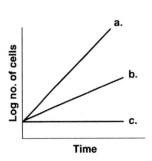

1) In Figure 6.1, which line best depicts a facultative anaerobe in the absence of O_2?
   A) a
   B) b
   C) c

   Answer: B
   Skill: Understanding

2) In Figure 6.1, which line best illustrates a mesophile at 5°C above its optimum temperature?
   A) a
   B) b
   C) c

   Answer: B
   Skill: Understanding

3) In Figure 6.1 ,which line best depicts an obligate anaerobe in the presence of O_2?
   A) a
   B) b
   C) c

   Answer: C
   Skill: Understanding

4) In Figure 6.1, which line best depicts a mesophile with an optimum temperature of 35°C incubated at 40°C?
   A) a
   B) b
   C) c

   Answer: B
   Skill: Understanding

5) In Figure 6.1, which line shows the growth of an obligate aerobe incubated anaerobically?
   A) a
   B) b
   C) c
Answer: C
Skill: Understanding

6) In Figure 6.1, which line best illustrates the growth of a facultative anaerobe incubated aerobically?
   A) a
   B) b
   C) c
Answer: A
Skill: Understanding

7) In Figure 6.1, which line best depicts a catalase–negative cell incubated aerobically?
   A) a
   B) b
   C) c
Answer: C
Skill: Understanding

8) Micrococci are facultative halophiles. In Figure 6.1, which line best depicts the growth of *Micrococcus luteus* in a nutrient medium containing 7.5% NaCl?
   A) a
   B) b
   C) c
Answer: B
Skill: Understanding

9) In Figure 6.1, which line best depicts a psychrophile incubated at room temperature?
   A) a
   B) b
   C) c
Answer: C
Skill: Understanding

10) In Figure 6.1, which line best depicts a psychrotroph incubated at 0°C?
   A) a
   B) b
   C) c
Answer: B
Skill: Understanding

11) In Figure 6.1, which line best depicts *Neisseria gonorrhoeae* when growing inside the human body?
 A) a
 B) b
 C) c

Answer: A
Skill: Understanding

12) The addition of which of the following to a culture medium will neutralize acids?
 A) Buffers
 B) Sugars
 C) pH
 D) Heat
 E) Carbon

Answer: A
Skill: Recall

13) Salts and sugars work to preserve foods by creating a
 A) Depletion of nutrients.
 B) Hypotonic environment.
 C) Lower osmotic pressure.
 D) Hypertonic environment.
 E) Lower pH.

Answer: D
Skill: Analysis

14) The term *facultative anaerobe* refers to an organism that
 A) Doesn't use oxygen but tolerates it.
 B) Is killed by oxygen.
 C) Uses oxygen or grows without oxygen.
 D) Requires less oxygen than is present in air.
 E) Prefers to grow without oxygen.

Answer: C
Skill: Analysis

15) Which of the following is an advantage of the standard plate count?
 A) Can readily count cells that form aggregates
 B) Requires incubation time
 C) Determines the number of viable cells
 D) Chemical and physical requirements are determined by media and incubation.
 E) Cannot be used to count bacteria in food

Answer: C
Skill: Recall

16) Which of the following is an advantage of the direct microscopic count?
  A) Can readily count organisms that are motile
  B) Enumerates dead cells
  C) Requires no incubation time
  D) Sample volume is unknown.
  E) Requires a large number of cells

Answer: C
Skill: Recall

17) Which of the following is *NOT* used to determine metabolic activity?
  A) Acid production from fermentation
  B) CO_2 produced from the Krebs cycle
  C) NO_2^- produced from the electron transport chain
  D) Decreased dissolved oxygen
  E) Turbidity

Answer: E
Skill: Understanding

18) Thirty–six colonies grew in nutrient agar from 1.0 ml of undiluted sample in a standard plate count. How many cells were in the original sample?
  A) 4
  B) 9
  C) 18
  D) 36
  E) 72

Answer: D
Skill: Understanding

Figure 6.2

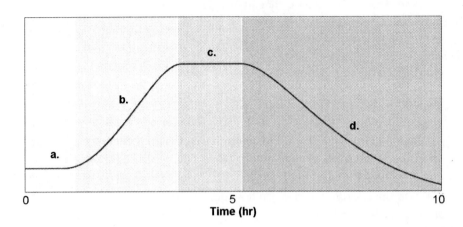

19) In Figure 6.2, which section shows a growth phase where the number of cells dying equals the number of cells dividing?
    A) a
    B) b
    C) c
    D) d
    E) a and c

Answer: C
Skill: Recall

20) In Figure 6.2, which sections of the graph illustrate a logarithmic change in cell numbers?
    A) a and c
    B) b and d
    C) a and b
    D) c and d
    E) b only

Answer: B
Skill: Analysis

21) Most bacteria grow best at pH
    A) 1.
    B) 5.
    C) 7.
    D) 9.
    E) 14.

Answer: C
Skill: Recall

Figure 6.3

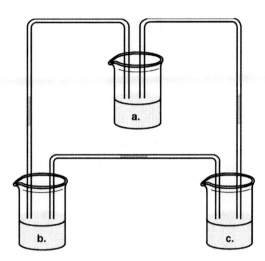

22) Figure 6.3 shows three containers of water connected by tubes. A selectively permeable membrane divides each tube. Solutes are added to each container to give final concentrations of 5% NaCl in (a); 10% NaCl in (b); and 5% sucrose in (c). When the experiment is first set up, the initial movement of water will be
    A) a to b; b to c; c to a.
    B) a to b; c to b; c to a.
    C) a to c; b to c; c to a.
    D) a to c; c to b; c to a.
    E) b to a; b to c; c to a.

Answer: B
Skill: Understanding

23) A culture medium on which only gram–positive organisms grow and a yellow halo surrounds *Staphylococcus aureus* colonies is called a(n)
    A) Selective medium.
    B) Differential medium.
    C) Enrichment culture.
    D) A and B
    E) B and C

Answer: D
Skill: Analysis

24) A culture medium consisting of agar, human blood, and beef heart is a
    A) Chemically defined medium.
    B) Complex medium.
    C) Selective medium.
    D) Differential medium.
    E) Reducing medium.

Answer: B
Skill: Analysis

25) Which of the following pairs is mismatched?
   A) Psychrotroph — growth at 0°C
   B) Thermophile — growth at 37°C
   C) Mesophile — growth at 25°C
   D) Psychrophile — growth at 15°C
   E) Hyperthermophiles — growth at 100°C

   Answer: B
   Skill: Recall

26) During which growth phase will gram–positive bacteria be most susceptible to penicillin?
   A) Lag phase
   B) Log phase
   C) Death phase
   D) Stationary phase
   E) The culture is equally susceptible during all phases.

   Answer: B
   Skill: Understanding

27) Which of the following is the best definition of *generation time*?
   A) The length of time needed for lag phase
   B) The length of time needed for a cell to divide
   C) The minimum rate of doubling
   D) The duration of log phase
   E) The time needed for nuclear division

   Answer: B
   Skill: Recall

28) Which of the following is *NOT* a direct method to measure microbial growth?
   A) Direct microscopic count
   B) Standard plate count
   C) Filtration
   D) Metabolic activity
   E) MPN

   Answer: D
   Skill: Analysis

29) Which group of microorganisms is most likely to spoil a freshwater trout preserved with salt?
   A) Psychrophiles
   B) Facultative halophiles
   C) Anaerobes
   D) Thermophiles
   E) Hyperthermophiles

   Answer: B
   Skill: Recall

30) Which of the following is an organic growth factor?
   A) Glucose
   B) NAD+
   C) Peptone
   D) $NH_4H_2PO_4$
   E) H_2O

Answer: B
Skill: Analysis

31) Which of the following is an example of a metabolic activity that could be used to measure microbial growth?
   A) Standard plate count
   B) Glucose consumption
   C) Direct microscopic count
   D) Turbidity
   E) MPN

Answer: B
Skill: Understanding

32) An experiment began with 4 cells and ended with 128 cells. How many generations did the cells go through?
   A) 64
   B) 32
   C) 6
   D) 5
   E) 4

Answer: D
Skill: Analysis

33) Three cells with generation times of 30 minutes are inoculated into a culture medium. How many cells are there after 5 hours?
   A) 3×2^{10}
   B) 1024
   C) 243
   D) 48
   E) 16

Answer: A
Skill: Analysis

Figure 6.4

34) In Figure 6.4, in which tube are microaerophiles growing?
    A) a
    B) b
    C) c
    D) d
    E) e

Answer: E
Skill: Analysis

35) In Figure 6.4, in which tube are facultative anaerobes growing?
    A) a
    B) b
    C) c
    D) d
    E) e

Answer: B
Skill: Analysis

36) In one hospital, *Pseudomonas aeruginosa* serotype 10 infected the biliary tract of 10% of 1300 patients who underwent gastrointestinal endoscopic procedures. After each use, endoscopes were washed with an automatic reprocessor that flushed detergent and glutaraldehyde through the endoscopes, followed by a tap water rinse. *P. aeruginosa* 10 was not isolated from the detergent, glutaraldehyde, or tap water. What was the source of the infections?
    A) Bacterial cell walls in the water
    B) A biofilm in the reprocessor
    C) Contaminated disinfectant
    D) Fecal contamination of the bile ducts

Answer: B
Skill: Analysis

Table 6.1
Three different culture media are shown below.

Medium A	Medium B	Medium C
Na_2HPO_4	Tide detergent	Glucose
KH_2PO_4	Na_2HPO_4	Peptone
$MgSO_4$	KH_2PO_4	$(NH_4)_2SO_4$
$CaCl_2$	$MgSO_4$	KH_2PO_2
$NaHCO_3$	$(NH_4)_2SO_4$	Na_2HPO_4

37) In Table 6.1, which medium (media) is (are) chemically defined?
   A) A
   B) B
   C) C
   D) A and B
   E) A and C

Answer: A
Skill: Analysis

38) In Table, 6.1, in which medium would an autotroph grow?
   A) A
   B) B
   C) C
   D) A and B
   E) A and C

Answer: A
Skill: Analysis

39) Assume you inoculated 100 cells into 100 ml of nutrient broth. You then inoculated 100 cells of the same species into 200 ml of nutrient broth. After incubation for 24 hours, you should have
   A) More cells in the 100 ml.
   B) More cells in the 200 ml.
   C) The same number of cells in both.

Answer: C
Skill: Understanding

40) The source of nutrients in nutrient agar is
   A) Agar.
   B) Nutrient.
   C) Peptone and beef extract.
   D) Peptone and NaCl.
   E) All of the above.

Answer: C
Skill: Analysis

41) Which enzyme catalyzes the reaction: $O_2^- + O_2^- + 2H^+ \rightarrow H_2O_2 + O_2$?

    A) Catalase
    B) Oxidase
    C) Peroxidase
    D) Superoxide dismutase

Answer: D
Skill: Recall

42) Which enzyme catalyzes the reaction: $2H_2O_2 \rightarrow 2H_2O + O_2$?

    A) Catalase
    B) Oxidase
    C) Peroxidase
    D) Superoxide dismutase

Answer: A
Skill: Recall

43) Which enzyme catalyzes the reaction: $H_2O_2 + 2H^+ \rightarrow 2H_2O$?

    A) Catalase
    B) Oxidase
    C) Peroxidase
    D) Superoxide dismutase

Answer: C
Skill: Recall

Table 6.2
The following data show growth of two bacteria on different media.

	Amount of Growth	
	Staphylococcus aureus	*Streptococcus pyogenes*
Nutrient agar	++	++
Nutrient agar + 7.5% NaCl	+	−

44) The data in Table 6.2 indicate that *S. aureus* is a(n)

    A) Mesophile.
    B) Facultative anaerobe.
    C) Facultative halophile.
    D) Aerobe.
    E) Halophile.

Answer: C
Skill: Analysis

45) Patients with indwelling catheters are susceptible to infections because
   A) Injected solutions are contaminated.
   B) Their immune systems are weakened.
   C) Infections can be transmitted from other people.
   D) Biofilms develop on catheters.
   E) Bacteria cause infections.

Answer: D
Skill: Recall

Essay Questions

Figure 6.5

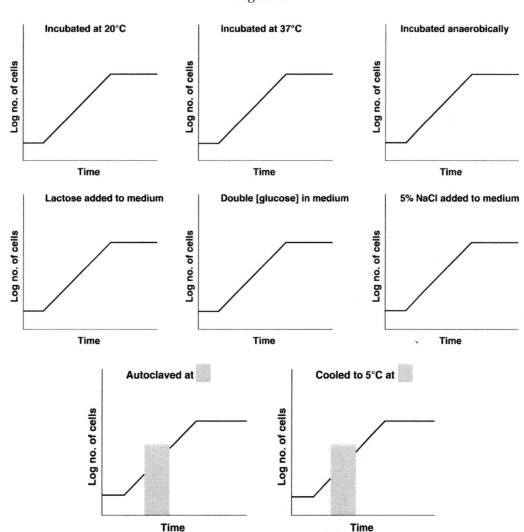

1) In each graph in Figure 6.5, the culture was incubated at 30°C in glucose minimal salts broth, aerobically. The bacterium is a facultative anaerobe with an optimum temperature of 37°C and can metabolize glucose and lactose. Indicate how each growth curve would change under the conditions indicated in each graph. Draw the new graphs, or write "no change."

2) A patient with a heart pacemaker received antibiotic therapy for streptococcal bacteremia (bacteria in the blood). One month later, he was treated for recurrence of the bacteremia. When he returned 6 weeks later, again with bacteremia, the physician recommended replacing the pacemaker. Why did this cure his condition?

Table 6.3
Bacterial generation times were calculated in the media shown below.
All media were prepared with tap water and incubated aerobically in the light.

| | Generation times (min.) | | | |
Medium	*Escherichia coli*	*Pseudomonas aeruginosa*	*Lactobacillus*	*Nitrobacter*
NaCl, NO_3^-, $MgSO_4$	0	0	0	80
Glucose	100	0	0	0
Glucose, NaCl	82	0	0	0
Glucose, NaCl, PO_4^{3-}	56	200	0	0
Glucose, NaCl, PO_4^{3-}, $MgSO_4$	43	100	0	0
Glucose, NaCl, PO_4^{3-}, $MgSO_4$, 8 amino acids	28	40	0	0
Glucose, NaCl, PO_4^{3-}, $MgSO_4$, 19 amino acids	25	25	80	0

3) Compare and contrast the growth requirements of the bacteria listed in Table 6.3. Which of the media, if any, are chemically defined?

Chapter 7 The Control of Microbial Growth

Objective Questions

1) Which of the following is the best method to sterilize heat–labile solutions?
   A) Dry heat
   B) Autoclave
   C) Membrane filtration
   D) Pasteurization
   E) Freezing
   Answer: C
   Skill: Recall

2) Which of the following best describes the pattern of microbial death?
   A) The cells in a population die at a constant rate.
   B) All the cells in a culture die at once.
   C) Not all of the cells in a culture are killed.
   D) The pattern varies depending on the antimicrobial agent.
   E) The pattern varies depending on the species.
   Answer: A
   Skill: Recall

3) Which of the following substances can sterilize?
   A) Alcohol
   B) Phenolics
   C) Ethylene oxide
   D) Chlorine
   E) Soap
   Answer: C
   Skill: Recall

4) Which of the following substances is used for surgical hand scrubs?
   A) Phenol
   B) Chlorine bleach
   C) Chlorhexidine
   D) Soap
   E) Glutaraldehyde
   Answer: C
   Skill: Recall

5) Place the following surfactants in order from the most effective to the least effective antimicrobial activity:
1-Soap; 2-Acid-anionic detergent; 3-Quats.
  A) 1, 2, 3
  B) 1, 3, 2
  C) 2, 1, 3
  D) 3, 2, 1
  E) 3, 1, 2
Answer: D
Skill: Analysis

6) The antimicrobial activity of chlorine is due to which of the following?
  A) The formation of hypochlorous acid
  B) The formation of hydrochloric acid
  C) The formation of ozone
  D) The formation of free O
  E) Disruption of the plasma membrane
Answer: A
Skill: Recall

7) Iodophors differ from iodine (I_2) in that iodophors
  A) Don't stain.
  B) Are less irritating.
  C) Are longer lasting.
  D) Are combined with a nonionic detergent.
  E) All of the above.
Answer: E
Skill: Analysis

8) Which of the following does *NOT* achieve sterilization?
  A) Dry heat
  B) Pasteurization
  C) Autoclave
  D) Formaldehyde
  E) Ethylene oxide
Answer: B
Skill: Recall

9) Which of the following is a limitation of the autoclave?
  A) Requires a long time to achieve sterilization
  B) Cannot inactivate viruses
  C) Cannot kill endospores
  D) Cannot be used with heat-labile materials
  E) Cannot be used with glassware
Answer: D
Skill: Analysis

10) Which of the following affects the elimination of bacteria from an object?
    A) Number of bacteria present
    B) Temperature
    C) pH
    D) Presence of organic matter
    E) All of the above
Answer: E
Skill: Recall

11) Which of the following does *NOT* directly result from application of heat?
    A) Breaking of hydrogen bonds
    B) Breaking of sulfhydryl bonds
    C) Denaturing of enzymes
    D) Cell lysis
    E) Damage to nucleic acids
Answer: D
Skill: Analysis

12) Which of these disinfectants acts by denaturing proteins?
    A) Alcohols
    B) Aldehydes
    C) Bisphenols
    D) Halogens
    E) Phenolics
Answer: C
Skill: Recall

13) Which of the following substances is *NOT* an oxidizing agent?
    A) Chlorine
    B) Glutaraldehyde
    C) Hydrogen peroxide
    D) Iodine
    E) Ozone
Answer: B
Skill: Recall

14) Which of the following is *NOT* used to disinfect water?
    A) Ozone
    B) Gamma radiation
    C) Chlorine
    D) Copper sulfate
    E) Heat
Answer: E
Skill: Analysis

15) Which of the following substances is *NOT* effective against nonenveloped viruses?
    A) Alcohol
    B) Chlorine
    C) Ethylene oxide
    D) Ozone
    E) All are equally effective.

Answer: A
Skill: Understanding

16) Glutaraldehyde is considered one of the most effective disinfectants for hospital use. Which of the following statements about glutaraldehyde is false?
    A) Stains and corrodes
    B) Is safe to transport
    C) Acts rapidly
    D) Is not hampered by organic material
    E) Attacks all microorganisms

Answer: A
Skill: Understanding

17) Which concentration of ethanol is the most effective bactericide?
    A) 100%
    B) 70%
    C) 50%
    D) 40%
    E) 30%

Answer: B
Skill: Recall

18) Which of the following is *NOT* a factor contributing to hospital–acquired infections?
    A) Some bacteria metabolize disinfectants.
    B) Gram–negative bacteria are often resistant to disinfectants.
    C) Invasive procedures can provide a portal of entry for bacteria.
    D) Bacteria may be present in commercial products such as mouthwash.
    E) All of the above may contribute to hospital–acquired infection.

Answer: E
Skill: Analysis

19) Which of the following treatments is the most effective for controlling microbial growth?
    A) 63°C for 30 min.
    B) 72°C for 15 sec.
    C) 140°C for 4 sec.
    D) They are equivalent treatments.
    E) None is effective.

Answer: D
Skill: Recall

20) Which of the following could be used to sterilize plastic Petri plates in a plastic wrapper?
    A) Autoclave
    B) Gamma radiation
    C) Microwaves
    D) Sunlight
    E) Ultraviolet radiation

Answer: B
Skill: Analysis

Figure 7.1

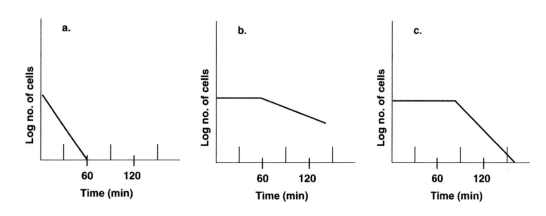

21) In Figure 7.1, what is the thermal death time for culture (a)?
    A) 150°C
    B) 60 min.
    C) 120 min.
    D) 100°C
    E) Can't tell

Answer: B
Skill: Analysis

22) Assume that one culture is a freshly opened package of dried yeast with 0.1% moisture, another culture is the same yeast with 7.5% moisture, and the third culture is a package of yeast mixed with water. Each culture was exposed to 130°C in a hot–air oven. Which graph in Figure 7.1 most likely shows the yeast with 0.1% moisture?
    A) a
    B) b
    C) c
    D) a and b
    E) b and c

Answer: C
Skill: Understanding

Figure 7.2

A suspension of 10^6 *Bacillus cereus* endospores was put in a hot–air oven at 170°C. Plate counts were used to determine the number of endospores surviving at the time intervals shown.

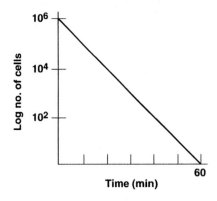

23) In Figure 7.2, the thermal death point for this culture is
   A) 15 min.
   B) 50°C.
   C) 30 min.
   D) 170°C.
   E) Can't tell from the data provided.

Answer: E
Skill: Understanding

24) In Figure 7.2, the decimal reduction time (D value) for the culture is approximately
   A) 0 min.
   B) 15 min.
   C) 30 min.
   D) 45 min.
   E) 60 min.

Answer: B
Skill: Understanding

25) In Figure 7.2, the thermal death time for this culture is
   A) 0 min.
   B) 10 min.
   C) 20 min.
   D) 40 min.
   E) 60 min.

Answer: E
Skill: Understanding

26) Which of the following pairs is mismatched?
    A) Ag — burns
    B) Alcohols — open wounds
    C) $CuSO_4$ — algicide
    D) H_2O_2 — open wounds
    E) Organic acids — food preservation

Answer: B
Skill: Recall

Figure 7.3

Assume 10^9 *E. coli* cells/ml are in a flask.

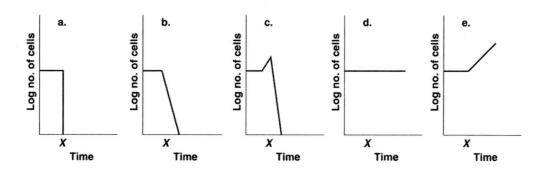

27) Which graph in Figure 7.3 best depicts the effect of placing the culture in an autoclave for 15 min. at time x?
    A) a
    B) b
    C) c
    D) d
    E) e

Answer: B
Skill: Understanding

28) Which graph in Figure 7.3 best depicts the effect of placing the culture at 7°C at time x?
    A) a
    B) b
    C) c
    D) d
    E) e

Answer: D
Skill: Understanding

Table 7.1
A disk–diffusion test using *Staphylococcus* gave the following results:

Disinfectant	Zone of inhibition (mm)
A	0
B	2.5
C	10
D	5

29) In Table 7.1, which compound was the most effective against *Staphylococcus*?
    A) A
    B) B
    C) C
    D) D
    E) Can't tell

Answer: C
Skill: Understanding

30) In Table 7.1, which compound was the most effective against *E. coli*?
    A) A
    B) B
    C) C
    D) D
    E) Can't tell

Answer: E
Skill: Understanding

31) In Table 7.1, which compound was bactericidal?
    A) A
    B) B
    C) C
    D) D
    E) Can't tell

Answer: E
Skill: Understanding

Table 7.2

The fate of *E. coli* O157:H7 in apple cider held at 8°C for 2 weeks, with and without preservatives, is shown below:

	Bacteria/ml
Cider only	2.2
Cider with potassium sorbate	2.0
Sodium benzoate	0
Sorbate + benzoate	0

32) In Table 7.2, which preservative is most effective?
    A) Sorbate
    B) Benzoate
    C) Sorbate + benzoate
    D) No preservative

Answer: B
Skill: Analysis

33) Which one of the following does *NOT* belong with the others?
    A) Acid–anionic detergents
    B) Benzoic acid
    C) Supercritical CO_2
    D) Pasteurization
    E) Peracetic acid

Answer: A
Skill: Analysis

34) Which one of the following does *NOT* belong with the others?
    A) Beta–propiolactone
    B) Glutaraldehyde
    C) Ethylene oxide
    D) Hydrogen peroxide
    E) Propylene oxide

Answer: D
Skill: Analysis

35) Which of the following substances is *NOT* used to preserve foods?
    A) Biguanides
    B) Nisin
    C) Potassium sorbate
    D) Sodium nitrite
    E) Sodium propionate

Answer: A
Skill: Recall

Table 7.3

The following data were obtained by incubating gram–positive bacteria in nutrient medium + disinfectant for

24 hr, then transferring one loopful to nutrient medium (subculturing). (+ = growth; – = no growth)

Dilution	Doom Initial	Doom Subculture	K.O. Initial	K.O. Subculture
1:16	–	+	+	+
1:32	–	+	+	+
1:64	–	+	+	+
1:128	+	+	+	+

Dilution	Mortum Initial	Mortum Subculture	Sterl Initial	Sterl Subculture
1:16	–	–	–	+
1:32	–	+	+	+
1:64	+	+	+	+
1:128	+	+	+	+

36) In Table 7.3, which disinfectant is the most effective at stopping bacterial growth?
   A) Doom
   B) K.O.
   C) Mortum
   D) Sterl
   E) Can't tell

Answer: A
Skill: Understanding

37) In Table 7.3, which disinfectant was bactericidal?
   A) Doom
   B) K.O.
   C) Mortum
   D) Sterl
   E) Can't tell

Answer: C
Skill: Understanding

38) In Table 7.3, which disinfectant was most effective against *Salmonella*?
   A) Doom
   B) K.O.
   C) Mortum
   D) Sterl
   E) Can't tell

Answer: E
Skill: Understanding

39) Which of the following will *NOT* destroy prions?
   A) Boiling
   B) Incineration
   C) NaOH + autoclaving at 134°C
   D) Proteases
   E) All of the above destroy prions.

Answer: A
Skill: Understanding

40) Which one of the following pairs is mismatched?
   A) Ionizing radiation — hydroxyl radicals
   B) Ozone — takes electrons from substances
   C) Plasma sterilization — free radicals
   D) Supercritical fluids — CO_2
   E) Ultraviolet radiation — desiccation

Answer: E
Skill: Understanding

41) Which of the following will *NOT* preserve foods?
   A) Desiccation
   B) High pressure
   C) Ionizing radiation
   D) Microwaves
   E) Osmotic pressure

Answer: D
Skill: Understanding

42) Which of the following will *NOT* inactivate endospores?
   A) Autoclave
   B) Chlorine dioxide
   C) High pressure
   D) Plasma
   E) Supercritical CO_2

Answer: C
Skill: Understanding

43) If you were preparing nutrient agar at home and didn't have an autoclave, what could you use to sterilize the nutrient agar?
   A) Bleach
   B) Boiling for 1 hour
   C) Hydrogen peroxide
   D) Oven at 121°C for 1 hour
   E) Pressure cooker at 121°C for 15 minutes

Answer: E
Skill: Understanding

44) Bone and tendons for transplant are decontaminated by
    A) Ethylene oxide.
    B) Glutaraldehyde.
    C) Peroxygens.
    D) Plasma sterilization.
    E) Supercritical fluids.

Answer: E
Skill: Understanding

45) Which one of the following is most resistant to chemical biocides?
    A) Gram–negative bacteria
    B) Gram–positive bacteria
    C) Mycobacteria
    D) Protozoan cysts
    E) Viruses with lipid envelopes

Answer: C
Skill: Recall

Essay Questions

Table 7.4

The results below were obtained from a use–dilution test of two disinfectants. Cultures were inoculated into tubes with varying concentrations of disinfectants and incubated for 24 hr at 20 °C, then subcultured in nutrient media without disinfectants. (+ = growth; – = no growth)

Concentration	Disinfectant 1 Initial	Disinfectant 1 Subculture	Disinfectant 2 Initial	Disinfectant 2 Subculture
1:10	–	+	–	–
1:90	+	+	–	–
1:900	+	+	–	–
1:90,000	+	+	–	–
1:900,000	+	+	–	+
1:9,000,000	+	+	–	+

1) a. In Table 7.4, what is the minimal bacteriostatic concentration of each disinfectant?
   b. Which compound is bactericidal? At what concentration?

2) Assume that you are responsible for decontaminating materials in a large hospital. How would you sterilize each of the following? Briefly justify your answers.
   a. A mattress used by a patient with bubonic plague.
   b. Intravenous glucose–saline solutions.
   c. Used disposable syringes.
   d. Tissues taken from patients.

Table 7.5

The following results were obtained from a use–dilution test of two disinfectants. Cultures were inoculated into tubes containing varying concentrations of the disinfectants, incubated for 10 min. at 20 °C, and then transferred to growth media without disinfectant. (+ = growth; – = no growth)

Concentration	Disinfectant A	
	Gram–positive bacteria	Gram–negative bacteria
1:10	–	–
1:20–70	–	+
1:80	+	+
1:90	+	+
1:100	+	+
1:110–500	+	+

Concentration	Disinfectant B	
	Gram–positive bacteria	Gram–negative bacteria
1:10	–	–
1:20–70	+	+
1:80	+	+
1:90	+	+
1:100	+	+
1:110–500	+	+

3) a. In Table 7.5, which disinfectant is most effective?
   b. Against which group of bacteria is disinfectant A most effective?

Chapter 8 Microbial Genetics

Objective Questions

1) A gene is best defined as
   A) A segment of DNA.
   B) Three nucleotides that code for an amino acid.
   C) A sequence of nucleotides in DNA that codes for a functional product.
   D) A sequence of nucleotides in RNA that codes for a functional product.
   E) A transcribed unit of DNA.

   Answer: C
   Skill: Recall

2) Which of the following pairs is mismatched?
   A) DNA polymerase — makes a molecule of DNA from a DNA template
   B) RNA polymerase — makes a molecule of RNA from an RNA template
   C) DNA ligase — joins segments of DNA
   D) Transposase — insertion of DNA segments into DNA
   E) DNA gyrase — coils and twists DNA

   Answer: B
   Skill: Recall

3) Which of the following statements is false?
   A) DNA polymerase joins nucleotides in one direction only.
   B) The leading strand of DNA is made continuously.
   C) The lagging strand of DNA is started by an RNA primer.
   D) DNA replication proceeds in one direction around the bacterial chromosome.
   E) Multiple replication forks are possible on a bacterial chromosome.

   Answer: D
   Skill: Analysis

4) DNA is constructed of
   A) A single strand of nucleotides with internal hydrogen bonding.
   B) Nucleotides bonded A—C and G—T.
   C) Two strands of nucleotides running antiparallel.
   D) Two strands of identical nucleotides with hydrogen bonds between them.
   E) None of the above.

   Answer: C
   Skill: Recall

5) Which of the following is *NOT* a product of transcription?
   A) A new strand of DNA
   B) rRNA
   C) tRNA
   D) mRNA
   E) None of the above

   Answer: A
   Skill: Understanding

6) Which of the following statements about bacteriocins is false?
    A) The genes coding for them are on plasmids.
    B) They cause food–poisoning symptoms.
    C) Nisin is a bacteriocin used as a food preservative.
    D) They can be used to identify certain bacteria.
    E) Bacteriocins kill baceria.

Answer: B
Skill: Analysis

Figure 8.1

The following results were obtained from a replica-plating experiment:

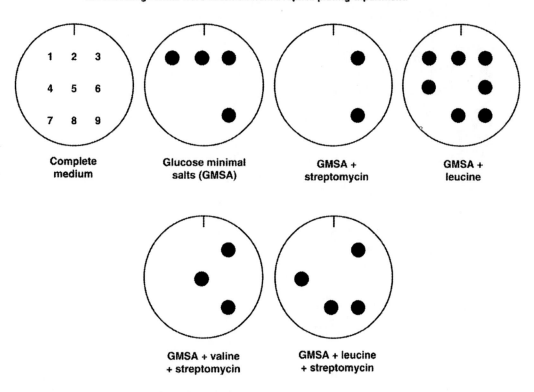

7) In Figure 8.1, which colonies are streptomycin–resistant and leucine–requiring?
    A) 1, 2, 3, and 9
    B) 3 and 9
    C) 4, 6, and 8
    D) 4 and 8
    E) 5 and 6

Answer: D
Skill: Understanding

Table 8.1

Culture 1: F$^+$, leucine$^+$, histidine$^+$

Culture 2: F$^-$, leucine$^-$, histidine$^-$

8) In Table 8.1, what will be the result of conjugation between cultures 1 and 2?
   A) 1 will remain the same;

      2 will become F$^+$, leucine$^-$, histidine$^-$
   B) 1 will become F$^-$, leu$^+$, his$^+$;

      2 will become F$^+$, leu$^-$, his$^-$
   C) 1 will become F$^-$, leu$^-$, his$^-$;
      2 will remain the same
   D) 1 will remain the same;

      2 will become F$^+$, leu$^+$, his$^+$
   E) 1 will remain the same;

      2 will become F$^+$ and recombination may occur

   Answer: A
   Skill: Understanding

9) In Table 8.1, if culture 1 mutates to Hfr, what will be the result of conjugation between the two
   cultures?
   A) They will both remain the same
   B) 1 will become F$^+$, leu$^+$, his$^+$;

      2 will become F$^+$, leu$^+$, his$^+$
   C) 1 will remain the same;
      Recombination will occur in 2
   D) 1 will become F$^-$, leu$^+$, his$^+$;

      2 will become Hfr, leu$^+$, his$^+$
   E) Can't tell

   Answer: C
   Skill: Understanding

10) An enzyme produced in response to the presence of a substrate is called
    A) An inducible enzyme.
    B) A repressible enzyme.
    C) A restriction enzyme.
    D) An operator.
    E) A promoter.

   Answer: A
   Skill: Recall

11) When glucose is high, cAMP is _____ : CAP _____ bind the lac operator, and RNA polymerase _____ bind the lac promoter.
   A) low, doesn't, doesn't
   B) high, does, does
   C) low, doesn't, doesn't
   D) high, doesn't, does
   E) low, does, does

Answer: C
Skill: Understanding

12) Transformation is the transfer of DNA from a donor to a recipient cell
   A) By a bacteriophage.
   B) As naked DNA in solution.
   C) By cell–to–cell contact.
   D) By crossing over.
   E) By sexual reproduction.

Answer: B
Skill: Recall

13) Genetic change in bacteria can be brought about by
   A) Mutation.
   B) Conjugation.
   C) Transduction.
   D) Transformation.
   E) All of the above.

Answer: E
Skill: Understanding

14) Which of the following statements is false regarding a bacterium that is R^+?
   A) It possesses a plasmid.
   B) R^+ can be transferred to a cell of the same species.
   C) It is resistant to certain drugs and heavy metals.
   D) It is F^+.
   E) R^+ can be transferred to a different species.

Answer: D
Skill: Analysis

15) The initial effect of ionizing radiation on a cell is that it causes
   A) DNA to break.
   B) Bonding between adjacent thymines.
   C) Base substitutions.
   D) The formation of highly reactive ions.
   E) The cells to get hot.

Answer: D
Skill: Recall

16) According to the operon model, for the synthesis of an inducible enzyme to occur, the
    A) End-product must not be in excess.
    B) Substrate must bind to the enzyme.
    C) Substrate must bind to the repressor.
    D) Repressor must bind to the operator.
    E) Repressor must not be synthesized.

Answer: C
Skill: Analysis

17) Synthesis of a repressible enzyme is stopped by
    A) The allosteric transition.
    B) The substrate binding to the repressor.
    C) The corepressor binding to the operator.
    D) The corepressor-repressor binding to the operator.
    E) The end-product binding to the promoter.

Answer: D
Skill: Analysis

Figure 8.2

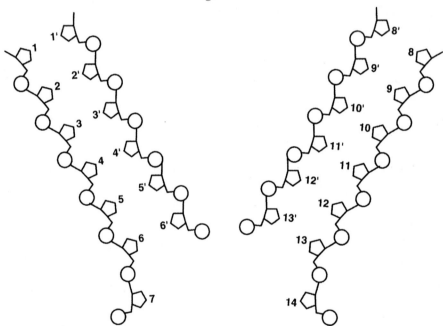

18) In Figure 8.2, if base 4 is thymine, what is base 4'?
    A) Adenine
    B) Thymine
    C) Cytosine
    D) Guanine
    E) Uracil

Answer: A
Skill: Understanding

19) In Figure 8.2, if base 4 is thymine, what is base 11'?
   A) Adenine
   B) Thymine
   C) Cytosine
   D) Guanine
   E) Uracil

Answer: B
Skill: Understanding

20) In Figure 8.2, base 2 is attached to
   A) Ribose.
   B) Phosphate.
   C) Deoxyribose.
   D) Thymine.
   E) Can't tell.

Answer: C
Skill: Recall

21) The damage caused by ultraviolet radiation is
   A) Never repaired.
   B) Repaired during transcription.
   C) Repaired during translation.
   D) Cut out and replaced.
   E) Repaired by DNA replication.

Answer: D
Skill: Recall

Table 8.2

Codon on mRNA and corresponding amino acid			
UUA	leucine	UAA	nonsense
GCA	alanine	AAU	sparagine
AAG	lysine	UGC	cysteine
GUU	valine	UCG, UCU	serine

22) (Use Table 8.2.) If the sequence of amino acids encoded by a strand of DNA is serine–alanine–lysine–leucine, what is the order of bases in the sense strand of DNA?
   A) 3′ UGUGCAAAGUUA
   B) 3′ AGACGTTTCAAT
   C) 3′ TCTCGTTTGTTA
   D) 5′ TGTGCTTTCTTA
   E) 5′ AGAGCTTTGAAT

Answer: B
Skill: Understanding

23) (Use Table 8.2.) If the sequence of amino acids encoded by a strand of DNA is serine–alanine–lysine–leucine, the coding for the antisense strand of DNA is
   A) 5′ ACAGTTTCAAT
   B) 5′ TCTGCAAAGTTA
   C) 3′ UGUGCAAAGUUA
   D) 3′ UCUCGAAAGUUA
   E) 3′ TCACGUUUCAAU

Answer: B
Skill: Understanding

24) (Use Table 8.2.) The anticodon for valine is
   A) GUU
   B) CUU
   C) CTT
   D) CAA
   E) GTA

Answer: D
Skill: Understanding

25) (Use Table 8.2.) What is the sequence of amino acids encoded by the following sequence of bases in a strand of DNA?

   3′ ATTACGCTTTGC

   A) Leucine–arginine–lysine–alanine
   B) Asparagine-arginine-lysine-alanine
   C) Asparagine-cysteine-valine-serine
   D) Transcription would stop at the first codon
   E) Can't tell

Answer: D
Skill: Understanding

26) (Use Table 8.2.) If a frameshift mutation occurred in the sequence of bases shown below, what would be the sequence of amino acids coded for?

   3′ ATTACGCTTTGC

   A) Leucine–arginine–lysine–alanine
   B) Asparagine-arginine-lysine–alanine
   C) Asparagine-cysteine-valine-serine
   D) Translation would stop at the first codon
   E) Can't tell

Answer: E
Skill: Understanding

Figure 8.3 – Metabolic Pathway

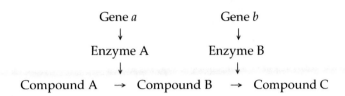

27) In Figure 8.3, if compound C reacts with the allosteric site of enzyme A, this would exemplify
    A) A mutation.
    B) Repression.
    C) Feedback inhibition.
    D) Competitive inhibition.
    E) Transcription.

Answer: C
Skill: Understanding

28) In Figure 8.3, if enzyme A is a repressible enzyme, compound C would
    A) Always be in excess.
    B) Bind to the enzyme.
    C) Bind to the corepressor.
    D) Bind to RNA polymerase.
    E) Bind to gene *a*.

Answer: C
Skill: Understanding

29) In Figure 8.3, if enzyme A is an inducible enzyme,
    A) Compound C would bind to the repressor.
    B) Compound A would bind to the repressor.
    C) Compound B would bind to enzyme A.
    D) Compound A would react with enzyme B.
    E) Compound C would react with gene *a*.

Answer: B
Skill: Understanding

30) Conjugation differs from reproduction because conjugation
    A) Replicates DNA.
    B) Transfers DNA vertically, to new cells.
    C) Transfers DNA horizontally, to cells in the same generation.
    D) Transcribes DNA to RNA.
    E) Copies RNA to make DNA.

Answer: C
Skill: Understanding

31) The necessary ingredients for DNA synthesis can be mixed together in a test tube. The DNA polymerase is from *Thermus aquaticus,* and the template is from a human cell. The DNA synthesized would be most similar to
    A) Human DNA.
    B) *T. aquaticus* DNA.
    C) A mixture of human and *T. aquaticus* DNA.
    D) Human RNA.
    E) *T. aquaticus* RNA.

Answer: A
Skill: Understanding

Table 8.3

Amino Acids Encoded by the Human p53 Gene

Bladder cancer																											
his	leu	thr	pro	glu	glu	lys	ser	ala	val	thr	ala	leu	trp	gly	lys	val	asn	val	asp	glu	val	gly	gly	glu	ala	leu	gly
Lung cancer A																											
his	leu	thr	pro	val	glu	lys	ser	ala	val	thr	ala	leu	trp	gly	lys	val	asn	val	asp	glu	val	gly	gly	glu	ala	leu	gly
Melanoma																											
his	leu	thr	pro	lys	glu	lys	ser	ala	val	thr	ala	leu	trp	gly	lys	val	asn	val	asp	glu	val	gly	gly	glu	ala	leu	gly
Prostate cancer																											
his	leu	thr	pro	glu	glu	lys	ser	ala	val	thr	ala	leu	trp	gly													
Breast cancer																											
his	leu	thr	pro	glu	glu	val	cys	arg	tyr	cys	pro	val	gly	glu	gly	glu	arg	ala									

32) Based on the information in Table 8.3, prostate cancer is probably the result of which kind of mutation?
    A) Analog
    B) Frameshift
    C) Missense
    D) Nonsense
    E) None of the above

Answer: D
Skill: Understanding

Figure 8.4

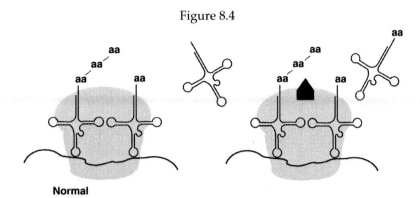

Normal

33) In Figure 8.4, the antibiotic chloramphenicol binds the 50S ribosome as shown. From this information you can conclude that chloramphenicol
    A) Prevents transcription in eukaryotes.
    B) Prevents translation in eukaryotes.
    C) Prevents transcription in prokaryotes.
    D) Prevents translation in prokaryotes.
    E) Prevents mRNA–ribosome binding.

Answer: D
Skill: Understanding

34) The mechanism by which the presence of glucose inhibits the arabinose operon is
    A) Catabolite repression.
    B) Translation.
    C) DNA polymerase.
    D) Repression.
    E) Induction.

Answer: A
Skill: Recall

35) The mechanism by which the presence of arabinose controls the arabinose operon is
    A) Catabolite repression.
    B) Translation.
    C) DNA polymerase.
    D) Repression.
    E) Induction.

Answer: E
Skill: Recall

36) If you knew the sequence of nucleotides within a gene, which one of the following could you determine with the most accuracy?
    A) The primary structure of the protein
    B) The secondary structure of the protein
    C) The tertiary structure of the protein
    D) The quaternary structure of the protein
    E) Can't tell

Answer: A
Skill: Analysis

37) An enzyme that makes covalent bonds between nucleotide sequences in DNA is
  A) RNA polymerase.
  B) DNA ligase.
  C) Restriction enzyme.
  D) Transposase.
  E) DNA polymerase.

Answer: B
Skill: Recall

38) An enzyme that copies DNA to make a molecule of RNA is
  A) RNA polymerase.
  B) DNA ligase.
  C) Restriction enzyme.
  D) Transposase.
  E) DNA polymerase.

Answer: A
Skill: Recall

39) An enzyme that cuts double–stranded DNA at specific nucleotide sequences.
  A) RNA polymerase
  B) DNA ligase
  C) Restriction enzyme
  D) Transposase
  E) DNA polymerase

Answer: C
Skill: Recall

40) Repair of damaged DNA might be viewed as a race between an endonuclease and
  A) DNA ligase.
  B) DNA polymerase.
  C) Helicase.
  D) Methylase.
  E) Primase.

Answer: D
Skill: Understanding

41) The cancer gene *ras* produces mRNA containing an extra exon that includes a number of UAA codons. Cancer cells produce ras mRNA missing this exon. This mistake most likely is due to a mistake by
  A) A chemical mutagen.
  B) DNA polymerase.
  C) Photolyases.
  D) snRNPs.
  E) UV radiation.

Answer: D
Skill: Understanding

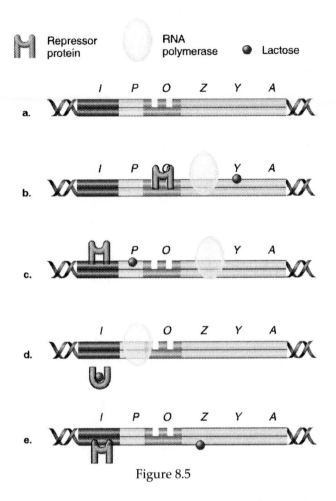

Figure 8.5

42) In Figure 8.5, which model of the *lac* operon correctly shows RNA polymerase, lactose, and repressor protein when the structural genes are being transcribed?
    A) a
    B) b
    C) c
    D) d
    E) e
Answer: D
Skill: Analysis

43) In transcription,
    A) DNA is changed to RNA.
    B) DNA is copied to RNA.
    C) DNA is replicated.
    D) RNA is copied to DNA.
    E) Proteins are made.
Answer: B
Skill: Recall

44) Assume the two *E.coli* strains shown below are allowed to conjugate.

Hfr: pro$^+$, arg$^+$, his$^+$, lys$^+$, met$^+$, ampicillin–sensitive

F: pro$^-$, arg$^-$, his$^-$, lys$^-$, met$^-$, ampicillin–resistant

What supplements would you add to glucose minimal salts agar to select for a recombinant cell that is lys$^+$, arg$^+$, amp–resistant?

A) Ampicillin, lysine, arginine
B) Lysine arginine
C) Ampicillin, proline, histidine, methionine
D) Proline, histidine, methionine
E) Ampicillin, prolein, histidine, lysine

Answer: C
Skill: Understanding

45) Protein synthesis in eukaryotes is similar to the process in prokaryotes in that both eukaryotes and prokaryotes

A) Have exons.
B) Have introns.
C) Require snRNPS.
D) Use methionine as the "start" amino acid.
E) Use codons to arrange amino acids.

Answer: E
Skill: Understanding

Essay Questions

1) What is the survival value of each of the following?
   a. Semiconservative replication of DNA.
   b. The degeneracy of the genetic code.

2) Scientists are concerned that bacteria will be resistant to all antibiotics within the next decade. Using your knowledge of genetics, describe how bacterial populations can develop drug resistance.

3) Explain why the following statement is false: Sexual reproduction is the only mechanism for genetic change.

Chapter 9 Biotechnology and Recombinant DNA

Objective Questions

1) The following steps are used to make DNA fingerprints. What is the third step?
   A) Collect DNA.
   B) Digest with a restriction enzyme.
   C) Perform electrophoresis.
   D) Lyse cells.
   E) Add stain.

Answer: B
Skill: Understanding

Figure 9.1

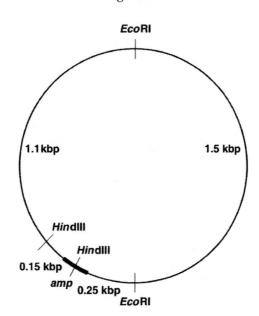

2) How many pieces will *Eco*RI produce from the plasmid shown in Figure 9.1?
   A) 1
   B) 2
   C) 3
   D) 4
   E) 5

Answer: B
Skill: Analysis

3) In Figure 9.1, after digestion with the appropriate restriction enzyme, what is the smallest piece containing the ampicillin–resistance (amp) gene?
   A) 0.17 kilobase pairs
   B) 0.25 kbp
   C) 1.08 kbp
   D) 1.50 kbp
   E) 3.00 kbp

Answer: D
Skill: Understanding

Figure 9.2

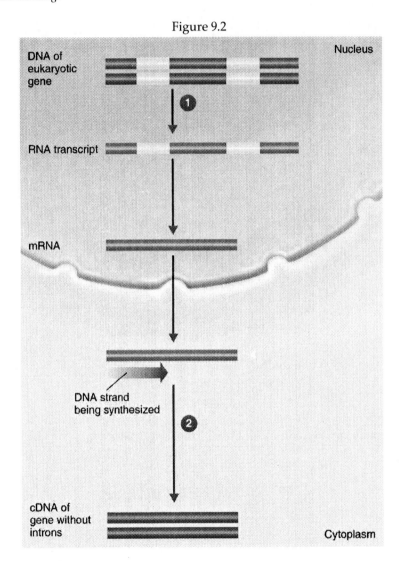

4) In Figure 9.2, the enzyme in step 1 is
   A) DNA polymerase.
   B) DNA ligase.
   C) RNA polymerase.
   D) Reverse transcriptase.
   E) Spliceosome.

Answer: C
Skill: Analysis

5) In Figure 9.2, the enzyme in step 2 is
    A) DNA polymerase.
    B) DNA ligase.
    C) RNA polymerase.
    D) Reverse transcriptase.
    E) Spliceosome.

Answer: D
Skill: Recall

6) The reaction catalyzed by DNA polymerase is
    A) DNA → mRNA
    B) mRNA → cDNA
    C) mRNA → protein
    D) DNA → DNA
    E) tRNA → mRNA

Answer: D
Skill: Recall

7) Which of the following is an advantage of using *E. coli* to make a human gene product?
    A) Endotoxin may be in the product.
    B) It doesn't secrete most proteins.
    C) Its genes are well known.
    D) It can't process introns.
    E) None of the above.

Answer: C
Skill: Recall

8) Which of the following is *NOT* an agricultural product made by DNA techniques?
    A) Frost retardant
    B) *Bacillus thuringiensis* insecticide
    C) Nitrogenase (nitrogen fixation)
    D) Glyphosate–resistant crops
    E) Pectinase

Answer: E
Skill: Recall

9) If you have inserted a gene in the Ti plasmid, the next step in genetic engineering is
    A) Transformation of *E. coli* with Ti plasmid.
    B) Splicing T DNA into a plasmid.
    C) Transformation of an animal cell.
    D) Inserting the Ti plasmid into *Agrobacterium*.
    E) Inserting the Ti plasmid into a plant cell.

Answer: D
Skill: Understanding

10) Which of the following methods of making rDNA could be described as "hit or miss"?
   A) Protoplast fusion
   B) Viral transduction
   C) Transformation
   D) Cloning
   E) Gene gun
   Answer: A
   Skill: Understanding

Figure 9.3

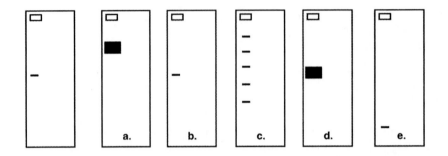

11) The figure at the left in Figure 9.3 shows a gene identified by Southern blotting. What will a Southern blot of the same gene look like after PCR?
   A) a
   B) b
   C) c
   D) d
   E) e
   Answer: D
   Skill: Understanding

12) Suicide genes can be controlled by the fimbriae–gene operator. This would result in the death of
   A) All cells.
   B) Cells making flagella.
   C) Cells making fimbriae.
   D) Cells at 37°C.
   E) Conjugating cells.
   Answer: C
   Skill: Analysis

13) Subunit vaccines can be made by genetic modification of yeast cells. A side effect of these vaccines might be
   A) The disease.
   B) A yeast infection.
   C) Due to extraneous material.
   D) Failure of the vaccine to provide immunity.
   E) None of the above.
   Answer: E
   Skill: Analysis

14) *E. coli* makes insulin because
    A) It needs to regulate its cell–glucose level.
    B) It's an ancient gene that now has no function.
    C) The insulin gene was inserted into it.
    D) It picked up the insulin gene from another cell.
    E) No reason; it doesn't make insulin.

Answer: C
Skill: Recall

15) The value of cDNA in recombinant DNA is that
    A) It lacks exons.
    B) It lacks introns.
    C) It's really RNA.
    D) It contains introns and exons.

Answer: B
Skill: Recall

16) Which enzyme does *NOT* make sticky ends?

	Enzyme	Recognition
A)	*Bam*HI	G↓GATCC
		CCTAG↑G
B)	*Eco*RI	G↓AATTC
		CTTAA↑G
C)	*Hae*III	GG↓CC
		CC↑GG
D)	*Hind*III	A↓AGCTT
		TTCGA↑A
E)	*Pst*I	CTGC↓G
		G↑ACGTC

Answer: C
Skill: Analysis

17) Which enzyme would cut this strand of DNA: GCATGGATCCCAATGC?

A) Enzyme	Recognition
*Bam*HI	G↓GATCC
	CCCTAG↑G
B) Enzyme	Recognition
*Eco*RI	G↓AATTC
	CTTAA↑G
C) Enzyme	Recognition
*Hae*III	GG↓CC
	CC↑GG
D) Enzyme	Recognition
*Hind*III	A↓AGCTT
	TTCGA↑A
E) Enzyme	Recognition
*Pst*I	CTGC↓G
	G↑ACGTC

Answer: A
Skill: Analysis

18) Pieces of DNA stored in yeast cells are called a
   A) Library.
   B) Clone.
   C) Vector.
   D) Southern blot.
   E) PCR.

Answer: A
Skill: Recall

19) A population of cells carrying a desired plasmid is called a
   A) Library.
   B) Clone.
   C) Vector.
   D) Southern blot.
   E) PCR.

Answer: B
Skill: Recall

20) Self–replicating DNA used to transmit a gene from one organism to another is a
   A) Library.
   B) Clone.
   C) Vector.
   D) Southern blot.
   E) PCR.

Answer: C
Skill: Recall

21) The purpose of the Human Genome Project was to
   A) Identify all of the human genes.
   B) Sequence the nucleotides in human DNA.
   C) Translate human DNA.
   D) Identify genes of all organisms.
   E) None of the above.

Answer: B
Skill: Analysis

22) A colleague has used computer modeling to design an improved enzyme. To produce this enzyme, the next step is to
   A) Look for a bacterium that makes the improved enzyme.
   B) Mutate bacteria until one makes the improved enzyme.
   C) Determine the nucleotide sequence for the improved enzyme.
   D) Synthesize the gene for the improved enzyme.
   E) Use siRNA to produce the enzyme.

Answer: C
Skill: Analysis

23) You have a small gene that you wish replicated by PCR. After 3 replication cycles, how many double–stranded DNA molecules do you have?
   A) 2
   B) 4
   C) 8
   D) 16
   E) Thousands

Answer: C
Skill: Understanding

24) You have a small gene that you wish replicated by PCR. You add radioactively labeled nucleotides to the PCR thermocycler. After 3 replication cycles, what percentage of the DNA single strands are radioactively labeled?
   A) 0%
   B) 12.5%
   C) 50%
   D) 87.5%
   E) 100%

Answer: D
Skill: Understanding

Figure 9.4

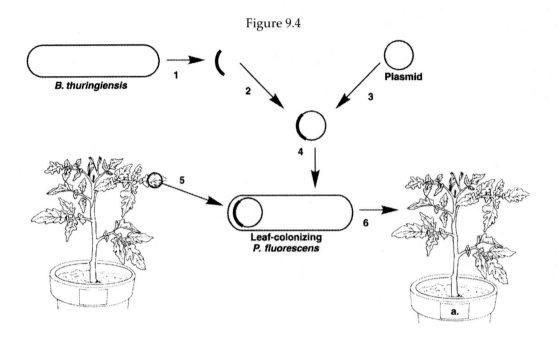

25) In Figure 9.4, the resulting organism (a) is
    A) *Bacillus thuringiensis*.
    B) *Pseudomonas fluorescens*.
    C) A tomato plant.
    D) *E. coli*.
    E) a plant × *Pseudomonas* hybrid.

Answer: C
Skill: Analysis

26) In Figure 9.4, the resulting *P. fluorescens* has
    A) A tomato gene.
    B) An *E. coli* gene.
    C) A *Bacillus* gene.
    D) A tomato and a *Bacillus* gene.
    E) No new gene.

Answer: C
Skill: Analysis

27) In Figure 9.4, the purpose of this experiment is to
    A) Put a gene into a plant.
    B) Put an insecticide on plant leaves.
    C) Put a gene in *Bacillus*.
    D) Isolate *Pseudomonas* from a plant.
    E) Make a better tomato.

Answer: B
Skill: Analysis

28) In Figure 9.4, the vector is
    A) A virus.
    B) A plasmid.
    C) A library.
    D) RNA.
    E) *Pseudomonas*.

Answer: B
Skill: Analysis

29) In Figure 9.4, the process required in step 5 is
    A) Transformation.
    B) Southern blotting.
    C) PCR.
    D) Transcription.
    E) Conjugation.

Answer: A
Skill: Analysis

30) A source of heat–stable DNA polymerase is
    A) *Agrobacterium tumefaciens*.
    B) *Thermus aquaticus*.
    C) *Saccharomyces cerevisiae*.
    D) *Bacillus thuringiensis*.
    E) *Pseudomonas*.

Answer: B
Skill: Recall

31) The Pap test for cervical cancer involves microscopic examination of cervical cells for cancerous cells. A new, rapid diagnostic test to detect human papilloma virus (HPV) DNA before cancer develops is done without microscopic exam. The steps involved in this FastHPV test are listed. What is the second step?
    A) Add an RNA probe for HPV DNA
    B) Lyse human cells
    C) Add enzyme–linked antibodies against DNA–RNA
    D) Add enzyme substrate
    E) It doesn't matter.

Answer: A
Skill: Understanding

32) Gene silencing blocks an undesirable product by
    A) Allosteric inhibition of an enzyme.
    B) End–product repression.
    C) Making double-stranded RNA.
    D) Blocking transcription.
    E) Blocking DNA replication.

Answer: C
Skill: Understanding

33) You want to determine whether a person has a certain mutant gene. The process involves using a primer and Taq. This process is
    A) Translation.
    B) Restriction mapping.
    C) Transformation.
    D) PCR.
    E) Site-directed mutagenesis.

Answer: D
Skill: Recall

34) To see the results of your work in question 33, you need to use
    A) Northern blotting.
    B) Southern blotting.
    C) Western blotting.
    D) Colony blotting.
    E) Selection.

Answer: B
Skill: Analysis

35) Assume you have discovered a cell that produces a lipase that works in cold water for a laundry additive. You can increase the efficiency of this enzyme by changing one amino acid. This is done by
    A) Irradiating the cells.
    B) Site-directed mutagenesis.
    C) Enrichment.
    D) Selective breeding.
    E) Selection.

Answer: B
Skill: Analysis

36) The use of an antibiotic-resistance gene on a plasmid used in genetic engineering makes
    A) Replica plating possible.
    B) Direct selection possible.
    C) The recombinant cell dangerous.
    D) The recombinant cell unable to survive.
    E) All of the above.

Answer: B
Skill: Analysis

37) The following steps must be performed to make a bacterium produce human protein X:
    1–Translation; 2–Restriction enzyme; 3–Prokaryotic transcription; 4–DNA ligase;
    5–Transformation; 6–Eukaryotic transcription; 7–Reverse transcription.
    Put the steps in the correct sequence.
    A) 5, 2, 3, 4, 7, 6, 1
    B) 1, 2, 3, 5, 4, 7, 6
    C) 6, 7, 2, 3, 4, 5, 1
    D) 6, 7, 2, 4, 5, 3, 1
    E) 6, 2, 1, 3, 4, 5, 7

Answer: D
Skill: Understanding

38) Large numbers of bacterial cells are *NOT* found in crown galls because
    A) The plant kills the bacteria.
    B) Cell walls protect the plant from bacterial invasion.
    C) A gene in plant cells is controlling growth.
    D) Bacteria kill plants.
    E) The assumption is not true; many bacteria are in the galls.

Answer: C
Skill: Recall

39) A restriction fragment is
    A) A gene.
    B) A segment of DNA.
    C) A segment of mRNA.
    D) A segment of tRNA.
    E) cDNA.

Answer: B
Skill: Recall

40) A specific gene can be inserted into a cell by all of the following *EXCEPT*
    A) Protoplast fusion.
    B) A gene gun.
    C) Microinjection.
    D) Electroporation.
    E) *Agrobacterium.*

Answer: A
Skill: Analysis

41) Which of the following processes is *NOT* involved in making cDNA?
    A) Reverse transcription
    B) RNA processing to remove introns
    C) Transcription
    D) Translation

Answer: D
Skill: Understanding

42) PCR can be used to identify an unknown bacterium because
    A) The RNA primer is specific.
    B) DNA polymerase will replicate DNA.
    C) DNA can be electrophoresed.
    D) All cells have DNA.
    E) All cells have RNA.

Answer: A
Skill: Analysis

43) PCR can be used to amplify DNA in a clinical sample. The following steps are used in PCR. What is the fourth step?
     A) Collect DNA.
     B) Incubate at 94°C.
     C) Incubate at 60°C.
     D) Incubate at 72°C.
     E) Add DNA polymerase.

Answer: C
Skill: Understanding

44) Restriction enzymes are
     A) Bacterial enzymes that splice DNA.
     B) Bacterial enzymes that destroy phage DNA.
     C) Animal enzymes that splice RNA.
     D) Viral enzymes that destroy host DNA.

Answer: B
Skill: Recall

45) Which of the following processes *CANNOT* be used to insert foreign DNA into cells?
     A) Transformation
     B) Electroporation
     C) Protoplast fusion
     D) A gene gun
     E) All of the above can be used to insert foreign DNA into cells.

Answer: E
Skill: Recall

Essay Questions

1) Some scientists are concerned that genetic engineering allows humans to tamper with evolution. Argue either for or against this position.

2) *Pseudomonas syringae* is found naturally in the soil. Sold as Snomax, it is used to make snow at ski resorts. The same bacterium with a gene deletion (Ice-minus) is used to prevent ice formation on plants. Should Snomax and Ice-minus be considered modified organisms and subject to precautions of releasing genetically modified organisms? Explain why or why not.

3) In the Human Genome Project, pieces of human DNA are stored in *E. coli* or yeast. Discuss the purpose of this activity.

Chapter 10 Classification of Microorganisms

Objective Questions

1) Which of the following statements about archaea is false?
    A) They are prokaryotes.
    B) They lack peptidoglycan in their cell walls.
    C) Some are thermoacidophiles; others are extreme halophiles.
    D) They evolved before bacteria.
    E) Some produce methane from carbon dioxide and hydrogen.

   Answer: D
   Skill: Recall

2) Which of the following characterizes the Domain Bacteria?
    A) Prokaryotic cells; ether linkages in phospholipids
    B) Eukaryotic cells; ester linkages in phospholipids
    C) Prokaryotic cells; ester linkages in phospholipids
    D) Complex cellular structures
    E) Multicellular

   Answer: C
   Skill: Recall

3) If two organisms have similar rRNA sequences, you can conclude that
    A) They live in the same place.
    B) They evolved from a common ancestor.
    C) They will have different G–C ratios.
    D) They will both ferment lactose.
    E) They mated with each other.

   Answer: B
   Skill: Understanding

4) What is the outstanding characteristic of the Kingdom Fungi?
    A) All members are photosynthetic.
    B) Members absorb dissolved organic matter.
    C) Members absorb dissolved inorganic matter.
    D) All members are microscopic.
    E) All members are macroscopic.

   Answer: B
   Skill: Analysis

5) Which of the following statements about the members of the Kingdom Plantae is false?
    A) They are multicellular.
    B) They have eukaryotic cells.
    C) They can photosynthesize.
    D) They use organic carbon sources.
    E) They use inorganic energy sources.

   Answer: D
   Skill: Recall

6) Which of the following statements about the members of the Kingdom Animalia is false?
    A) They are multicellular.
    B) They have eukaryotic cells.
    C) They can photosynthesize.
    D) They use organic carbon sources.
    E) They use organic energy sources.

Answer: C
Skill: Recall

7) A *genus* can best be defined as
    A) A taxon composed of families.
    B) A taxon composed of one or more species and below family.
    C) A taxon belonging to a species.
    D) A taxon comprised of classes.
    E) The most specific taxon.

Answer: B
Skill: Understanding

8) A bacterial species differs from a species of eukaryotic organisms in that a bacterial species
    A) Does not breed with other species.
    B) Has a limited geographical distribution.
    C) Can be distinguished from other bacterial species.
    D) Is a population of cells with similar characteristics.
    E) Breeds with its own species.

Answer: D
Skill: Understanding

9) Which of the following is the best evidence for a three–domain system?
    A) There are three distinctly different types of ribosomes.
    B) There are three distinctly different cellular chemical compositions.
    C) There are three distinctly different Gram reactions.
    D) Some bacteria live in extreme environments.
    E) There are three distinctly different types of nuclei.

Answer: B
Skill: Analysis

10) Biochemical tests are used to determine
    A) Staining characteristics.
    B) Amino acid sequences.
    C) Nucleic acid–base composition.
    D) Enzymatic activities.
    E) All of the above.

Answer: D
Skill: Understanding

11) Which of the following is *NOT* based on nucleic–acid hybridization?
    A) DNA chip
    B) FISH
    C) PCR
    D) Southern blotting
    E) Western blotting

Answer: D
Skill: Understanding

12) The phylogenetic classification of bacteria is based on
    A) Cell morphology.
    B) Gram reaction.
    C) rRNA sequences.
    D) Habitat.
    E) Diseases.

Answer: C
Skill: Recall

13) Which of the following statements is *NOT* a reason for classifying viruses in the three domains rather than in a fourth domain?
    A) Some viruses can incorporate their genome into a host's genome.
    B) Viruses direct anabolic pathways of host cells.
    C) Viruses are obligate parasites.
    D) Viruses are not composed of cells.
    E) None of the above.

Answer: D
Skill: Understanding

14) Which of the following provides taxonomic information that includes the others?
    A) Nucleic acid hybridization
    B) Nucleic acid–base composition
    C) Amino acid sequencing
    D) Biochemical tests
    E) Cladogram

Answer: E
Skill: Analysis

15) Fossil evidence indicates that prokaryotic cells first existed on the Earth
    A) 350 years ago.
    B) 3500 years ago.
    C) 3.5 million years ago.
    D) 3.5 billion years ago.
    E) 3.5×10^{12} years ago.

Answer: D
Skill: Recall

Figure 10.1

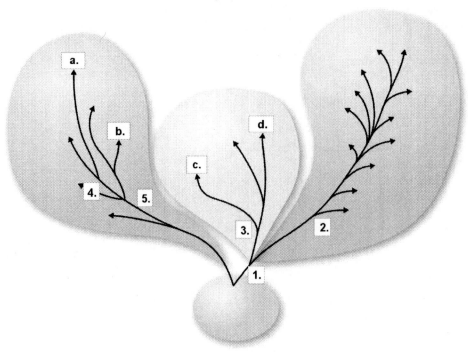

16) In Figure 10.1, species "c." is most closely related to
   A) a
   B) b
   C) c
   D) d
   E) e

Answer: D
Skill: Understanding

17) In Figure 10.1, the closest ancestor for both species "a." and species "b." would be
   A) 1
   B) 2
   C) 3
   D) 4
   E) 5

Answer: E
Skill: Understanding

18) Protist is a diverse group of organisms that are similar in
   A) rRNA sequences.
   B) Metabolic type.
   C) Motility.
   D) Ecology.
   E) None of the above.

Answer: E
Skill: Analysis

19) In the scientific name *Enterobacter aerogenes*, *Enterobacter* is the
    A) Specific epithet.
    B) Genus.
    C) Family.
    D) Order.
    E) Kingdom.

Answer: B
Skill: Analysis

20) The arrangement of organisms into taxa
    A) Shows degrees of relatedness between organisms.
    B) Shows relationships to common ancestors.
    C) Was designed by Charles Darwin.
    D) Is arbitrary.
    E) Is based on evolution.

Answer: A
Skill: Analysis

21) Bacteria and archaea are similar in which of the following?
    A) Peptidoglycan cell walls
    B) Methionine as the start signal for protein synthesis
    C) Sensitivity to antibiotics
    D) Possessing prokaryotic cells
    E) Plasma membrane ester linkage

Answer: D
Skill: Recall

22) Which of the following best defines a *strain*?
    A) A population of cells that differs from other members of the species
    B) A group of organisms with a limited geographical distribution
    C) A pure culture
    D) A group of cells all derived from a single parent
    E) The same as a species

Answer: D
Skill: Recall

23) Serological testing is based on the fact that
    A) All bacteria have the same antigens.
    B) Antibodies react specifically with an antigen.
    C) The human body makes antibodies against bacteria.
    D) Antibodies cause the formation of antigens.
    E) Bacteria clump together when mixed with any antibodies.

Answer: B
Skill: Analysis

24) Phage typing is based on the fact that
    A) Bacteria are destroyed by viruses.
    B) Viruses cause disease.
    C) Bacterial viruses attack specific cells.
    D) *Staphylococcus* causes infections.
    E) Phages and bacteria are related.

Answer: C
Skill: Analysis

25) Organism A has 70 moles % G+C, and organism B has 40 moles % G+C. Which of the
    following can be concluded from these data?
    A) The two organisms are related.
    B) The two organisms are unrelated.
    C) The organisms make entirely different enzymes.
    D) Their nucleic acids will not hybridize.
    E) None of the above.

Answer: B
Skill: Understanding

26) Nucleic acid hybridization is based on the fact that
    A) The strands of DNA can be separated.
    B) A chromosome is composed of complementary strands.
    C) Pairing between complementary bases occurs.
    D) DNA is composed of genes.
    E) All cells have DNA.

Answer: C
Skill: Recall

27) One of the most popular taxonomic tools is DNA fingerprinting to develop profiles of
    organisms. These profiles provide direct information about
    A) Enzymatic activities.
    B) Protein composition.
    C) The presence of specific genes.
    D) Antigenic composition.
    E) Nucleotide sequences.

Answer: E
Skill: Understanding

28) Which of the following statements is *NOT* a reason why fluorescent in situ hybridization
    (FISH) has become a valuable tool for environmental microbiologists?
    A) It allows for detection of uncultured microbes.
    B) It demonstrates the diversity of microbes in an environment.
    C) It allows observation of microbes in their natural environment in association with other
       microbes.
    D) To obtain pure cultures of microbes.
    E) All of the above.

Answer: D
Skill: Understanding

29) Which of the following criteria is most useful in determining whether two organisms are related?
    A) Both ferment lactose.
    B) Both are gram–positive.
    C) Both are motile.
    D) Both are aerobic.
    E) All are equally important.

Answer: B
Skill: Recall

30) A clone is
    A) Genetically identical cells derived from a single cell.
    B) A genetically engineered cell.
    C) A taxon composed of species.
    D) A mound of cells on an agar medium.
    E) None of the above.

Answer: A
Skill: Recall

Figure 10.2
A nucleic acid hybridization experiment produced the following results.

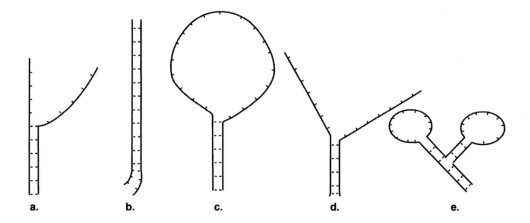

a.   b.   c.   d.   e.

31) In Figure 10.2, which figure shows the most closely related organisms?
    A) a
    B) b
    C) c
    D) d
    E) e

Answer: B
Skill: Analysis

Table 10.1

1. 9+2 flagella
2. Nucleus
3. Plasma membrane
4. Peptidoglycan
5. Mitochondrion
6. Fimbriae

32) In Table 10.1, which features are found in all Eukarya?
   A) 2, 3, 5
   B) 1, 4, 6
   C) 3, 5
   D) 2, 3
   E) 1, 2, 5

Answer: D
Skill: Analysis

33) In Table 10.1, which feature(s) is (are) found *only* in prokaryotes?
   A) 1, 2, 3
   B) 4, 6
   C) 2
   D) 1
   E) 2, 4, 5

Answer: B
Skill: Analysis

Figure 10.3

This figure shows the results of a gel electrophoresis separation of restriction fragments of the DNA of different organisms.

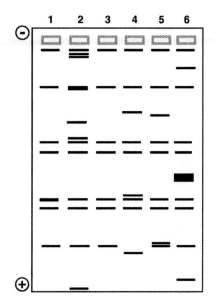

34) In Figure 10.3, which two are most closely related?
   A) 1 and 3
   B) 2 and 4
   C) 3 and 5
   D) 2 and 5
   E) 4 and 5

Answer: A
Skill: Analysis

35) Into which group would you place a photosynthetic cell that lacks a nucleus?
   A) Animalia
   B) Bacteria
   C) Fungi
   D) Plantae
   E) Protista

Answer: B
Skill: Analysis

36) Into which group would you place a multicellular heterotroph with chitin cell walls?
   A) Animalia
   B) Archaea
   C) Bacteria
   D) Fungi
   E) Plantae

Answer: D
Skill: Understanding

37) You discovered a unicellular organism that lacks a nucleus and peptidoglycan. You suspect the organism is in the group
    A) Animalia.
    B) Archaea.
    C) Bacteria.
    D) Fungi.
    E) Plantae.

Answer: B
Skill: Understanding

38) Into which group would you place a unicellular organism that has 70S ribosomes and a peptidoglycan cell wall?
    A) Animalia
    B) Bacteria
    C) Fungi
    D) Plantae
    E) Protist

Answer: B
Skill: Analysis

Table 10.2

I.   Gram–positive
    A. Catalase+
        1.   Acid from glucose..................................   *Staphylococcus*
        2.   Glucose–..   *Micrococcus*
    B. Catalase–
        1.   Coccus..   *Streptococcus*
        2.   Rod..   *Lactobacillus*
II. Gram–negative
    A. Oxidase–
        1.   Acid from lactose
            a.   Uses citric acid..............................   *Citrobacter*
            b.   Citric acid–....................................   *Escherichia*
        2.   Lactose–
            a. H_2S produced
                (1) Urease positive.........................   *Proteus*
                (2) Urease negative.......................   *Salmonella*
    B. Oxidase+
        1.   Rod...   *Pseudomonas*
        2.   Coccus...   *Neisseria*

39) Use the dichotomous key in Table 10.2 to identify a gram–negative rod that ferments lactose and uses citric acid as its sole carbon source.
    A) *Citrobacter*
    B) *Escherichia*
    C) *Lactobacillus*
    D) *Pseudomonas*
    E) *Staphylococcus*

Answer: A
Skill: Understanding

40) Use the dichotomous key in Table 10.2 to identify a gram–negative coccus.
    A) *Neisseria*
    B) *Pseudomonas*
    C) *Staphylococcus*
    D) *Streptococcus*
    E) *Micrococcus*

Answer: A
Skill: Understanding

41) Into which group would you place a multicellular organism that has a mouth and lives inside the human liver?
    A) Animalia
    B) Fungi
    C) Plantae
    D) Firmicutes (gram–positive bacteria)
    E) Proteobacteria (gram–negative bacteria)

Answer: A
Skill: Analysis

42) Into which group would you place a photosynthetic organism that lacks a nucleus and has a thin peptidoglycan wall surrounded by an outer membrane?
    A) Animalia
    B) Fungi
    C) Plantae
    D) Firmicutes (gram–positive bacteria)
    E) Proteobacteria (gram–negative bacteria)

Answer: E
Skill: Analysis

Figure 10.4

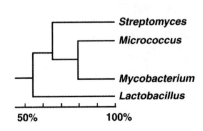

43) In the cladogram shown in Figure 10.4, which two organisms are most closely related?
    A) *Streptomyces* and *Micrococcus*
    B) *Micrococcus* and *Mycobacterium*
    C) *Mycobacterium* and *Lactobacillus*
    D) *Streptomyces* and *Lactobacillus*
    E) *Streptomyces* and *Mycobacterium*

Answer: B
Skill: Understanding

44) Which of the following characteristics indicates that two organisms are closely related?
    A) Both are cocci.
    B) Both ferment lactose.
    C) Their DNA can hybridize.
    D) Both normally live in clams.
    E) Both are motile.

Answer: C
Skill: Recall

45) Data collected to date indicate that
    A) Humans and marine mammals cannot be infected by the same pathogens.
    B) Marine mammals do not get infectious diseases.
    C) New species of bacteria may be discovered in wild animals.
    D) Marine mammals don't have an immune system.
    E) None of the above.

Answer: E
Skill: Recall

Essay Questions

Figure 10.5

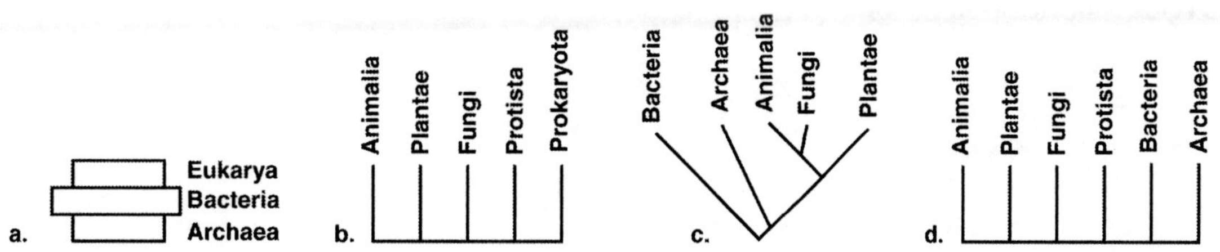

1) Choose one of the phylogenetic schemes in Figure 10.5 and explain why you feel this one is preferable to the others.

Table 10.3

	Organism				
Characteristic	A	B	C	D	E
Morphology	Rod	Rod	Coccus	Coccus	Rod
Motile	Yes	Yes	No	No	Yes
Gram Reaction	–	–	+	–	–
Glucose Utilization	Oxid.	Ferm.	Ferm.	Ferm.	None
% G+C	58–70	50–51	30–40	47–52	58–70
Cytochrome oxidase	Present	Absent	Absent	Present	Present

2) Use the information given in Table 10.3 to answer questions (a) and (b). Note to instructors: A=*Pseudomonas*; B=*Escherichia*; C=*Staphylococcus*; D=*Neisseria*; E=*Alcaligenes*.
   a. Which organisms are most closely related? On what did you base your answer?
   b. DNA from which organisms will probably hybridize?

3) One of the advantages of some newly developed rapid identification tools is that pure cultures aren't needed. Why is a pure culture necessary for biochemical tests such as the Enterotube, but not for DNA probes?

Chapter 11 The Prokaryotes: Domains Bacteria and Archaea

Objective Questions

1) Which of the following are found primarily in the intestines of humans?
    A) Gram–negative aerobic rods and cocci
    B) Aerobic, helical bacteria
    C) Facultatively anaerobic gram–negative rods
    D) Gram–positive cocci
    E) Endospore–forming rods

Answer: C
Skill: Recall

Figure 11.1

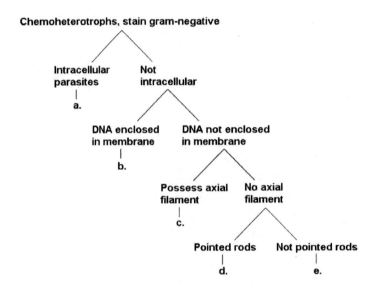

2) What is group "c." in the key shown in Figure 11.1?
    A) Bacteroidetes
    B) Chlamydiae
    C) Fusobacteria
    D) Planctomycetes
    E) Spirochaetes

Answer: E
Skill: Analysis

3) Which of the following is *NOT* a characteristic of the non–endospore-forming gram-positive rods?
   A) Are aerotolerant
   B) Carry out fermentative metabolism
   C) Don't produce endospores
   D) Are nonpathogenic
   E) Lack cell walls

Answer: D
Skill: Analysis

4) Which of the following is *NOT* a characteristic of *Neisseria*?
   A) Requires X and V factors
   B) Cocci
   C) Gram–negative
   D) Oxidase–positive
   E) Some species are human pathogens.

Answer: A
Skill: Analysis

5) *Staphylococcus* and *Streptococcus* can be easily differentiated in a laboratory by which one of the following?
   A) Cell shape
   B) Gram stain reaction
   C) Growth in high salt concentrations
   D) Ability to cause disease
   E) Glucose fermentation

Answer: C
Skill: Analysis

6) Which of the following genera is an anaerobic gram–negative rod?
   A) *Escherichia*
   B) *Staphylococcus*
   C) *Bacteroides*
   D) *Treponema*
   E) *Neisseria*

Answer: C
Skill: Recall

7) Which of the following do you expect to be most resistant to high temperatures?
   A) *Bacillus subtilis*
   B) *Eschericia coli*
   C) *Neisseria gonorrhoeae*
   D) *Staphylococcus aureus*
   E) *Streptococcocus pyogenes*

Answer: A
Skill: Analysis

8) Which of the following is *NOT* an enteric?
   A) *Salmonella*
   B) *Shigella*
   C) *Escherichia*
   D) *Enterobacter*
   E) *Campylobacter*

   Answer: E
   Skill: Recall

9) Which of the following is *NOT* a characteristic of spirochetes?
   A) Possess an axial filament
   B) Gram–negative
   C) Helical shape
   D) Easily observed with brightfield microscopy
   E) Difficult to culture in vitro

   Answer: D
   Skill: Recall

10) You have isolated a bacterium that grows in a medium containing an organic substrate and nitrate in the absence of oxygen. The nitrate is reduced to nitrogen gas. You can be sure that this bacterium is
   A) Gram–positive.
   B) Using anaerobic respiration.
   C) A chemoautotroph.
   D) A photoautotroph.
   E) A photoheterotroph.

   Answer: B
   Skill: Understanding

11) Which of the following lacks a cell wall?
   A) *Borrelia*
   B) *Mycoplasma*
   C) *Mycobacterium*
   D) *Clostridium*
   E) *Nocardia*

   Answer: B
   Skill: Recall

12) Which of the following bacteria is gram–negative?
   A) *Treponema*
   B) *Corynebacterium*
   C) *Bacillus*
   D) *Staphylococcus*
   E) *Mycobacterium*

   Answer: A
   Skill: Analysis

13) Which of the following form conidiospores?
    A) Endospore–forming gram–positive rods and cocci
    B) Actinomycetes and related organisms
    C) Rickettsias
    D) Anaerobic gram–negative cocci
    E) Spiral and curved bacteria

Answer: B
Skill: Recall

14) Which of the following pairs is mismatched?
    A) Dissimilatory sulfate–reducing bacteria — produce H_2S
    B) Archaea — extremophiles
    C) Chemoautotrophic bacteria — fix atmospheric nitrogen
    D) Actinomycetes — reproduce by fragmentation
    E) *Cytophaga* — a gliding, nonfruiting bacterium

Answer: C
Skill: Analysis

15) Rickettsias differ from chlamydias in that rickettsias
    A) Are gram–negative.
    B) Are intracellular parasites.
    C) Require an arthropod for transmission.
    D) Form elementary bodies.
    E) Lack cell walls.

Answer: C
Skill: Recall

16) Requirements for X and V factors are used to identify
    A) *Staphylococcus.*
    B) *Escherichia.*
    C) *Neisseria.*
    D) *Haemophilus.*
    E) *Pseudomonas.*

Answer: D
Skill: Recall

17) You have isolated a bacterium that grows in a medium containing only inorganic nutrients. Ammonia is oxidized to nitrate ion. This bacterium is
    A) Gram–negative.
    B) Using anaerobic respiration.
    C) A chemoautotroph.
    D) A photoautotroph
    E) A photoheterotroph.

Answer: C
Skill: Understanding

18) Which of the following bacteria is gram-positive?
    A) *Pseudomonas*
    B) *Salmonella*
    C) *Streptococcus*
    D) *Bacteroides*
    E) *Rickettsia*

    Answer: C
    Skill: Analysis

19) *Escherichia coli* belongs to the
    A) Proteobacteria.
    B) Gram-positive bacteria.
    C) Green sulfur bacteria.
    D) Spirochetes.
    E) Actinomycetes.

    Answer: A
    Skill: Recall

20) Which one of the following bacteria does *NOT* belong with the others?
    A) *Bacillus*
    B) *Escherichia*
    C) *Lactobacillus*
    D) *Staphylococcus*
    E) *Streptococcus*

    Answer: B
    Skill: Analysis

21) Which of the following statements about the causative agent of Rocky Mountain spotted fever is false?
    A) It is an intracellular parasite.
    B) It is transmitted by ticks.
    C) It is in the genus *Rickettsia*.
    D) It is gram-negative.
    E) It is found in soil and water.

    Answer: E
    Skill: Recall

22) A primary difference between cyanobacteria and purple and green phototrophic bacteria is
    A) Energy source.
    B) Cell wall type.
    C) Electron donor for CO_2 reduction.
    D) Cell type.
    E) Color.

    Answer: C
    Skill: Analysis

23) Which one of the following bacteria does *NOT* belong with the others?
   A) *Bordetella*
   B) *Burkholderia*
   C) *Campylobacter*
   D) *Pseudomonas*
   E) *Salmonella*

Answer: E
Skill: Analysis

24) Which of the following bacteria are responsible for more infections and more different kinds of infections?
   A) *Streptococcus*
   B) *Staphylococcus*
   C) *Salmonella*
   D) *Pseudomonas*
   E) *Neisseria*

Answer: A
Skill: Recall

25) Both *Beggiatoa* and the purple sulfur bacteria use H_2S. These bacteria differ in that *Beggiatoa*
   A) Uses H_2S for an energy source.
   B) Uses H_2S for a carbon source.
   C) Uses light energy.
   D) Belongs to the gammaproteobacteria.
   E) Is a heterotroph.

Answer: A
Skill: Understanding

26) The nonsulfur photosynthetic bacteria use organic compounds as
   A) Carbon sources.
   B) Electron donors to reduce CO_2.
   C) Energy sources.
   D) Electron acceptors.
   E) Oxygen sources.

Answer: B
Skill: Understanding

27) Which of the following is the best reason to classify *Streptococcus* in the Lactobacillales?
   A) Gram reaction
   B) Morphology
   C) Fermentation of lactose
   D) rRNA sequences
   E) Found in dairy products

Answer: D
Skill: Understanding

28) *Streptomyces* differs from *Actinomyces* because *Streptomyces*
 A) Makes antibiotics.
 B) Produces conidia.
 C) Forms filaments.
 D) Is aerobic.
 E) Is a bacterium.

Answer: D
Skill: Recall

29) All of the following bacteria are gram-positive. Which does *NOT* belong with the others?
 A) *Actinomyces*
 B) *Bacillus*
 C) *Corynebacterium*
 D) *Listeria*
 E) *Mycobacterium*

Answer: E
Skill: Understanding

30) *Salmonella, Shigella, Yersinia,* and *Serratia* are all
 A) Pathogens.
 B) Gram–negative facultatively anaerobic rods.
 C) Gram–positive aerobic cocci.
 D) Fermentative.
 E) Endospore–forming bacteria.

Answer: B
Skill: Analysis

31) You have isolated a gram–positive rod. What should you do next?
 A) Gram stain
 B) Lactose fermentation
 C) Endospore stain
 D) Flagella stain
 E) Enterotube

Answer: C
Skill: Understanding

32) *Borrelia* is classified as a spirochete because it
 A) Is aerobic.
 B) Possesses an axial filament.
 C) Is a rod.
 D) Is a pathogen.
 E) Is transmitted by ticks.

Answer: B
Skill: Analysis

33) *Thiobacillus* oxidizes inorganic sulfur compounds and reduces CO_2. This bacterium is a
    A) Chemoheterotroph.
    B) Chemoautotroph.
    C) Photoautotroph.
    D) Gammaproteobacteria.
    E) Photoheterotroph.

Answer: B
Skill: Understanding

34) You have isolated a prokaryotic cell. The first step in identification is a(n)
    A) Gram stain.
    B) Lactose fermentation test.
    C) Endospore stain.
    D) Flagella stain.
    E) DNA fingerprint.

Answer: A
Skill: Understanding

35) Actinomycetes differ from fungi in that actinomycetes
    A) Are chemoheterotrophs.
    B) Lack a membrane-bounded nucleus.
    C) Require light.
    D) Are decomposers.
    E) Cause disease.

Answer: B
Skill: Understanding

36) You have isolated an aerobic gram-positive, endospore-forming bacterium that grows well on nutrient agar. To which of the following groups does it most likely belong?
    A) Phototrophic bacteria
    B) Gammaproteobacteria
    C) Deltaproteobacteria
    D) Bacillales
    E) Can't tell

Answer: D
Skill: Analysis

37) Which of the following pairs is mismatched?
    A) Spirochete — axial filament
    B) Aerobic, helical bacteria — gram-negative
    C) Enterics — gram-negative
    D) Mycobacteria — acid-fast
    E) Pseudomonas — gram-positive

Answer: E
Skill: Analysis

38) Which one of the following does *NOT* belong with the others?
   A) *Coxiella*
   B) *Ehrlichia*
   C) *Rickettsia*
   D) *Staphylococcus*
   E) *Wolbachia*

Answer: D
Skill: Analysis

39) *Caulobacter* are different from most bacteria in that
   A) They are gram–negative.
   B) They are gram–positive.
   C) They have stalks.
   D) They lack cell walls.
   E) They are motile.

Answer: C
Skill: Recall

40) All of the following bacteria are motile; which does (do) *NOT* have flagella?
   A) *Escherichia*
   B) Helical bacteria
   C) *Pseudomonas*
   D) Spirochetes
   E) *Salmonella*

Answer: D
Skill: Analysis

41) Which of the following bacteria does *NOT* belong with the others?
   A) *Halobacterium*
   B) *Halococcus*
   C) *Methanobacterium*
   D) *Staphylococcus*
   E) *Sulfolobus*

Answer: D
Skill: Analysis

42) Mycoplasmas differ from other bacteria in that they
   A) Grow inside host cells.
   B) Lack a cell wall.
   C) Are acid–fast.
   D) Are motile.
   E) Are gram–negative.

Answer: B
Skill: Recall

43) Which of the following pairs is *NOT* correctly matched?
   A) Elementary body — *Escherichia*
   B) Endospore — *Bacillus*
   C) Endospore — *Clostridium*
   D) Heterocyst — cyanobacteria
   E) Myxospore — gliding bacteria

   Answer: A
   Skill: Analysis

44) *Burkholderia* was reclassified from the gammaproteobacteria to the betaproteobacteria because
   A) It grows in disinfectants.
   B) It is a gram–negative rod.
   C) It causes infections in cystic fibrosis patients.
   D) It causes melioidosis.
   E) Its rRNA sequence is similar to that of *Neisseria*.

   Answer: E
   Skill: Analysis

45) The crab industry needs female crabs for growing more crabs. What bacterium might be used to ensure development of female crabs and shrimp?
   A) *Acinetobacter*
   B) *Gemmata*
   C) *Neisseria*
   D) *Pelagibacter*
   E) *Wolbachia*

   Answer: E
   Skill: Recall

Essay Questions

1) Discuss the use of *Bergey's Manual* as a tool of classification. Of identification.

2) Provide a reason to classify bacteria.

3) *Bacteroides* and *Escherichia* are both gram–negative rods found in the large intestine. Why are they in different phyla?

Chapter 12 The Eukaryotes: Fungi, Algae, Protozoa, and Helminths

Objective Questions

1) Which of the following statements about fungi is false?
    A) All fungi are unicellular.
    B) All fungi have eukaryotic cells.
    C) Fungi are heterotrophic.
    D) Most fungi are aerobic.
    E) Few fungi are pathogenic to humans.

    Answer: A
    Skill: Analysis

2) Which of the following statements about helminths is false?
    A) They are heterotrophic.
    B) They are multicellular animals.
    C) They have eukaryotic cells.
    D) All are parasites.
    E) Some have male and female reproductive organs in one animal.

    Answer: D
    Skill: Analysis

3) Which of the following statements about the Oomycote algae is false?
    A) They form hyphae.
    B) They produce zoospores in a sporangium.
    C) They cause plant diseases.
    D) They have chlorophyll.
    E) They reproduce sexually.

    Answer: D
    Skill: Understanding

4) Seventeen patients in ten hospitals had cutaneous infections caused by *Rhizopus*. In all 17 patients, Elastoplast bandages were placed over sterile gauze pads to cover wounds. Fourteen of the patients had surgical wounds, two had venous line insertion sites, and one had a bite wound. Lesions present when the bandages were removed ranged from vesiculopustular eruptions to ulcerations and skin necrosis requiring debridement. Fungi are more likely than bacteria to contaminate bandages because
    A) They are aerobic.
    B) They can tolerate low-moisture conditions.
    C) They prefer a neutral environment (pH 7).
    D) They have a fermentative metabolism.
    E) They cannot tolerate high osmotic pressure.

    Answer: B
    Skill: Analysis

5) Which of the following statements is false?
   A) A lichen doesn't exist if the fungal and algal partners are separated.
   B) Lichens are parasites.
   C) In a lichen, the alga produces carbohydrates.
   D) In a lichen, the fungus provides the holdfast.
   E) Lichens are important soil producers.

Answer: B
Skill: Recall

6) Which of the following pairs is mismatched?
   A) Plasmogamy — union of two haploid cells
   B) Karyogamy — fusion of nucleus
   C) Meiosis — cell division resulting in haploid cells
   D) Anamorph — produces asexual spores
   E) Deuteromycota — a phylum of fungi

Answer: E
Skill: Recall

Table 12.1

1–Arthroconidium   5–Chlamydoconidium
2–Ascospore   6–Conidiospore
3–Basidiospore   7–Sporangiospore
4–Blastoconidium   8–Zygospore

7) In Table 12.1, which of these spores are characteristic of *Penicillium*?
   A) 1 and 2
   B) 3 and 4
   C) 2 and 6
   D) 1 and 4
   E) 4 and 6

Answer: C
Skill: Recall

8) In Table 12.1, which of these spores are characteristic of *Rhizopus*?
   A) 1 and 2
   B) 6 and 7
   C) 2 and 8
   D) 1 and 4
   E) 7 and 8

Answer: E
Skill: Recall

9) In Table 12.1, which spore is in a sac and results from the fusion of two nuclei from different strains of the same fungi?
   A) 1
   B) 2
   C) 4
   D) 6
   E) 8

Answer: B
Skill: Recall

10) In Table 12.1, which spore is found externally on a pedestal?
   A) 1
   B) 3
   C) 5
   D) 7
   E) None

Answer: B
Skill: Recall

11) In Table 12.1, which is a thick–walled spore formed as a segment within a hypha?
   A) 1
   B) 3
   C) 5
   D) 7
   E) None

Answer: C
Skill: Recall

12) In Table 12.1, which of these spores are asexual spores?
   A) 1, 4, 5, 6, 7
   B) 2, 3, 6, 8
   C) 1, 3, 5, 8
   D) 2, 4, 6, 7, 8
   E) All

Answer: A
Skill: Recall

13) In mid-December, a woman with insulin-dependent diabetes who had been on prednisone fell and received an abrasion on the dorsal side of her right hand. She was placed on penicillin. By the end of January, the ulcer had not healed, and she was referred to a plastic surgeon. On January 30, a swab of the wound was cultured at 35°C on blood agar. On the same day, a smear was made for Gram staining. The Gram stain showed large (10 μm) cells. Brownish, waxy colonies grew on the blood agar. Slide cultures set up on February 1 and incubated at 25°C showed septate hyphae and single conidia. The most likely cause of the infection is a
   A) Gram-negative bacterium.
   B) Dimorphic fungus.
   C) Parasitic alga.
   D) Yeast.
   E) Protozoan.

Answer: B
Skill: Analysis

14) Which of the following tends to be more complex in a parasitic helminth than in free-living helminths?
   A) Digestive system
   B) Nervous system
   C) Locomotion
   D) Reproductive system
   E) All of the above are more complex in a parasitic helminth.

Answer: D
Skill: Recall

15) Which of the following statements is false?
   A) Fungi produce sexual spores.
   B) Fungi produce asexual spores.
   C) Fungal spores are used in identification of fungi.
   D) Fungal spores are resting spores to protect the fungus from adverse environmental conditions.
   E) Fungal spores are for reproduction.

Answer: D
Skill: Analysis

16) Which of the following pairs are mismatched?
   1.   Arthroconidium — formed by fragmentation
   2.   Sporangiospore — formed within hyphae
   3.   Conidiospore — formed in a chain
   4.   Blastoconidium — formed from a bud
   5.   Chlamydoconidium — formed in a sac
   A) 1 and 2
   B) 2 and 3
   C) 2 and 5
   D) 3 and 4
   E) 4 and 5

Answer: C
Skill: Recall

17) Which of the following pairs is mismatched?
   A) Dinoflagellates — paralytic shellfish poisoning
   B) Brown algae — algin
   C) Red algae — agar
   D) Diatoms — petroleum
   E) Green algae — prokaryotic

Answer: E
Skill: Recall

18) Helminthic diseases are usually transmitted to humans by
   A) Respiratory route.
   B) Genitourinary route.
   C) Gastrointestinal route.
   D) Vectors.
   E) Aerosols.

Answer: C
Skill: Analysis

19) Which of the following is *NOT* a characteristic of parasitic platyhelminths?
   A) They are hermaphroditic.
   B) They are dorsoventrally flattened.
   C) They have a complete digestive system.
   D) They can be divided into flukes and tapeworms.
   E) They are multicellular animals.

Answer: C
Skill: Recall

20) Cercariae, metacercaria, miracidia, and rediae are stages in the life cycle of
   A) Cestodes.
   B) Trematodes.
   C) Nematodes.
   D) Sporozoans.
   E) Sarcodina.

Answer: C
Skill: Recall

21) Which stage immediately precedes the adult?
   A) Cercaria
   B) Metacercaria
   C) Miracidium
   D) Redia
   E) Proglottid

Answer: B
Skill: Recall

22) The encysted larva of the beef tapeworm is called a
    A) Redia.
    B) Cercaria.
    C) Cysticercus.
    D) Metacercaria.
    E) Proglottid.

Answer: C
Skill: Recall

23) Which of the following arthropods does *NOT* transmit diseases by sucking blood from a human host?
    A) Lice
    B) Fleas
    C) Houseflies
    D) Mosquitoes
    E) Kissing bugs

Answer: C
Skill: Analysis

24) Which of the following statements about algae is false?
    A) They use light as their energy source.
    B) They use CO_2 as their carbon source.
    C) They produce oxygen from hydrolysis of water.
    D) All are unicellular.
    E) Some are capable of sexual reproduction.

Answer: D
Skill: Analysis

25) Below are several paired items referring to the heartworm *Dirofilaria immitis*. Which of the pairs is mismatched?
    A) Dog — definitive host
    B) Dog — sexual reproduction
    C) Mosquito — vector
    D) Mosquito — definitive host
    E) All of the above are correctly matched.

Answer: D
Skill: Analysis

26) All algae are
    A) Photoautotrophs.
    B) Plants.
    C) Unicellular.
    D) Toxic.
    E) None of the above.

Answer: E
Skill: Understanding

27) A definitive host harbors which stage of a parasite?
    A) Miracidium
    B) Cyst
    C) Adult
    D) Larva
    E) All of the above
Answer: C
Skill: Recall

28) What do tapeworms eat?
    A) Intestinal bacteria
    B) Host tissues
    C) Red blood cells
    D) Intestinal contents
    E) Plant matter
Answer: D
Skill: Recall

29) The microspora and archaezoa are unusual eukaryotes because they
    A) Are motile.
    B) Lack mitochondria.
    C) Lack nuclei.
    D) Don't produce cysts.
    E) Do produce cysts.
Answer: B
Skill: Analysis

30) The life cycle of the fish tapeworm is similar to that of the beef tapeworm. Which of the
    following is the most effective preventive measure?
    A) Salting fish before eating
    B) Refrigerating stored fish
    C) Cooking fish before eating
    D) Wearing gloves while handling fish
    E) Not swimming in fish–infested waters
Answer: C
Skill: Understanding

31) Which of the following is the most effective control for malaria?
    A) Vaccination
    B) Treating patients
    C) Eliminate *Anopheles*
    D) Eliminate the intermediate host
    E) None of the above is an effective control.
Answer: A
Skill: Analysis

32) Multinucleated amoebalike cells that produce funguslike spores.
    A) Ascomycete
    B) Cellular slime mold
    C) Euglenozoa
    D) Tapeworm
    E) Plasmodial slime mold

Answer: E
Skill: Analysis

33) Amoebalike vegetative structures that produce sporangia.
    A) Ascomycete
    B) Cellular slime mold
    C) Euglenozoa
    D) Tapeworm
    E) Plasmodial slime mold

Answer: B
Skill: Analysis

34) A multicellular organism; the digestive tract has one opening.
    A) Ascomycete
    B) Cellular slime mold
    C) Euglenozoa
    D) Tapeworm
    E) Plasmodial slime mold

Answer: D
Skill: Analysis

35) A nucleated, unicellular organism; when you change the incubation temperature, it forms filaments with conidiospores.
    A) Ascomycete
    B) Cellular slime mold
    C) Euglenozoa
    D) Tapeworm
    E) Plasmodial slime mold

Answer: A
Skill: Analysis

36) An organism that can grow photoautotrophically in the light and chemoheterotrophically in the dark.
    A) Oomycote
    B) Cellular slime mold
    C) *Euglena*
    D) *Phytophthora*
    E) Plasmodial slime mold

Answer: C
Skill: Analysis

37) Which of the following pairs is mismatched?
   A) Tick — Rocky Mountain spotted fever
   B) Tick — Lyme disease
   C) Mosquito — malaria
   D) Mosquito — *Pneumocystis*
   E) Mosquito — encephalitis

   Answer: D
   Skill: Recall

38) Which of the following groups of algae does *NOT* produce compounds that are toxic to humans?
   A) Diatoms
   B) Dinoflagellates
   C) Green algae
   D) Red algae
   E) All of the above produce compounds toxic to humans.

   Answer: C
   Skill: Recall

39) The cells of plasmodial slime molds can grow to several centimeters in diameter because
   A) They have organelles.
   B) They distribute nutrients by cytoplasmic streaming.
   C) The large surface can absorb nutrients.
   D) They form spores.
   E) None of the above.

   Answer: B
   Skill: Understanding

40) Assume you have isolated a multicellular heterotrophic organism that produces coenocytic hyphae, motile zoospores, and cellulose cell walls. It is most likely a(n)
   A) Ascomycete fungus.
   B) Green alga.
   C) Oomycote alga.
   D) Tapeworm.
   E) Zygomycete fungus.

   Answer: C
   Skill: Analysis

41) If a larva of *Echinococcus granulosus* is found in humans, humans are the
   A) Definitive host.
   B) Infected host.
   C) Intermediate host.
   D) Reservoir.
   E) None of the above.

   Answer: C
   Skill: Analysis

42) Ringworm is caused by a(n)
   A) Ascomycete.
   B) Cestode.
   C) Nematode.
   D) Protozoan.
   E) Trematode.

Answer: A
Skill: Recall

43) Yeast infections are caused by
   A) *Aspergillus.*
   B) *Candida albicans.*
   C) *Histoplasma.*
   D) *Penicillium.*
   E) *Saccharomyces cerevisiae.*

Answer: B
Skill: Recall

44) In a food chain consisting of the following organisms, which acts as a producer?
   A) Fungi
   B) Lichens
   C) Protozoa
   D) Slime molds

Answer: B
Skill: Analysis

45) You see acid–fast oocysts in a fecal sample from a patient who has diarrhea. What is the most likely cause?
   A) *Cryptosporidium*
   B) Diatoms
   C) *Entamoeba*
   D) *Giardia*
   E) *Taenia*

Answer: A
Skill: Recall

Essay Questions

1) Provide an explanation for the complex life cycles exhibited by parasitic helminths. Cite specific examples in your discussion.

2) Explain how the presence of algae can indicate either pollution or productivity of a body of water.

Chapter 13 Viruses, Viroids, and Prions

Objective Questions

1) In which of the following ways do viruses differ from bacteria?
   A) Viruses are filterable.
   B) Viruses are obligate intracellular parasites.
   C) Viruses don't have any nucleic acid.
   D) Viruses are not composed of cells.
   E) Viruses don't reproduce.

   Answer: D
   Skill: Recall

2) Which of the following statements provides the most significant support for the idea that viruses are nonliving chemicals?
   A) They are not composed of cells.
   B) They are filterable.
   C) They cannot reproduce themselves outside a host.
   D) They cause diseases similar to those caused by chemicals.
   E) They are chemically simple.

   Answer: C
   Skill: Analysis

3) Which of the following statements about spikes is false?
   A) They are used for penetration.
   B) They are used for absorption.
   C) They may cause hemagglutination.
   D) They are found only on enveloped viruses.
   E) They are found only on nonenveloped viruses.

   Answer: A
   Skill: Recall

4) Which of the following is *NOT* used as a criterion to classify viruses?
   A) Biochemical tests
   B) Morphology
   C) Nucleic acid
   D) Size
   E) Number of capsomeres

   Answer: A
   Skill: Analysis

5) Which of the following is *NOT* a method of culturing viruses?
   A) In laboratory animals
   B) In culture media
   C) In embryonated eggs
   D) In cell culture
   E) None of the above

   Answer: B
   Skill: Recall

6) Bacteriophages and animal viruses do *NOT* differ significantly in which one of the following steps?
    A) Adsorption
    B) Penetration
    C) Uncoating
    D) Biosynthesis
    E) Release

Answer: D
Skill: Understanding

7) The definition of *lysogeny* is
    A) Phage DNA is incorporated into host cell DNA.
    B) Lysis of the host cell due to a phage.
    C) The period during replication when virions are not present.
    D) When the burst time takes an unusually long time.
    E) Attachment of a phage to a cell.

Answer: A
Skill: Analysis

8) A viroid is
    A) A complete, infectious virus particle.
    B) A nonenveloped, infectious piece of RNA.
    C) A capsid without a nucleic acid.
    D) A provirus.
    E) An infectious protein.

Answer: B
Skill: Recall

Figure 13.1

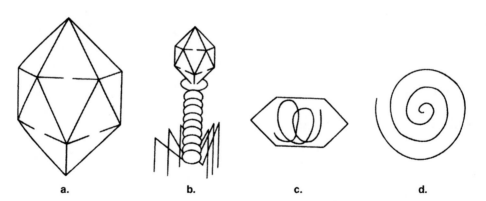

a.   b.   c.   d.

9) In Figure 13.1, which structure is a complex virus?
    A) a
    B) b
    C) c
    D) d
    E) All of the above

Answer: B
Skill: Recall

10) In Figure 13.1, the structures illustrated are composed of
    A) DNA.
    B) RNA.
    C) DNA or RNA.
    D) Capsomeres.
    E) Capsids.
Answer: D
Skill: Recall

11) A clear area against a confluent "lawn" of bacteria is called a
    A) Phage.
    B) Pock.
    C) Cell lysis.
    D) Plaque.
    E) Rash.
Answer: D
Skill: Recall

12) Continuous cell lines differ from primary cell lines in that
    A) Viruses can be grown in continuous cell lines.
    B) Continuous cell lines always have to be reisolated from animal tissues.
    C) Continuous cell lines are derived from primary cell lines.
    D) Continuous cell lines can be maintained through an indefinite number of generations.
    E) Continuous cell lines are from human embryos.
Answer: D
Skill: Recall

13) Which of the following is necessary for replication of a prion?
    A) DNA
    B) DNA polymerase
    C) Lysozyme
    D) P^{Sc}
    E) RNA
Answer: D
Skill: Understanding

14) A persistent infection is an infection in which
    A) The virus remains in equilibrium with the host without causing a disease.
    B) Viral replication is unusually slow.
    C) The disease process occurs gradually over a long period.
    D) Host cells are gradually lysed.
    E) Host cells are transformed.
Answer: C
Skill: Recall

15) Which of the following statements is false?
    A) A prophage is phage DNA inserted into a bacterial chromosome.
    B) A prophage can pop out of the chromosome.
    C) Prophage genes are represented by a repressor protein coded for by the prophage.
    D) A prophage may result in new properties of the host cell.
    E) The prophage makes the host cell immune to infection by other phages.

Answer: E
Skill: Analysis

16) Lysogeny can result in all of the following *EXCEPT*
    A) Immunity to reinfection by the same phage.
    B) Acquisition of new characteristics by the host cell.
    C) Immunity to reinfection by any phage.
    D) Transduction of specific genes.
    E) None of the above.

Answer: C
Skill: Analysis

17) Which of the following would be the first step in biosynthesis of a virus with a – strand of RNA?
    A) Synthesis of DNA from an RNA template
    B) Synthesis of double–stranded RNA from an RNA template
    C) Synthesis of double–stranded RNA from a DNA template
    D) Transcription of mRNA from DNA
    E) Synthesis of DNA from a DNA template

Answer: B
Skill: Understanding

18) An infectious protein is a
    A) Bacteriophage.
    B) Prion.
    C) Retrovirus.
    D) Viroid.
    E) Papovavirus.

Answer: B
Skill: Recall

19) An envelope is acquired during which of the following steps?
    A) Penetration
    B) Adsorption
    C) Uncoating
    D) Biosynthesis
    E) Release

Answer: E
Skill: Analysis

20) Which of the following contributes to the difficulty in establishing the etiology of cancer?
  A) Most viral particles can infect cells without inducing cancer.
  B) Cancer may not develop until long after infection.
  C) Cancers do not seem to be contagious.
  D) Viruses are difficult to observe.
  E) All of the above.

Answer: E
Skill: Analysis

21) An example of a latent viral infection is
  A) Subacute sclerosing panencephalitis.
  B) Cold sores.
  C) Influenza.
  D) Smallpox.
  E) Mumps.

Answer: B
Skill: Recall

22) The most common route of accidental AIDS transmission to health care workers is
  A) Mouth to mouth.
  B) Fecal—oral.
  C) Needlestick.
  D) Aerosol.
  E) Environmental surface contact.

Answer: C
Skill: Recall

23) Assume you have isolated an unknown virus. It is a single–stranded RNA, enveloped virus. To which group does it most likely belong?
  A) Herpesvirus
  B) Picornavirus
  C) Retrovirus
  D) Togavirus
  E) Papovavirus

Answer: D
Skill: Recall

24) To which group does a small, nonenveloped single–stranded RNA virus most likely belong?
  A) Herpesvirus
  B) Picornavirus
  C) Retrovirus
  D) Togavirus
  E) Papovavirus

Answer: B
Skill: Recall

25) The most conclusive evidence that viruses cause cancers is provided by
    A) Finding oncogenes in viruses.
    B) The presence of antibodies against viruses in cancer patients.
    C) Cancer following injection of cell–free filtrates.
    D) Treating cancer with antibodies.
    E) Some liver cancer patients having had hepatitis.

Answer: C
Skill: Analysis

26) Bacteriophages derive all of the following from the host cell *EXCEPT*
    A) Lysozyme.
    B) tRNA.
    C) Amino acids.
    D) Nucleotides.
    E) A.T.P.

Answer: A
Skill: Analysis

27) Generalized transduction differs from specialized transduction in that generalized transduction
    A) Kills the host.
    B) Transfers DNA from one cell to another.
    C) Transfers specific DNA.
    D) Involves lysogeny.
    E) Lyses the host cell.

Answer: C
Skill: Understanding

28) Generally, in a DNA–containing virus infection, the host animal cell supplies all of the following *EXCEPT*
    A) RNA polymerase.
    B) Nucleotides.
    C) DNA polymerase.
    D) tRNA.
    E) All of the above are supplied by the host animal cell.

Answer: C
Skill: Analysis

29) Put the following in the correct order for DNA–virus replication:
1–Maturation; 2–DNA synthesis; 3–Transcription; 4–Translation.
    A) 1, 2, 3, 4
    B) 2, 3, 4, 1
    C) 3, 4, 1, 2
    D) 4, 1, 2, 3
    E) 4, 3, 2, 1

Answer: B
Skill: Analysis

30) A viral species is a group of viruses that
  A) Have the same morphology and nucleic acid.
  B) Have the same genetic information and ecological niche.
  C) Infect the same cells and cause the same disease.
  D) Can't be defined.

Answer: B
Skill: Recall

31) Viruses that have reverse transcriptase are in the
  A) Retroviridae and Picornaviridae.
  B) Herpesviridae and Retroviridae.
  C) Hepadnaviridae and Retroviridae.
  D) Bacteriophage families.
  E) Influenzavirus.

Answer: C
Skill: Recall

32) DNA made from an RNA template will be incorporated into the virus capsid of
  A) Retroviridae.
  B) Herpesviridae.
  C) Hepadnaviridae.
  D) Bacteriophage families.
  E) Influenzavirus.

Answer: C
Skill: Analysis

33) Which of the following statements about viruses is false?
  A) Viruses contain DNA or RNA but never both.
  B) Viruses contain a protein coat.
  C) Viruses use the anabolic machinery of the cell.
  D) Viruses use their own catabolic enzymes.
  E) Viruses have genes.

Answer: D
Skill: Analysis

34) Approximately how many virus particles could fit along a 1-millimeter line?
  A) 2
  B) 20
  C) 200
  D) 20,000
  E) 2,000,000

Answer: D
Skill: Analysis

35) Some viruses, such as human herpesvirus 1, infect a cell without causing symptoms; these are called
   A) Latent viruses.
   B) Lytic viruses.
   C) Phages.
   D) Slow viruses.
   E) Unconventional viruses.

Answer: A
Skill: Recall

Figure 13.2

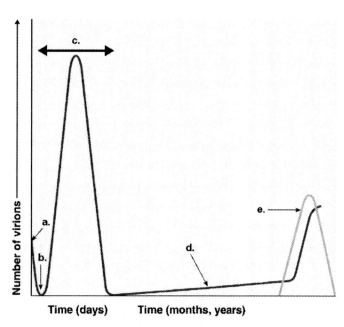

36) Assume a patient had chickenpox (human herpesvirus 3) as a child. Which line on the graph in Figure 13.2 would show the number of viruses present in this person as a 60–year–old with shingles (human herpesvirus 3)?
   A) a
   B) b
   C) c
   D) d
   E) e

Answer: E
Skill: Analysis

37) Assume a patient has influenza. During which time (on the graph in Figure 13.2) would the patient show the symptoms of the illness?
   A) a
   B) b
   C) c
   D) d
   E) e

Answer: C
Skill: Analysis

38) The following steps occur during multiplication of herpesviruses. What is the third step?
   A) Attachment
   B) Biosynthesis
   C) Penetration
   D) Release
   E) Uncoating

Answer: E
Skill: Recall

39) The following steps occur during multiplication of retroviruses. What is the fourth step?
   A) Synthesis of double–stranded DNA
   B) Synthesis of + RNA
   C) Attachment
   D) Penetration
   E) Uncoating

Answer: A
Skill: Analysis

40) Nontoxic strains of *Vibrio cholerae* can become toxic when they are in the human intestine with toxic strains of bacteria. This suggests that the toxin genes are acquired by
   A) Host enzymes.
   B) Prions.
   C) Reverse transcriptase.
   D) Transduction.
   E) None of the above.

Answer: D
Skill: Analysis

41) Which one of the following steps does *NOT* occur during multiplication of a picornavirus?
   A) Synthesis of + strands of RNA
   B) Synthesis of – strands of RNA
   C) Synthesis of viral proteins
   D) Synthesis of DNA
   E) None of the above

Answer: D
Skill: Understanding

42) Which of the following is most likely a product of an early gene?
    A) Capsid proteins
    B) DNA polymerase
    C) Envelope proteins
    D) Spike proteins
    E) Lysozyme

Answer: B
Skill: Understanding

43) Most RNA viruses carry which of the following enzymes?
    A) DNA–dependent DNA polymerase
    B) Lysozyme
    C) RNA–dependent RNA polymerase
    D) Reverse transcriptase
    E) ATP synthase

Answer: C
Skill: Understanding

44) The following steps occur during biosynthesis of a + strand RNA virus. What is the third step?
    A) Attachment
    B) Penetration and uncoating
    C) Synthesis of – strand RNA
    D) Synthesis of + strand RNA
    E) Synthesis of viral proteins

Answer: C
Skill: Analysis

45) What contributes to antigenic shift in influenza viruses?
    A) Worldwide distribution
    B) Segmented genome
    C) Attachment spikes
    D) Ease of transmission
    E) Different subtypes

Answer: B
Skill: Recall

Essay Questions

1) Bacteriophages are used as vectors in genetic engineering to insert new genes into bacteria. Describe the process that makes this genetic recombination possible.

2) Compare and contrast the lytic cycle of infection of a DNA virus and an RNA virus.

3) Why was it previously believed that only DNA viruses could cause cancer? How can RNA viruses cause cancer?

4) You are growing *Bacillus subtilis* in nine 16,000–liter fermenters to produce enzymes for industrial use. The *Bacillus* cultures had been growing for 2 days when the cells in one of the fermenters lysed. Explain what happened in this fermenter.

Chapter 14 Principles of Disease and Epidemiology

Objective Questions

1) A commensal bacterium
   A) Does not receive any benefit from its host.
   B) Is beneficial to its host.
   C) May be an opportunistic pathogen.
   D) Does not infect its host.
   E) B and D only.

   Answer: C
   Skill: Analysis

2) Which of the following statements is true?
   A) Symbiosis refers to different organisms living together.
   B) Members of a symbiotic relationship cannot live without each other.
   C) A parasite is not in symbiosis with its host.
   D) Symbiosis refers to different organisms living together and benefiting from each other.
   E) At least one member must benefit in a symbiotic relationship.

   Answer: A
   Skill: Analysis

3) A nosocomial infection is
   A) Always present but is inapparent at the time of hospitalization.
   B) Acquired during the course of hospitalization.
   C) Always caused by medical personnel.
   D) Only a result of surgery.
   E) Always caused by pathogenic bacteria.

   Answer: B
   Skill: Recall

4) The major significance of Koch's work was that
   A) Microorganisms are present in a diseased animal.
   B) Diseases can be transmitted from one animal to another.
   C) Microorganisms can be cultured.
   D) Microorganisms cause disease.
   E) Microorganisms are the result of disease.

   Answer: D
   Skill: Recall

5) Koch's postulates don't apply to all diseases because
   A) Some microorganisms can't be cultured in laboratory media.
   B) Some microorganisms don't cause the same disease in laboratory animals.
   C) Some microorganisms cause different symptoms under different conditions.
   D) Some microorganisms can't be observed.
   E) Not all diseases are caused by microorganisms.

   Answer: E
   Skill: Recall

6) Which of the following diseases is *NOT* spread by droplet infection?
   A) Botulism
   B) Tuberculosis
   C) Measles
   D) Common cold
   E) Diphtheria

Answer: A
Skill: Understanding

7) Mechanical transmission differs from biological transmission in that mechanical transmission
   A) Doesn't require an arthropod.
   B) Involves fomites.
   C) Doesn't involve specific diseases.
   D) Requires direct contact.
   E) Doesn't work with noncommunicable diseases.

Answer: C
Skill: Analysis

8) Which of the following definitions is incorrect?
   A) Endemic — a disease that is constantly present in a population
   B) Epidemic — fraction of the population having a disease at a specified time
   C) Pandemic — a disease that affects a large number of people in the world in a short time
   D) Sporadic — a disease that affects a population occasionally
   E) Incidence — number of new cases of a disease

Answer: B
Skill: Recall

9) Which of these infections can cause septicemia?
   A) Bacteremia
   B) Focal infection
   C) Local infection
   D) Septicemia
   E) Systemic infection

Answer: B
Skill: Understanding

10) Which type of infection can be caused by septicemia?
   A) Bacteremia
   B) Focal infection
   C) Local infection
   D) Viremia
   E) Systemic infection

Answer: E
Skill: Understanding

11) Koch observed *Bacillus anthracis* multiplying in the blood of cattle. What is this condition called?
   A) Bacteremia
   B) Focal infection
   C) Local infection
   D) Septicemia
   E) Systemic infection

Answer: D
Skill: Understanding

12) Which one of the following does *NOT* contribute to the incidence of nosocomial infections?
   A) Formation of biofilms
   B) Lapse in aseptic techniques
   C) Gram-negative cell walls
   D) Lack of handwashing
   E) Lack of insect control

Answer: C
Skill: Analysis

13) Transient microbiota differ from normal microbiota because transient microbiota
   A) Cause diseases.
   B) Are found in a certain location on the host.
   C) Are acquired by direct contact.
   D) Are present for a relatively short time.
   E) Never cause disease.

Answer: D
Skill: Recall

14) Which of the following statements about nosocomial infections is false?
   A) They occur in compromised patients.
   B) They are caused by opportunists.
   C) They are caused by drug-resistant bacteria.
   D) They are caused by normal microbiota.
   E) The patient was infected before hospitalization.

Answer: E
Skill: Recall

15) One effect of washing regularly with antibacterial agents is the removal of normal microbiota. This can result in
   A) Body odor.
   B) Fewer diseases.
   C) Increased susceptibility to disease.
   D) Normal microbiota returning immediately.
   E) No bacterial growth because washing removes their food source.

Answer: C
Skill: Analysis

16) Which of the following is *NOT* a reservoir of infection?
    A) A sick person
    B) A healthy person
    C) A sick animal
    D) A hospital
    E) All of the above can be reservoirs of infection.

Answer: E
Skill: Analysis

17) Which of the following is *NOT* a communicable diseases?
    A) Malaria
    B) AIDS
    C) Tuberculosis
    D) Tetanus
    E) Typhoid fever

Answer: D
Skill: Analysis

18) Which of the following is a fomite?
    A) Water
    B) Droplets from a sneeze
    C) Pus
    D) Insects
    E) A hypodermic needle

Answer: E
Skill: Analysis

19) Which of the following statements about biological transmission is false?
    A) The pathogen reproduces in the vector.
    B) The pathogen may enter the host in the vector's feces.
    C) Houseflies are an important vector.
    D) The pathogen may be injected by the bite of the vector.
    E) The pathogen may require the vector as a host.

Answer: C
Skill: Recall

20) Which of the following definitions is incorrect?
    A) Acute — a short–lasting primary infection
    B) Inapparent — infection characteristic of a carrier state
    C) Chronic — a disease that develops slowly and lasts for months
    D) Primary infection — an initial illness
    E) Secondary infection — a long–lasting illness

Answer: E
Skill: Recall

21) Symptoms of disease differ from signs of disease in that symptoms
   A) Are changes felt by the patient.
   B) Are changes observed by the physician.
   C) Are specific for a particular disease.
   D) Always occur as part of a syndrome.
   E) None of the above.

   Answer: A
   Skill: Recall

22) The science that deals with when diseases occur and how they are transmitted is called
   A) Ecology.
   B) Epidemiology.
   C) Communicable disease.
   D) Morbidity and mortality.
   E) Public health.

   Answer: B
   Skill: Recall

Figure 14.1

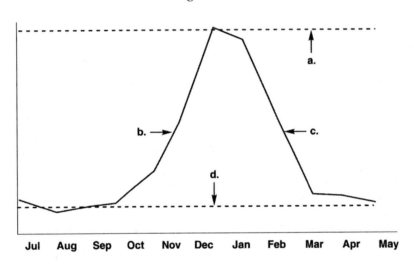

23) Figure 14.1 shows the incidence of influenza during a typical year. Which letter on the graph indicates the endemic level?
   A) a
   B) b
   C) c
   D) d

   Answer: D
   Skill: Analysis

24) Emergence of infectious diseases can be due to all of the following *EXCEPT*
      A) Antibiotic resistance.
      B) Climatic changes.
      C) Digging up soil.
      D) Microbes trying to cause disease.
      E) Travel.

Answer: D
Skill: Understanding

25) Which of the following pairs is mismatched?
      A) Malaria — vector
      B) Salmonellosis — vehicle transmission
      C) Syphilis — direct contact
      D) Influenza — droplet infection
      E) All of the above are correctly matched.

Answer: E
Skill: Analysis

26) Which of the following can contribute to postoperative infections?
      A) Using syringes more than once
      B) Normal microbiota on the operating room staff
      C) Errors in aseptic technique
      D) Antibiotic resistance
      E) All of the above

Answer: E
Skill: Analysis

Figure 14.2

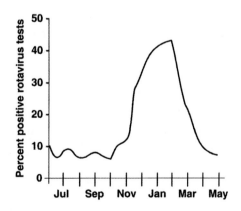

27) In Figure 14.2, what is the endemic level of rotavirus infections?
      A) 0%
      B) Approximately 10%
      C) Approximately 20%
      D) 35%
      E) The month of January

Answer: B
Skill: Analysis

28) A cold transmitted by a facial tissue is an example of
  A) Direct contact.
  B) Droplet transmission.
  C) Fomite.
  D) Vector.
  E) Vehicle transmission.

Answer: E
Skill: Analysis

29) Influenza transmitted by an unprotected sneeze is an example of
  A) Direct contact.
  B) Droplet transmission.
  C) Fomite.
  D) Vector.
  E) Vehicle transmission.

Answer: B
Skill: Analysis

30) A sexually transmitted disease is an example of
  A) Direct contact.
  B) Droplet transmission.
  C) Fomite.
  D) Vector.
  E) Vehicle transmission.

Answer: A
Skill: Analysis

31) Gastroenteritis acquired from roast beef is an example of
  A) Direct contact.
  B) Droplet transmission.
  C) Fomite.
  D) Vector.
  E) Vehicle transmission.

Answer: E
Skill: Analysis

32) A needlestick is an example of
  A) Direct contact.
  B) Droplet transmission.
  C) Fomite.
  D) Vector.
  E) Vehicle transmission.

Answer: C
Skill: Analysis

33) Legionellosis transmitted by a grocery store mist machine is an example of
  A) Direct contact.
  B) Droplet transmission.
  C) Fomite.
  D) Vector.
  E) Vehicle transmission.

Answer: E
Skill: Analysis

34) Plague transmitted by a flea is an example of
  A) Direct contact.
  B) Droplet transmission.
  C) Fomite.
  D) Vector.
  E) Vehicle transmission.

Answer: D
Skill: Analysis

35) The most likely mode of transmission of pneumonic plague between humans is
  A) Direct contact.
  B) Droplet transmission.
  C) Fomite.
  D) Vector.
  E) Vehicle transmission.

Answer: B
Skill: Analysis

Situation 14.1
During a 6-month period, 239 cases of pneumonia occurred in a town of 300 people. A clinical case was defined as fever ≥39°C lasting >2 days with three or more symptoms (i.e., chills, sweats, severe headache, cough, aching muscles/joints, fatigue, or feeling ill). A laboratory-confirmed case was defined as a positive result for antibodies against *Coxiella burnetii*. Before the outbreak, 2000 sheep were kept northwest of the town. Of the 20 sheep tested from the flock, 15 were positive for *C. burnetii* antibodies. Wind blew from the northwest, and rainfall was 0.5 cm compared with 7 to 10 cm during each of the previous 3 years.

36) Situation 14.1 is an example of
  A) Human reservoirs.
  B) A zoonosis.
  C) A nonliving reservoir.
  D) A vector.
  E) A focal infection.

Answer: B
Skill: Understanding

37) In Situation 14.1, the etiologic agent of the disease is
    A) Sheep.
    B) Soil.
    C) *Coxiella burnetii.*
    D) Pneumonia.
    E) Wind.

Answer: C
Skill: Understanding

38) In Situation 14.1, the method of transmission of this disease was
    A) Direct contact.
    B) Droplet.
    C) Indirect contact.
    D) Vector–borne.
    E) Vehicle.

Answer: E
Skill: Understanding

39) Which one of the following is *NOT* an example of microbial antagonism?
    A) Acid production by bacteria
    B) Bacteriocin production
    C) Bacteria occupying host receptors
    D) Bacteria causing disease
    E) Bacteria producing vitamin K

Answer: D
Skill: Analysis

40) The yeast *Candida albicans* does not normally cause disease because of
    A) Symbiotic bacteria.
    B) Antagonistic bacteria.
    C) Parasitic bacteria.
    D) Commensal bacteria.
    E) Other fungi.

Answer: B
Skill: Analysis

41) *Haemophilus* bacteria require heme protein produced by *Staphylococcus* bacteria. This is an example of
    A) Antagonism.
    B) Commensalism.
    C) Parasitism.
    D) Synergism.
    E) Competitive exclusion.

Answer: D
Skill: Analysis

42) Which one of the following is *NOT* a zoonosis?
    A) Cat–scratch disease
    B) *Hantavirus* pulmonary syndrome
    C) Rabies
    D) Tapeworm
    E) All of the above are zoonoses.

Answer: E
Skill: Recall

43) *Pseudomonas* bacteria colonized the bile duct of a patient following his liver transplant surgery. This is an example of a
    A) Communicable disease.
    B) Latent infection.
    C) Nosocomial infection.
    D) Sporadic disease.
    E) None of the above.

Answer: C
Skill: Analysis

Figure 14.3

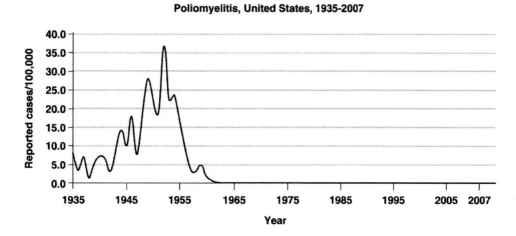

44) The graph in Figure 14.3 shows the incidence of polio in the United States. The period between 1945 and 1955 indicates
    A) An endemic level.
    B) An epidemic level.
    C) A sporadic infection.
    D) A communicable disease.
    E) A pandemic.

Answer: B
Skill: Analysis

45) Which one of the following statements is false?
   A) Antimicrobial therapy for hemodialysis–associated infections increases antibiotic
      resistance.
   B) *S. aureus* is differentiated from other mannitol+ cocci by the coagulase test.
   C) The M in MRSA stands for mannitol.
   D) USA100 accounts for most hospital–acquired MRSA.
   E) USA300 accounts for most community–acquired MRSA.

Answer: C
Skill: Recall

Essay Questions

Situation 14.2

A 37–week–old infant was delivered by cesarean section and discharged from a Connecticut hospital when
he was 10 days old. Two days later he was lethargic and had a fever. When he was readmitted to the
hospital, he had multiple brain abscesses caused by *Citrobacter diversus*. After a prolonged illness, the baby
died. A second infant with a normal pregnancy and delivery died of *C. diversus* meningitis after a short
illness. Nine infants in the hospital nursery had umbilical cord colonization by *C. diversus*. Environmental
cultures were negative for hospital equipment.

1) a.   What is the normal habitat of this gram–negative, facultatively anaerobic,
      non–endospore–forming, lactose–positive rod?
   b.   Provide a plan for identifying the source of infection and preventing further infection.

Figure 14.4

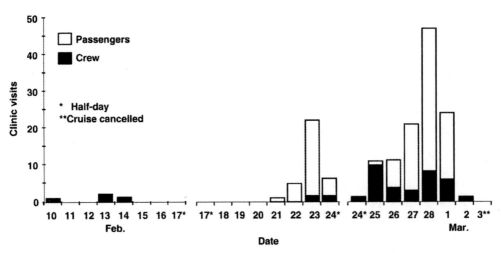

2) *Salmonella heidelberg* gastroenteritis occurred on three cruises aboard the T.S.S. *Festivale*. Figure
   14.4 shows on–board clinic visits for diarrheal illness between February 10 and March 3.

   a.   Explain the incidence pattern shown on the graph.
   b.   What are probable modes of transmission?
   c.   What changes would you recommend before the ship books more cruises after March 3?

Chapter 15 Microbial Mechanisms of Pathogenicity

Objective Questions

1) The most frequently used portal of entry for pathogens is the
    A) Mucous membranes of the respiratory tract.
    B) Mucous membranes of the gastrointestinal tract.
    C) Skin.
    D) Parenteral route.
    E) All are used equally.

    Answer: A
    Skill: Recall

2) Which of the following diseases is *NOT* usually contracted by the respiratory route?
    A) Pneumonia
    B) Infectious hepatitis
    C) Tuberculosis
    D) Whooping cough
    E) All of the above are usually contracted by the respiratory route.

    Answer: B
    Skill: Understanding

3) Most pathogens that gain access through the skin
    A) Can penetrate intact skin.
    B) Just infect the skin itself.
    C) Enter through hair follicles and sweat ducts.
    D) Must adhere first while their invasive factors allow them to penetrate.
    E) Must be injected.

    Answer: C
    Skill: Analysis

4) The ID_{50} is a
    A) Measure of pathogenicity.
    B) Dose that will cause an infection in 50% of the test population.
    C) Dose that will kill some of the test population.
    D) Dose that will cause an infection in some of the test population.
    E) Dose that will kill 50% of the test population.

    Answer: B
    Skill: Recall

5) Which of the following does *NOT* contribute to a pathogen's invasiveness?
    A) Toxins
    B) Capsule
    C) Cell wall
    D) Hyaluronidase
    E) Ligands

    Answer: A
    Skill: Understanding

6) Which of the following statements is false?
   A) Leukocidins destroy neutrophils.
   B) Hemolysins lyse red blood cells.
   C) Hyaluronidase breaks down substances between cells.
   D) Kinase destroys fibrin clots.
   E) Coagulase destroys blood clots.

   Answer: E
   Skill: Recall

7) Which of the following statements about exotoxins is generally false?
   A) They are more potent than endotoxins.
   B) They are composed of proteins.
   C) They are not destroyed by heat.
   D) They have specific methods of action.
   E) They are produced by gram-positive bacteria.

   Answer: C
   Skill: Analysis

8) Endotoxins are
   A) Associated with gram-positive bacteria.
   B) Specific in their method of action.
   C) Part of the gram-negative cell wall.
   D) Excreted from the cell.
   E) A-B toxins.

   Answer: C
   Skill: Analysis

9) Which of the following is *NOT* a membrane-disrupting toxin?
   A) A-B toxin
   B) Hemolysin
   C) Leukocidin
   D) Streptolysin O
   E) Streptolysin S

   Answer: A
   Skill: Recall

10) Cytopathic effects are changes in host cells due to
   A) Viral infections.
   B) Protozoan infections.
   C) Fungal infections.
   D) Bacterial infections.
   E) Helminthic infections.

   Answer: A
   Skill: Recall

11) Which of the following does *NOT* contribute to the symptoms of a fungal disease?
    A) Capsules
    B) Toxins
    C) Allergic response of the host
    D) Cell walls
    E) Metabolic products

Answer: D
Skill: Recall

12) Which of the following is *NOT* a method of avoiding host antibodies?
    A) Antigenic change
    B) IgA protease
    C) Invasins
    D) Membrane–disrupting toxins
    E) Inducing endocytosis

Answer: D
Skill: Understanding

13) Siderophores are bacterial proteins that compete with animal
    A) Antibodies.
    B) Red blood cells.
    C) Transferrin.
    D) White blood cells.
    E) Receptors.

Answer: C
Skill: Recall

14) Which of the following *CANNOT* be used for adherence?
    A) Fimbriae
    B) Cell membrane mannose
    C) Glycoproteins
    D) Lipoproteins
    E) Capsules

Answer: B
Skill: Recall

15) Which of the following is *NOT* considered entry via the parenteral route?
    A) Injection
    B) Bite
    C) Surgery
    D) Hair follicle
    E) Skin cut

Answer: D
Skill: Analysis

16) A cell wall can increase a bacterium's virulence because cell wall lipid A
    A) Resists phagocytosis.
    B) Helps the bacterium attach.
    C) Destroys host tissues.
    D) Is toxic.
    E) All bacteria have a cell wall and all are not pathogenic; therefore, cell walls do not
       contribute to virulence.

Answer: D
Skill: Recall

17) Botulism is caused by a proteinaceous exotoxin; therefore it can easily be prevented by
    A) Boiling food prior to consumption.
    B) Administering antibiotics to patients.
    C) Not eating canned food.
    D) Preventing fecal contamination of food.
    E) Filtering food.

Answer: A
Skill: Recall

18) Which of the following organisms does *NOT* produce an exotoxin?
    A) *Salmonella typhi*
    B) *Clostridium botulinum*
    C) *Corynebacterium diphtheriae*
    D) *Clostridium tetani*
    E) *Staphylococcus aureus*

Answer: A
Skill: Understanding

19) Which of the following cytopathic effects is cytocidal?
    A) Inclusion bodies
    B) Giant cells
    C) Antigenic changes
    D) Transformation
    E) Release of enzymes from lysosomes

Answer: E
Skill: Analysis

20) Which of the following is *NOT* used by bacteria for attachment to a host?
    A) M protein
    B) Ligands
    C) Fimbriae
    D) Capsules
    E) A–B toxin

Answer: E
Skill: Analysis

21) Symptoms of protozoan and helminthic diseases are due to
    A) Tissue damage due to growth of the parasite on the tissues.
    B) Waste products excreted by the parasite.
    C) Products released from damaged tissues.
    D) All of the above.
    E) None of the above.

Answer: D
Skill: Recall

22) Which of the following statements about staphylococcal enterotoxin is false?
    A) It causes vomiting.
    B) It causes diarrhea.
    C) It is an exotoxin.
    D) It is produced by *Staphylococcus aureus* growing in the host's intestines.
    E) It is a superantigen.

Answer: D
Skill: Analysis

23) Which of the following does *NOT* contribute to the virulence of a pathogen?
    A) Numbers of microorganisms that gain access to a host
    B) Cell wall
    C) Toxins
    D) Enzymes
    E) All of the above contribute to a pathogen's virulence.

Answer: E
Skill: Analysis

24) Lysogenic bacteriophages contribute to bacterial virulence because bacteriophages
    A) Give new gene sequences to the host bacteria.
    B) Produce toxins.
    C) Carry plasmids.
    D) Kill the bacteria causing release of endotoxins.
    E) Kill human cells.

Answer: A
Skill: Analysis

25) Thirty-two people in San Francisco who ate jackfish caught at Midway Island developed malaise, nausea, blurred vision, breathing difficulty, and numbness from 3 to 6 hours after eating. The most likely cause of this food intoxication is
    A) A mycotoxin.
    B) Aflatoxin.
    C) Staphylococcal enterotoxin.
    D) Ciguatera.
    E) Cholera toxin.

Answer: D
Skill: Understanding

26) Which of the following statements about M protein is false?
   A) It is found on *Streptococcus pyogenes*.
   B) It is found on fimbriae.
   C) It is heat- and acid-resistant.
   D) It is readily digested by phagocytes.
   E) It is a protein.

   Answer: D
   Skill: Recall

27) Septic shock due to gram-positive bacteria is caused by
   A) A–B toxins.
   B) Lipid A.
   C) Membrane-disrupting toxins.
   D) Superantigens.
   E) Erythrogenic toxin.

   Answer: D
   Skill: Understanding

28) A needlestick is an example of which portal of entry?
   A) Skin
   B) Parenteral route
   C) Mucous membranes
   D) All of the above
   E) None of the above

   Answer: B
   Skill: Recall

29) Poliovirus is ingested and gains access to tissues by which portal of entry?
   A) Skin
   B) Parenteral
   C) Mucous membranes
   D) All of the above
   E) None of the above

   Answer: C
   Skill: Analysis

30) *Pseudomonas aeruginosa* produces a two-part exotoxin. The most likely pathologic effect of this toxin is
   A) Inhibition of protein synthesis.
   B) Flaccid paralysis.
   C) Tetani or lockjaw.
   D) A red rash.
   E) The bacteria will be able to grow in phagocytes.

   Answer: A
   Skill: Understanding

31) Cholera toxin polypeptide A binds to surface gangliosides on target cells. If the gangliosides were removed,
   A) Polypeptide A would bind to target cells.
   B) Polypeptide A would enter the cells.
   C) Polypeptide B would not be able to enter the cells.
   D) *Vibrio* would not produce cholera toxin.
   E) *Vibrio* would bind to target cells.

Answer: C
Skill: Analysis

32) Which is a method of avoiding phagocytosis?
   A) Producing fimbriae
   B) Inducing endocytosis
   C) Producing toxins
   D) Inducing TNF
   E) Producing iron–binding proteins

Answer: B
Skill: Understanding

33) The mechanism by which gram–negative bacteria can cross the blood–brain barrier?
   A) Producing fimbriae
   B) Inducing endocytosis
   C) Producing toxins
   D) Inducing TNF
   E) All of the above

Answer: D
Skill: Understanding

34) Injectable drugs are tested for endotoxins by
   A) The *Limulus* amoebocyte lysate test.
   B) Counting the viable bacteria.
   C) Filtering out the cells.
   D) Looking for turbidity.
   E) Culturing bacteria.

Answer: A
Skill: Recall

35) Endotoxins in sterile injectable drugs could cause
   A) Infection.
   B) Septic shock symptoms.
   C) Giant cell formation.
   D) Nerve damage.
   E) No damage, because they are sterile.

Answer: B
Skill: Recall

36) Gram–negative septic shock results from the following events. What is the second step?
    A) Body temperature is reset in the hypothalamus.
    B) Fever occurs.
    C) IL–1 is released.
    D) LPS is released from gram–negative bacteria.
    E) Phagocytes ingest gram–negative bacteria.

Answer: D
Skill: Analysis

37) Antibiotics can lead to septic shock if used to treat
    A) Viral infections.
    B) Gram–negative bacterial infections.
    C) Gram–positive bacterial infections.
    D) Protozoan infections.
    E) Helminth infestations.

Answer: B
Skill: Recall

38) Which of the following is *NOT* a cytopathic effect of viruses?
    A) Cell death
    B) Host cells fusing to form multinucleated syncytia
    C) Inclusion bodies forming in the cytoplasm or nucleus
    D) Increased cell growth
    E) Toxin production

Answer: E
Skill: Recall

39) Which of the following organisms causes the most severe disease?
    A) *E. coli* O157:H7 $ID_{50}=20$
    B) *Rhinovirus* $ID_{50}=200$
    C) *Shigella* $ID_{50}=10$
    D) *Treponema pallidum* $ID_{50}=57$
    E) Can't tell

Answer: E
Skill: Understanding

Table 15.1
Use these data to answer the following question:

Bacteria	Portal of entry	ID_{50}
Staphylococcus aureus	Wound	<10
S. aureus	Wound+ampicillin	300

40) The administration of ampicillin before surgery
    A) Decreases the risk of staphylococcal infection.
    B) Increases the risk of staphylococcal infection.
    C) Has no effect on risk of infection.
    D) Replaces tetracycline.
    E) Can't tell.

Answer: A
Skill: Understanding

41) Which organism most easily causes an infection?
    A) *E. coli* O157:H7 $ID_{50}=20$
    B) *Legionella pneumophila* $ID_{50}=1$
    C) *Shigella* $ID_{50}=10$
    D) *Treponema pallidum* $ID_{50}=57$
    E) Can't tell

Answer: B
Skill: Understanding

42) Bacteria that cause periodontal disease have adhesins for receptors on streptococci that colonize on teeth. This indicates that
    A) Streptococci get bacterial infections.
    B) Streptococcal colonization is necessary for periodontal disease.
    C) Bacteria that cause periodontal disease adhere to gums and teeth.
    D) Bacteria that cause periodontal disease adhere to teeth.
    E) Streptococci cause periodontal disease.

Answer: B
Skill: Analysis

43) Nonpathogenic *Vibrio cholerae* can acquire the cholera toxin gene by
    A) Phagocytosis.
    B) Transduction.
    C) Conjugation.
    D) Transformation.
    E) Infecting a pathogenic *Vibrio cholerae*.

Answer: B
Skill: Analysis

44) In response to the presence of endotoxin, phagocytes secrete tumor necrosis factor. This causes
    A) The disease to subside.
    B) A decrease in blood pressure.
    C) A fever.
    D) A gram–negative infection.
    E) An increase in red blood cells.

Answer: B
Skill: Recall

45) Patients developed inflammation a few hours following eye surgery. Instruments and solutions were sterile, and the *Limulus* assay was positive. The patients' inflammation was due to
    A) Bacterial infection.
    B) Viral infection.
    C) Endotoxin.
    D) Exotoxin.
    E) Can't tell.

Answer: C
Skill: Analysis

Essay Questions

1) Antibiotics can kill gram–negative bacteria, but symptoms of fever and low blood pressure can persist. Why?

2) Why is diagnosis of botulism difficult?

Chapter 16 Innate Immunity: Nonspecific Defenses of the Host

Objective Questions

1) Innate immunity is
    A) The body's ability to ward off diseases.
    B) The body's defenses against any kind of pathogen.
    C) The body's defense against a particular pathogen.
    D) The lack of resistance.
    E) Increased susceptibility to disease.

Answer: B
Skill: Recall

2) Which of the following is *NOT* a physical factor protecting the skin and mucous membranes from infection?
    A) Layers of cells
    B) Tears
    C) Saliva
    D) Lysozyme
    E) Ciliary escalator

Answer: D
Skill: Analysis

3) The function of the "ciliary escalator" is to
    A) Kill microorganisms.
    B) Remove microorganisms from body cavities.
    C) Remove microorganisms from the lower respiratory tract.
    D) Remove microorganisms from the upper respiratory tract.
    E) All of the above.

Answer: C
Skill: Recall

4) Which of the following exhibits the highest phagocytic activity?
    A) Neutrophils
    B) Erythrocytes
    C) Lymphocytes
    D) Basophils
    E) Eosinophils

Answer: A
Skill: Recall

5) TLRs attach to all of the following *EXCEPT*
    A) AMPs.
    B) Flagellin.
    C) LPS.
    D) PAMPs.
    E) Peptidoglycan.

Answer: A
Skill: Recall

6) Which of the following *CANNOT* be determined from a differential count?
    A) The number of white blood cells
    B) The numbers of each type of white blood cell
    C) The number of red blood cells
    D) The possibility of a state of disease
    E) None of the above

Answer: C
Skill: Recall

7) The complement protein cascade is the same for the classical pathway, alternative pathway, and lectin pathway beginning with the activation of
    A) C1.
    B) C2.
    C) C3.
    D) C5.
    E) C6.

Answer: C
Skill: Understanding

8) Which of the following does *NOT* increase blood vessel permeability?
    A) Kinins
    B) Prostaglandins
    C) Lysozymes
    D) Histamine
    E) Leukotrienes

Answer: C
Skill: Recall

9) Which of the following choices shows the order in which white blood cells migrate to infected tissues?
    A) Macrophages — monocytes
    B) Lymphocytes — macrophages
    C) Neutrophils — macrophages
    D) Neutrophils — monocytes
    E) Macrophages — neutrophils

Answer: D
Skill: Recall

10) *Margination* refers to
    A) The adherence of phagocytes to microorganisms.
    B) The chemotactic response of phagocytes.
    C) Adherence of phagocytes to the lining of blood vessels.
    D) Dilation of blood vessels.
    E) The movement of phagocytes through walls of blood vessels.

Answer: C
Skill: Recall

11) Which of the following statements is true?
    A) Alpha interferon is an antiviral protein.
    B) Alpha interferon promotes phagocytosis.
    C) Gamma interferon causes bactericidal activity by macrophages.
    D) Alpha interferon acts against specific viruses.
    E) Beta interferon attacks invading viruses.

Answer: C
Skill: Analysis

12) Which of the following is found normally in serum?
    A) Complement
    B) Interferon
    C) Histamine
    D) Leukocytosis–promoting factor
    E) TLRs

Answer: A
Skill: Analysis

13) Which of the following is *NOT* an effect of complement activation?
    A) Interference with viral replication
    B) Bacterial cell lysis
    C) Opsonization
    D) Increased phagocytic activity
    E) Increased blood vessel permeability

Answer: A
Skill: Analysis

14) Which of the following is an effect of opsonization?
    A) Increased adherence of phagocytes to microorganisms
    B) Increased margination of phagocytes
    C) Increased diapedesis of phagocytes
    D) Inflammation
    E) Cytolysis

Answer: A
Skill: Recall

15) Which of the following is *NOT* a way in which normal microbiota provide protection from infection?
    A) They provide antibacterial chemicals.
    B) They outcompete newcomers.
    C) They make the chemical environment unsuitable for nonresident bacteria.
    D) They produce lysozyme.
    E) They change the pH of the environment.

Answer: D
Skill: Analysis

16) Which of the following does *NOT* provide protection from phagocytic digestion?
    A) Preventing formation of phagolysosomes
    B) Killing white blood cells
    C) Causing formation of phagolysosomes
    D) Ability to grow at a low pH
    E) Biofilms

Answer: C
Skill: Analysis

17) Defensive cells such as T cells identify pathogens by binding which of the following?
    A) Toll-like receptors
    B) Lysozyme
    C) Complement
    D) Lectins
    E) Cytokines

Answer: A
Skill: Recall

18) The swelling associated with inflammation decreases when the fluid
    A) Returns to the blood.
    B) Goes into lymph capillaries.
    C) Is excreted in urine.
    D) Is lost as perspiration.
    E) None of the above

Answer: B
Skill: Recall

19) Which of the following statements about fixed macrophages is false?
    A) They are found in certain tissues and organs.
    B) They develop from neutrophils.
    C) They are cells of the mononuclear phagocytic system.
    D) They are mature monocytes.
    E) All of the above statements are true.

Answer: B
Skill: Analysis

20) Which of the following is *NOT* used by phagocytes to adhere to a microorganism?
   A) Trapping a bacterium against a rough surface
   B) Opsonization
   C) Chemotaxis
   D) Lysozyme
   E) Complement

   Answer: D
   Skill: Analysis

21) Which of the following is *NOT* an effect of histamine?
   A) Vasodilation
   B) Fever
   C) Swelling
   D) Redness
   E) Pain

   Answer: B
   Skill: Recall

22) Which of the following is *NOT* a function of inflammation?
   A) To destroy an injurious agent
   B) To remove an injurious agent
   C) To wall off an injurious agent
   D) To repair damaged tissue
   E) To produce antibodies

   Answer: E
   Skill: Recall

23) Chill is a sign that
   A) Body temperature is falling.
   B) Body temperature is rising.
   C) Body temperature will remain the same.
   D) Sweating will follow.
   E) None of the above.

   Answer: B
   Skill: Recall

24) Which of the following statements is true?
   A) There are at least 30 complement proteins.
   B) All of the complement proteins are always active in serum.
   C) Factors B, D, and P cause cytolysis.
   D) Complement activity is antigen specific.
   E) Complement increases after immunization.

   Answer: A
   Skill: Recall

25) Which of the following is *NOT* a result of complement fixation?
   A) Activation of C3b
   B) Immune adherence
   C) Acute local inflammation
   D) Opsonization
   E) Cell lysis

   Answer: C
   Skill: Recall

26) Which of the following is *NOT* part of the mechanism of action of alpha and beta interferons?
   A) They bind to the surface of uninfected cells.
   B) They inactivate viruses.
   C) They initiate manufacture of antiviral proteins.
   D) They work in cells not producing INF.
   E) They initiate transcription.

   Answer: B
   Skill: Analysis

27) The alternative pathway for complement activation is initiated by
   A) Polysaccharides and C3b.
   B) C5—C9.
   C) Antigen—antibody reactions.
   D) Factors released from phagocytes.
   E) Factors released from damaged tissues.

   Answer: A
   Skill: Recall

28) The classical pathway for complement activation is initiated by
   A) Polysaccharides and C3b.
   B) C5—C9.
   C) Antigen—antibody reactions.
   D) Factors released from phagocytes.
   E) Factors released from damaged tissues.

   Answer: C
   Skill: Recall

29) Activation of C3a results in
   A) Acute inflammation.
   B) Increased blood vessel permeability.
   C) Fever.
   D) Attraction of phagocytes.
   E) Cell lysis.

   Answer: C
   Skill: Analysis

30) Neutrophils with defective lysosomes are unable to
      A) Move by chemotaxis.
      B) Migrate.
      C) Produce toxic oxygen products.
      D) Live.
      E) None of the above.

Answer: C
Skill: Analysis

Figure 16.1

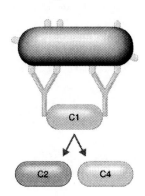

31) In Figure 16.1, what happens next?
      A) C2 causes bacterial lyses.
      B) C2a and C4b activate C3.
      C) C1 binds C2.
      D) C4 activates phagocytes.
      E) C5a activates C6.

Answer: B
Skill: Analysis

32) After ingesting a pathogen, lysosomal enzymes produce all of the following *EXCEPT*
      A) Complement.
      B) O_2^-.
      C) H_2O_2.
      D) OH•.
      E) HOCl.

Answer: A
Skill: Analysis

33) Activation of C5–C9 results in
      A) Activation of C3.
      B) Fixation of complement.
      C) Leakage of cell contents.
      D) Phagocytosis.
      E) Inflammation.

Answer: C
Skill: Recall

34) A C–reactive protein (CRP) test was ordered for a patient who recently underwent surgery. The results revealed CRP levels 10 times greater than normal. This indicates
    A) Inflammation.
    B) A normal response to the trauma of surgery.
    C) Abnormally high blood protein.
    D) Internal bleeding.
    E) None of the above.

Answer: A
Skill: Analysis

35) Which of the following is involved in resistance to parasitic helminths?
    A) Basophil
    B) Eosinophil
    C) Lymphocyte
    D) Monocyte
    E) Neutrophil

Answer: B
Skill: Recall

36) Macrophages arise from which of the following?
    A) Basophil
    B) Eosinophil
    C) Lymphocyte
    D) Monocyte
    E) Neutrophil

Answer: D
Skill: Recall

37) Which one of the following does *NOT* belong with the others?
    A) Basophil
    B) Eosinophil
    C) Dendritic cell
    D) Natural killer cell
    E) Neutrophil

Answer: D
Skill: Analysis

38) Bacteria have siderophores that capture iron; humans counter this by
    A) Producing iron.
    B) Transferrins.
    C) Toxin production.
    D) Iron–degrading enzymes.
    E) Interferon.

Answer: B
Skill: Recall

39) All of the following occur during inflammation. What is the first step?
    A) Diapedesis
    B) Margination
    C) Phagocyte migration
    D) Repair
    E) Vasodilation

Answer: E
Skill: Analysis

40) The lectin pathway for complement action is initiated by
    A) Mannose on host membranes.
    B) Mannose on the parasite.
    C) Lectins of the parasite.
    D) Gram–negative cell walls.
    E) Gram–positive cell walls.

Answer: B
Skill: Recall

41) Which one of the following is *NOT* an effect of fever?
    A) Increases production of T cells.
    B) Increases alpha interferon activity.
    C) Increases transferrin production.
    D) Kills pathogens.
    E) Increases interleukin–1.

Answer: D
Skill: Analysis

42) Several inherited deficiencies in the complement system occur in humans. Which of the following would be the most severe?
    A) Deficiency of C3
    B) Deficiency of C5
    C) Deficiency of C6
    D) Deficiency of C7
    E) Deficiency of C8

Answer: A
Skill: Understanding

43) Which of the following statements about the classical pathway of complement activation is false?
    A) C1 is the first protein activated in the classical pathway.
    B) The C1 protein complex is initiated by antigen–antibody complexes.
    C) C3 is not involved in the classical pathway.
    D) Cleaved fragments of some of the proteins act to increase inflammation.
    E) C3b causes opsonization.

Answer: C
Skill: Analysis

44) Bacterial enzymes such as catalase and superoxide dismutase can protect bacteria from
   A) Complement.
   B) Histamine.
   C) Gamma interferon.
   D) Phagocytic digestion.
   E) Phagocytosis.

   Answer: D
   Skill: Understanding

45) Serum is obtained from blood by
   A) Centrifuging whole blood.
   B) Coagulating whole blood.
   C) Lysing red blood cells.
   D) Lysing white blood cells.
   E) All of the above.

   Answer: B
   Skill: Recall

Essay Questions

1) Explain how each of the following avoids being killed by phagocytes.
   a.   *Streptococcus pneumoniae*
   b.   *Mycobacterium tuberculosis*
   c.   *Streptococcus pyogenes*
   d.   *Shigella dysenteriae*

2) A patient consulted a physician for symptoms that included a swollen toe, a red streak along his ankle, and enlarged lymph nodes in his groin. Explain the cause of these symptoms.

Chapter 17 Adaptive Immunity: Specific Defenses of the Host

Objective Questions

1) What type of immunity results from vaccination?
    A) Innate immunity
    B) Naturally acquired active immunity
    C) Naturally acquired passive immunity
    D) Artificially acquired active immunity
    E) Artificially acquired passive immunity

Answer: D
Skill: Understanding

2) What type of immunity results from transfer of antibodies from one individual to a susceptible individual by means of injection?
    A) Innate immunity
    B) Naturally acquired active immunity
    C) Naturally acquired passive immunity
    D) Artificially acquired active immunity
    E) Artificially acquired passive immunity

Answer: E
Skill: Understanding

3) What type of immunity results from recovery from mumps?
    A) Innate immunity
    B) Naturally acquired active immunity
    C) Naturally acquired passive immunity
    D) Artificially acquired active immunity
    E) Artificially acquired passive immunity

Answer: B
Skill: Understanding

4) A human's resistance to canine distemper is an example of
    A) Innate immunity.
    B) Naturally acquired active immunity.
    C) Naturally acquired passive immunity.
    D) Artificially acquired active immunity.
    E) Artificially acquired passive immunity.

Answer: A
Skill: Understanding

5) Newborns' immunity due to the transfer of antibodies across the placenta is an example of
    A) Innate immunity.
    B) Naturally acquired active immunity.
    C) Naturally acquired passive immunity.
    D) Artificially acquired active immunity.
    E) Artificially acquired passive immunity.

Answer: C
Skill: Understanding

6) What type of immunity is *NOT* due to antibodies?
    A) Innate immunity
    B) Naturally acquired active immunity
    C) Naturally acquired passive immunity
    D) Artificially acquired active immunity
    E) Artificially acquired passive immunity

Answer: A
Skill: Understanding

7) What type of immunity results from injection of tetanus toxoid?
    A) Innate immunity
    B) Naturally acquired active immunity
    C) Naturally acquired passive immunity
    D) Artificially acquired active immunity
    E) Artificially acquired passive immunity

Answer: D
Skill: Understanding

8) Immunity due to injection of an antigen is an example of
    A) Innate immunity.
    B) Naturally acquired active immunity.
    C) Naturally acquired passive immunity.
    D) Artificially acquired active immunity.
    E) Artificially acquired passive immunity.

Answer: E
Skill: Understanding

9) CD4$^+$ T cells are activated by
    A) Interaction between CD4$^+$ and MHC II.
    B) Interaction between TCRs and MHC II.
    C) Cytokines released by dendtritic cells.
    D) Cytokines released by B cells.
    E) Complement.

Answer: A
Skill: Analysis

10) Which of the following recognizes antigens displayed on host cells with MHC II?
    A) T_C cell
    B) B cell
    C) T_H cell
    D) Natural killer cell
    E) Basophil

Answer: C
Skill: Analysis

11) The specificity of an antibody is due to
    A) Its valence.
    B) The H chains.
    C) The L chains.
    D) The constant portions of the H and L chains.
    E) The variable portions of the H and L chains.

Answer: E
Skill: Recall

12) Which of the following is *NOT* a characteristic of B cells?
    A) They originate in bone marrow.
    B) They have antibodies on their surfaces.
    C) They are responsible for the memory response.
    D) They are responsible for antibody formation.
    E) They recognize antigens associated with MHC I.

Answer: E
Skill: Analysis

13) Which of the following is *NOT* a characteristic of cellular immunity?
    A) The cells originate in bone marrow.
    B) Cells are processed in the thymus gland.
    C) It can inhibit the immune response.
    D) B cells make antibodies.
    E) T cells react with antigens.

Answer: D
Skill: Analysis

14) Plasma cells are activated by a(n)
    A) Antigen.
    B) T cell.
    C) B cell.
    D) Memory cell.
    E) APC.

Answer: A
Skill: Recall

15) The antibodies found in mucus, saliva, and tears are
    A) IgG.
    B) IgM.
    C) IgA.
    D) IgD.
    E) IgE.

Answer: C
Skill: Recall

16) The antibodies found on B cells are
    A) IgG.
    B) IgM.
    C) IgA.
    D) IgD.
    E) IgE.

Answer: D
Skill: Recall

17) The antibodies that can bind to large parasites are
    A) IgG.
    B) IgM.
    C) IgA.
    D) IgD.
    E) IgE.

Answer: E
Skill: Recall

18) In addition to IgG, the antibodies that can fix complement are
    A) IgG.
    B) IgM.
    C) IgA.
    D) IgD.
    E) IgE.

Answer: B
Skill: Recall

19) Large antibodies that agglutinate antigens are
    A) IgG.
    B) IgM.
    C) IgA.
    D) IgD.
    E) IgE.

Answer: B
Skill: Recall

20) The most abundant class of antibodies in serum is
　　A) IgG.
　　B) IgM.
　　C) IgA.
　　D) IgD.
　　E) IgE.
Answer: A
Skill: Recall

Figure 17.1

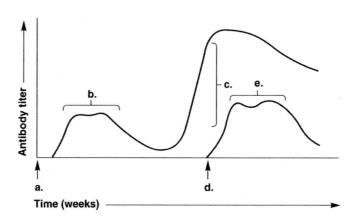

21) In Figure 17.1, which letter on the graph indicates the patient's secondary response to an antigen?
　　A) a
　　B) b
　　C) c
　　D) d
　　E) e
Answer: C
Skill: Analysis

22) In Figure 17.1, which letter on the graph indicates the patient's response to a second antigen?
　　A) a
　　B) b
　　C) c
　　D) d
　　E) e
Answer: E
Skill: Analysis

23) In Figure 17.1, the arrow at time (d) indicates
　　A) The time of exposure to the same antigen as at time (a).
　　B) The secondary response.
　　C) The primary response.
　　D) Exposure to a new antigen.
　　E) The T-cell response.
Answer: D
Skill: Analysis

24) Which statement is false?
   A) The variable region of a heavy chain binds with antigen.
   B) The variable region of a light chain binds with antigen.
   C) The Fc region attaches to a host cell.
   D) The constant region of a heavy chain is the same for all antibodies.
   E) All of the above statements are true.

Answer: D
Skill: Analysis

25) The best definition of *antigen* is
   A) Something foreign in the body.
   B) A chemical that elicits an antibody response and can combine with these antibodies.
   C) A chemical that combines with antibodies.
   D) A pathogen.
   E) A protein that combines with antibodies.

Answer: B
Skill: Recall

26) The best definition *antibody* is
   A) A serum protein.
   B) A protein that inactivates or kills an antigen.
   C) A protein made in response to an antigen that can combine with that antigen.
   D) An immunoglobulin.
   E) A protein that combines with a protein or carbohydrate.

Answer: C
Skill: Recall

27) The following events elicit an antibody response. What is the third step?
   A) Antigen–digest goes to surface of APC.
   B) APC phagocytizes antigen.
   C) B cell is activated.
   D) T_H cell recognizes antigen–digest and MHC II.
   E) T_H cell produces cytokines.

Answer: D
Skill: Analysis

Figure 17.2

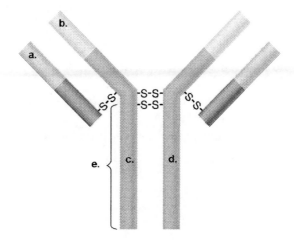

28) In Figure 17.2, which areas are similar for all IgG antibodies?
    A) a and b
    B) a and c
    C) b and c
    D) c and d
    E) b and d
    Answer: D
    Skill: Understanding

29) In Figure 17.2, which areas are different for all IgM antibodies?
    A) a and b
    B) a and c
    C) b and c
    D) c and d
    Answer: A
    Skill: Analysis

30) In Figure 17.2, which areas represent antigen–binding sites?
    A) a and b
    B) a and c
    C) b and c
    D) c and d
    E) b and d
    Answer: A
    Skill: Analysis

31) In Figure 17.2, what can attach to a host cell?
    A) a and c
    B) b and c
    C) b
    D) d
    E) e
    Answer: E
    Skill: Analysis

32) Figure 17.2 could be any of the following *EXCEPT*
    A) IgM.
    B) IgG.
    C) IgD.
    D) IgE.
    E) The figure could represent any of the above.

Answer: A
Skill: Analysis

33) The presence of which of the following indicates a current infection rather than a previous infection or vaccination?
    A) IgA
    B) IgG
    C) IgM
    D) IgD
    E) IgE

Answer: C
Skill: Recall

34) Which of the following destroys virus–infected cells?
    A) CTL
    B) T_{reg}
    C) T_H
    D) Dendritic cells
    E) B cells

Answer: A
Skill: Recall

35) The following events occur in cellular immunity. What is the third step?
    A) Antibodies are produced.
    B) Dendritic cell takes up antigen.
    C) Antigen enters M cell
    D) T_H cell produces cytokines.
    E) T_H cells proliferate.

Answer: E
Skill: Analysis

36) Cytokines released by T_H1 cells
    A) Activate $CD8^+$ cells to CTLs.
    B) Convert T_H1 cells to T_H2 cells.
    C) Convert T_H2 cells to T_H1 cells.
    D) Kill parasites.
    E) Convert B cells to T cells.

Answer: A
Skill: Recall

37) Which one of the following causes transmembrane channels in target cells?
   A) Antigen
   B) Hapten
   C) IL–1
   D) IL–2
   E) Perforin

Answer: E
Skill: Recall

38) Patients with an inherited type of colon cancer called familial adenomatous polyposis have a mutation in the gene that codes for
   A) Apoptosis.
   B) IgE antibodies.
   C) T helper cells.
   D) ADCC.
   E) Phagocytosis.

Answer: A
Skill: Understanding

39) Thymic selection
   A) Destroys T cells that don't recognize self–molecules of MHC.
   B) Destroys B cells that make antibodies against self.
   C) Destroys MHC molecules.
   D) Destroys CD4$^+$ cells that attack self.
   E) Activates B cells.

Answer: A
Skill: Recall

40) Which of the following statements about natural killer cells is false?
   A) They destroy virus–infected cells.
   B) They destroy tumor cells.
   C) They destroy cells lacking MHC I.
   D) They are stimulated by an antigen.
   E) All of the above statements are true.

Answer: D
Skill: Analysis

41) An antibody's Fc region can be bound by
   A) Antibodies.
   B) Macrophages.
   C) T helper cells.
   D) B cells.
   E) CTLs

Answer: B
Skill: Analysis

42) A T_{reg} cell deficiency could result in
   A) Increased number of viral infections.
   B) Increased number of bacterial infections.
   C) Autoimmunity.
   D) Increased severity of bacterial infections.
   E) Transplant rejection.

Answer: C
Skill: Understanding

43) Cell death caused by perforin and granzymes is caused by
   A) CTLs.
   B) T_H1 cells.
   C) T_H2 cells.
   D) B cells.
   E) TLRs.

Answer: A
Skill: Recall

44) IL-2, produced by T_H cells,
   A) Activates macrophages.
   B) Stimulates T_H cell maturation.
   C) Causes phagocytosis.
   D) Activates antigen–presenting cells.
   E) Activates T_C cells to CTLs.

Answer: B
Skill: Recall

45) Which of the following statements about IL–12 is false?
   A) It activates macrophages.
   B) It inhibits some tumor cells.
   C) It activates the T_H1 pathway.
   D) It causes autoimmune diseases.
   E) It causes T_H cells to respond to HIV.

Answer: D
Skill: Recall

Essay Questions

1) A person has antibodies against the measles virus. Identify three ways in which these antibodies could be acquired.

2) Describe the production of antibodies using the clonal selection theory.

3) Positive diagnosis of AIDS is made when a patient has antibodies against the human immunodeficiency virus (HIV). Why does a patient have an immune deficiency if he or she is making antibodies?

Chapter 18 Practical Applications of Immunology

Objective Questions

1) Which of the following is *NOT* normally used in a vaccine?
   A) Toxoid
   B) Parts of bacterial cells
   C) Live, attenuated bacteria
   D) Inactivated viruses
   E) Antibodies

   Answer: E
   Skill: Recall

2) Patient's serum, influenza virus, and red blood cells are mixed in a tube. What happens if the patient has antibodies against influenza virus?
   A) Agglutination
   B) Hemagglutination
   C) Complement fixation
   D) Hemolysis
   E) Hemagglutination–inhibition

   Answer: E
   Skill: Analysis

3) A patient shows the presence of antibodies against diphtheria toxin. Which of the following statements is false?
   A) The patient may have the disease.
   B) The patient may have had the disease and has recovered.
   C) The patient may have been vaccinated.
   D) A recent transfusion may have passively introduced the antibodies.
   E) The patient was near someone who had the disease.

   Answer: E
   Skill: Recall

4) In an agglutination test, eight serial dilutions to determine antibody titer were set up: tube #1 contained a 1:2 dilution; tube #2, a 1:4, etc. If tube #6 is the last tube showing agglutination, what is the antibody titer?
   A) 6
   B) 1:6
   C) 64
   D) 1:32
   E) 32

   Answer: C
   Skill: Analysis

5) Which of the following is *NOT* a disadvantage of a live virus vaccine?
   A) The live vaccine may revert to a more virulent form.
   B) Exogenous protein contaminants may be present.
   C) Antibody response is not as good as with inactivated viruses.
   D) Live viruses generally require refrigeration.
   E) All of the above are disadvantages of live virus vaccine.

Answer: C
Skill: Recall

6) Which of the following *CANNOT* yield antibodies for serological testing?
   A) Vaccinated humans
   B) Vaccinated animals
   C) Monoclonal antibodies
   D) Viral cultures
   E) All of the above may yield antibodies for serological testing.

Answer: D
Skill: Analysis

7) A reaction between an antibody and soluble antigen–forming lattices is called a(n)
   A) Agglutination reaction.
   B) Complement fixation.
   C) Immunofluorescence.
   D) Neutralization reaction.
   E) Precipitation reaction.

Answer: E
Skill: Recall

8) A reaction between antibody and particulate antigen is called a(n)
   A) Agglutination reaction.
   B) Complement fixation.
   C) Immunofluorescence.
   D) Neutralization reaction.
   E) Precipitation reaction.

Answer: A
Skill: Recall

9) A reaction using red blood cells as the indicator and hemolysis indicates an antigen—antibody reaction is called a(n)
   A) Agglutination reaction.
   B) Complement fixation.
   C) Immunofluorescence.
   D) Neutralization reaction.
   E) Precipitation reaction.

Answer: B
Skill: Recall

10) An indirect version of which test using antihuman globulin may be used to detect patient's antibodies against *Treponema pallidum*?
    A) Agglutination reaction
    B) Complement fixation
    C) Immunofluorescence
    D) Neutralization reaction
    E) Precipitation reaction

Answer: C
Skill: Recall

11) Toxoid vaccines such as the vaccines against diphtheria and tetanus elicit a(n)
    A) T$_C$ cell response.
    B) Immune complex.
    C) Dendritic cell proliferation.
    D) Antibody response against these bacterial toxins.
    E) Antibody response against gram–positive bacteria.

Answer: D
Skill: Analysis

12) What type of vaccine is *Streptococcus pyogenes* capsule?
    A) Conjugated vaccine
    B) Subunit vaccine
    C) Nucleic acid vaccine
    D) Attenuated whole–agent vaccine
    E) Toxoid vaccine

Answer: B
Skill: Recall

13) What type of vaccine involves host synthesis of viral antigens?
    A) Conjugated vaccine
    B) Subunit vaccine
    C) Nucleic acid vaccine
    D) Attenuated whole–agent vaccine
    E) Toxoid vaccine

Answer: C
Skill: Recall

14) Purified protein from *Bordetella pertussis* is a(n)
    A) Conjugated vaccine.
    B) Subunit vaccine.
    C) Nucleic acid vaccine.
    D) Attenuated whole–agent vaccine.
    E) Toxoid vaccine.

Answer: B
Skill: Recall

15) What type of vaccine is live measles virus?
     A) Conjugated vaccine
     B) Subunit vaccine
     C) Nucleic acid vaccine
     D) Attenuated whole-agent vaccine
     E) Toxoid vaccine

   Answer: D
   Skill: Recall

16) A test used to identify antibodies against *Treponema pallidum* in a patient is the
     A) Direct fluorescent-antibody test.
     B) Indirect fluorescent-antibody test.
     C) Direct agglutination test.
     D) Direct ELISA test.
     E) Hemagglutination-inhibition test.

   Answer: B
   Skill: Analysis

17) A test used to identify *Streptococcus pyogenes* in a patient is the
     A) Direct fluorescent-antibody test.
     B) Indirect fluorescent-antibody test.
     C) Hemagglutination.
     D) Hemagglutination-inhibition.
     E) Indirect ELISA.

   Answer: A
   Skill: Analysis

18) A test used to detect anti-*Rickettsia* antibodies in a patient is the
     A) Direct fluorescent-antibody test.
     B) Indirect fluorescent-antibody test.

   Answer: B
   Skill: Analysis

19) Which of the following is a pregnancy test used to find the fetal hormone HCG in a woman's
    urine using anti-HCG and latex spheres?
     A) Direct agglutination reaction
     B) Passive agglutination reaction
     C) Immunofluorescence
     D) Neutralization reaction
     E) Precipitation reaction

   Answer: B
   Skill: Analysis

20) Which of the following is a test to determine patient's blood type by mixing patient's red blood cells with antisera?
    A) Direct agglutination reaction
    B) Passive agglutination reaction
    C) Immunofluorescence
    D) Neutralization reaction
    E) Precipitation reaction

Answer: A
Skill: Analysis

21) Which of the following is a test to determine the presence of soluble antigens in patient's saliva?
    A) Direct agglutination reaction
    B) Passive agglutination reaction
    C) Immunofluorescence
    D) Neutralization reaction
    E) Precipitation reaction

Answer: E
Skill: Analysis

22) Patient's serum, *Rickettsia,* guinea pig complement, sheep red blood cells, and anti–sheep red blood cells are mixed in a tube. What happens if the patient has epidemic typhus?
    A) Bacteria fluoresce.
    B) Hemagglutination occurs.
    C) Hemagglutination-inhibition occurs.
    D) Hemolysis occurs.
    E) *Rickettsia* grow.

Answer: E
Skill: Understanding

23) A vaccine against HIV proteins made by vaccinia virus is a(n)
    A) Conjugated vaccine.
    B) Subunit vaccine.
    C) Nucleic acid vaccine.
    D) Inactivated whole-agent vaccine.
    E) Toxoid vaccine.

Answer: B
Skill: Analysis

24) Inactivated tetanus toxin is a(n)
    A) Conjugated vaccine.
    B) Subunit vaccine.
    C) Nucleic acid vaccine.
    D) Inactivated whole-agent vaccine.
    E) Toxoid vaccine.

Answer: E
Skill: Analysis

25) *Haemophilus influenzae* b capsular polysaccharide with a protein is a(n)
    A) Conjugated vaccine.
    B) Subunit vaccine.
    C) Nucleic acid vaccine.
    D) Inactivated whole-agent vaccine.
    E) Toxoid vaccine.

Answer: A
Skill: Analysis

Table 18.1

	Antibody Titer			
	Day 1	Day 7	Day 14	Day 21
Patient A	0	0	256	512
Patient B	128	256	512	1024
Patient C	0	0	0	0
Patient D	128	128	128	128

26) In Table 18.1, who probably has the disease?
    A) A and B
    B) B and C
    C) A and C
    D) C and D
    E) A and D

Answer: A
Skill: Analysis

27) In Table 18.1, who is most likely protected from the disease?
    A) A
    B) B
    C) C
    D) D

Answer: D
Skill: Analysis

28) In Table 18.1, who showed seroconversion during these observations?
    A) A
    B) B
    C) C
    D) D

Answer: A
Skill: Analysis

Figure 18.1

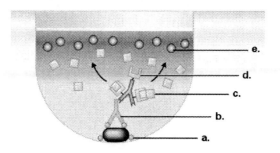

29) In Figure 18.1, which component came from the patient in this ELISA test?
    A) a
    B) b
    C) c
    D) d
    E) e

Answer: B
Skill: Analysis

30) Which of the following tests is *NOT* correctly matched to its positive reaction?
    A) Hemagglutination — clumping of red blood cells
    B) Complement fixation — no hemolysis
    C) Neutralization — no tissue/animal death
    D) ELISA — enzyme–substrate reaction
    E) Western blot — agglutination

Answer: E
Skill: Recall

31) To detect botulinum toxin in food, suspect food is injected into two guinea pigs. The guinea pig that was vaccinated against botulism survives, but the one that was not vaccinated dies. This is an example of
    A) Agglutination.
    B) Neutralization.
    C) Hemagglutination.
    D) Fluorescent antibodies.
    E) ELISA.

Answer: B
Skill: Understanding

32) The following steps are used to produce monoclonal antibodies. What is the fourth step?
    A) A B cell is activated to produce antibodies.
    B) Culture the hybridoma.
    C) Fuse a B cell to a myeloma cell.
    D) Isolate antibody-producing B cells.
    E) Vaccinate a mouse.

Answer: C
Skill: Analysis

33) Palivizumab is used to treat respiratory syncytial virus disease. The antiviral drug is
    A) A toxoid.
    B) A monoclonal antibody.
    C) A vaccine.
    D) An immunosuppressive.
    E) A nucleoside analog.

Answer: B
Skill: Analysis

34) Live polio virus can be used in a(n)
    A) Inactivated whole-agent vaccine.
    B) Attenuated whole-agent vaccine.
    C) Conjugated vaccine.
    D) Subunit vaccine.
    E) Toxoid vaccine.

Answer: B
Skill: Analysis

35) *Haemophilus* capsule polysaccharide plus diphtheria toxoid is a(n)
    A) Inactivated whole-agent vaccine.
    B) Attenuated whole-agent vaccine.
    C) Conjugated vaccine.
    D) Subunit vaccine.
    E) Toxoid vaccine.

Answer: C
Skill: Analysis

36) Dead *Bordetella pertussis* can be used in a(n)
    A) Inactivated whole-agent vaccine.
    B) Attenuated whole-agent vaccine.
    C) Conjugated vaccine.
    D) Subunit vaccine.
    E) Toxoid vaccine.

Answer: A
Skill: Analysis

37) Hepatitis B virus surface antigen can be used in a(n)
    A) Inactivated whole-agent vaccine.
    B) Attenuated whole-agent vaccine.
    C) Conjugated vaccine.
    D) Subunit vaccine.
    E) Toxoid vaccine.

Answer: D
Skill: Analysis

38) Which is the third step in a direct ELISA test?
    A) Substrate for the enzyme
    B) Antigen
    C) Antihuman immune serum
    D) Antibodies against the antigen

Answer: C
Skill: Understanding

39) Which item is from the patient in a direct ELISA test?
    A) Substrate for the enzyme
    B) Antigen
    C) Antihuman immune serum
    D) Antibodies against the antigen

Answer: B
Skill: Understanding

40) Which of the following tests is most useful in determining the presence of AIDS antibodies?
    A) Agglutination
    B) Complement fixation
    C) Neutralization
    D) Indirect ELISA
    E) Direct fluorescent–antibody

Answer: D
Skill: Understanding

41) Which of the following uses fluorescent–labeled antibodies?
    A) Agglutination
    B) Complement fixation
    C) Precipitation
    D) Flow cytometry
    E) Neutralization

Answer: D
Skill: Recall

42) Which of the following uses red blood cells as the indicator?
    A) Agglutination
    B) Complement fixation
    C) Precipitation
    D) Flow cytometry
    E) Neutralization

Answer: B
Skill: Recall

Situation 18.1

In an immunodiffusion test to diagnose histoplasmosis, patient's serum is placed in a well in an agar plate. In a positive test, a precipitate forms as the serum diffuses from the well and meets material diffusing from a second well.

43) In Situation 18.1, what is in the second well?
   A) Antibodies
   B) A fungal antigen
   C) Fungal cells
   D) Mycelia
   E) Red blood cells

Answer: B
Skill: Understanding

44) The immunodiffusion test described in Situation 18.1 is
   A) An agglutination reaction.
   B) A precipitation reaction.
   C) A complement–fixation test.
   D) An ELISA test.
   E) A direct test.

Answer: B
Skill: Understanding

45) Which one of the following statements about measles is true?
   A) It is not a serious disease.
   B) It is endemic in the United States.
   C) Annually, it kills thousands of children worldwide.
   D) It is not preventable.
   E) All children should get the disease.

Answer: C
Skill: Recall

Essay Questions

1) Explain the ELISA test to detect the presence of HIV antibodies in a patient.

2) Design a serological test to detect botulinum toxin in food.

3) A person has an antibody titer of 28. What do you know about this person?

Chapter 19 Disorders Associated with the Immune System

Objective Questions

1) Hypersensitivity is due to
    A) The presence of an antigen.
    B) Immunity.
    C) The presence of antibodies.
    D) An altered immune response.
    E) Allergies.

Answer: D
Skill: Recall

2) The chemical mediators of anaphylaxis are
    A) Found in basophils and mast cells.
    B) Antibodies.
    C) Antigens.
    D) Antigen–antibody complexes.
    E) The proteins of the complement system.

Answer: A
Skill: Analysis

3) Which of the following may result from systemic anaphylaxis?
    A) Hay fever
    B) Asthma
    C) Shock
    D) Hives
    E) Immunodeficiency

Answer: C
Skill: Analysis

4) Which antibodies will be in the serum of a person with blood type B, Rh⁻?
    A) Anti–A, anti–B, anti–Rh
    B) Anti–A, anti–Rh
    C) Anti–A
    D) Anti–B, anti–Rh
    E) Anti–B

Answer: C
Skill: Understanding

5) Which type of transplant is least compatible?
   A) Autograft
   B) Allograft
   C) Isograft
   D) Xenotransplant
   E) All of the above are equally compatible.

   Answer: D
   Skill: Analysis

6) Which of the following is *NOT* used to determine relatedness between a donor and a recipient for transplants?
   A) ABO antigens
   B) ABO antibodies
   C) MHC antigens
   D) MHC antibodies
   E) All of the above are used to determine relatedness between donor and recipient.

   Answer: E
   Skill: Analysis

7) Graft–versus–host disease will most likely be a complication of
   A) A skin graft.
   B) A bone marrow transplant.
   C) A blood transfusion.
   D) An Rh incompatibility between mother and fetus.
   E) All of the above.

   Answer: B
   Skill: Analysis

8) Immune complexes include
   A) Antibodies against self and complement.
   B) Viruses and antiviruses.
   C) IgE antibodies.
   D) Macrophages and T cells.
   E) CTLs.

   Answer: A
   Skill: Recall

9) A healthy immune system destroys cancer cells with
   A) Tumor–specific antigens.
   B) CTLs.
   C) IgG antibodies.
   D) IgE antibodies.
   E) CD4$^+$ T cells.

   Answer: B
   Skill: Recall

10) The symptoms of an immune complex reaction are due to
    A) Destruction of the antigen.
    B) Complement fixation.
    C) Phagocytosis.
    D) Antibodies against self.
    E) Cytokines.

Answer: B
Skill: Analysis

11) Autoimmunity is due to
    A) IgG and IgM antibodies.
    B) IgA antibodies.
    C) IgD antibodies.
    D) IgE antibodies.
    E) CTLs.

Answer: A
Skill: Recall

12) Allergic contact dermatitis is due to
    A) Sensitized T cells.
    B) IgG antibodies.
    C) IgE antibodies.
    D) IgM antibodies.
    E) Activated macrophages.

Answer: A
Skill: Analysis

13) Which of these causes of glomerulonephritis leads to all the others?
    A) Antibodies against *Streptococcus*
    B) Circulating immune complexes
    C) Complement fixation
    D) Formation of immune complexes
    E) Production of IgG

Answer: A
Skill: Understanding

14) Which of these causes damage to kidney cells in glomerulonephritis?
    A) Antibodies against *Streptococcus*
    B) Circulating immune complexes
    C) Complement fixation
    D) Formation of immune complexes
    E) Production of IgG

Answer: C
Skill: Understanding

15) A hypersensitivity reaction occurs
    A) During the first exposure to an antigen.
    B) On a second or subsequent exposure to an antigen.
    C) In immunologically tolerant individuals.
    D) During autoimmune diseases.
    E) In individuals with diseases of the immune system.

Answer: B
Skill: Recall

16) Which of the following statements about type I hypersensitivities is false?
    A) They are cell–mediated.
    B) They involve IgE antibodies.
    C) The symptoms are due to histamine.
    D) Antibodies are bound to host cells.
    E) The symptoms occur soon after exposure to an antigen.

Answer: A
Skill: Analysis

17) Which of the following statements about type IV hypersensitivities is false?
    A) They are cell–mediated.
    B) The symptoms occur within a few days after exposure to an antigen.
    C) They can be passively transferred with serum.
    D) The symptoms are due to lymphokines.
    E) They contribute to the symptoms of certain diseases.

Answer: C
Skill: Analysis

18) Which of the following blood transfusions are *incompatible*?

Donor	Recipient
1. AB, Rh⁻	AB, Rh⁺
2. A, Rh⁺	A, Rh⁻
3. A, Rh⁺	O, Rh⁺
4. B, Rh⁻	B, Rh⁺
5. B, Rh⁺	A, Rh⁺

    A) 2 and 5
    B) 1, 2, and 3
    C) 2, 3, and 5
    D) 3 and 4
    E) 1 and 2

Answer: C
Skill: Understanding

19) Hemolytic disease of the newborn can result from
    A) An Rh$^+$ mother with an Rh$^-$ fetus.
    B) An Rh$^-$ mother with an Rh$^+$ fetus.
    C) An AB mother with a B fetus.
    D) An AB mother with an O fetus.
    E) An Rh$^-$ mother and an A fetus.

Answer: B
Skill: Understanding

20) Reaction of antigen with IgE antibodies attached to mast cells causes
    A) Lysis of the cells.
    B) Release of chemical mediators.
    C) Complement fixation.
    D) Agglutination.
    E) Hemolysis.

Answer: B
Skill: Analysis

21) Which of the following involves a monoclonal antitumor antibody and a toxin?
    A) Immunologic enhancement
    B) Immunologic surveillance
    C) Immunotherapy
    D) Immunosuppression
    E) Immune complex

Answer: C
Skill: Analysis

22) Which of the following may be inherited or result from HIV infection?
    A) Immunologic enhancement
    B) Immunologic surveillance
    C) Immunotherapy
    D) Immunosuppression
    E) Autoimmunity

Answer: D
Skill: Analysis

23) Treatment with certain drugs to reduce transplant rejection can cause
    A) Immunologic enhancement.
    B) Immunologic surveillance.
    C) Immunotherapy.
    D) Immunosuppression.
    E) Autoimmunity

Answer: D
Skill: Analysis

24) Which of the following statements about human embryonic stem cells is false?
   A) They produce MHC I antigens.
   B) They produce MHC II antigens.
   C) They are pluripotent.
   D) They are undifferentiated.

Answer: B
Skill: Analysis

Figure 19.1

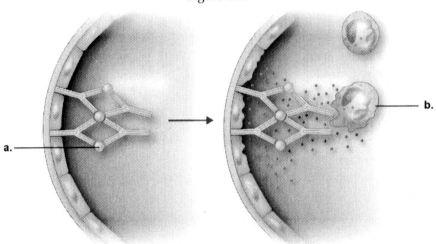

25) In the immune complex reaction shown in Figure 19.1, what is the structure labeled a?
   A) Antibody
   B) Antigen
   C) Complement
   D) Neutrophil
   E) Mast cell

Answer: B
Skill: Analysis

26) In the immune complex reaction shown in Figure 19.1, what is the structure labeled b?
   A) Antibody
   B) Antigen
   C) Complement
   D) Neutrophil
   E) Mast cell

Answer: D
Skill: Analysis

27) Worldwide, the primary method of transmission of HIV is
   A) Heterosexual intercourse.
   B) Homosexual intercourse.
   C) Intravenous drug use.
   D) Blood transfusions.
   E) Nosocomial.

Answer: A
Skill: Recall

28) Someone with AIDS probably
   A) Does not make any antibodies.
   B) Makes T–dependent antibodies.
   C) Makes T–independent antibodies.
   D) Makes T_C- and T^{reg}-dependent antibodies.
   E) None of the above.

Answer: C
Skill: Understanding

29) Which of the following is the *LEAST* likely vaccine against HIV?
   A) Attenuated virus
   B) Glycoprotein
   C) Protein core
   D) Subunit
   E) All of the above are equally likely.

Answer: A
Skill: Analysis

30) Which of the following is a possible outcome of an HIV infection?
   A) Latency
   B) Slow production of new viruses
   C) T_C-killing of infected cells
   D) Viral–killing of infected cells
   E) All of the above

Answer: E
Skill: Recall

31) Which of the following does *NOT* transmit HIV?
   A) Homosexual activity
   B) Heterosexual activity
   C) Hypodermic needles
   D) Mosquitoes
   E) Human milk

Answer: D
Skill: Recall

32) Drugs, such as AZT and ddC, currently used to treat AIDS act by
   A) Stimulatory T_H cells.
   B) Stopping DNA synthesis.
   C) Promoting antibody formation.
   D) Neutralizing the virus.
   E) All of the above.

Answer: B
Skill: Analysis

33) During asymptomatic phase I of HIV disease, HIV infection is diagnosed by
   A) Measuring viral RNA.
   B) Measuring antibodies against HIV.
   C) Counting CD4$^+$ T cells.
   D) Counting CD8$^+$ T cells.
   E) Testing for seroconversion.

Answer: A
Skill: Analysis

34) Which one of the following statements about HIV is false?
   A) CD8$^+$ T cells decrease the viral load.
   B) HIV can be transmitted by cell–to–cell contact.
   C) Bone marrow can be a reservoir for future infection.
   D) Viral infection of T$_H$ cells results in signs elsewhere in the patient.
   E) Long–term nonprogessors lack CD4 molecules.

Answer: E
Skill: Understanding

35) Which of the following is *NOT* an immune complex disease?
   A) Rheumatic fever
   B) Systemic lupus erythematosus
   C) Hemolytic disease of the newborn
   D) Glomerulonephritis
   E) Psoriasis

Answer: C
Skill: Recall

36) Which of the following is *NOT* considered a type I hypersensitivity?
   A) Asthma
   B) Dust allergies
   C) Penicillin allergic reactions
   D) Pollen allergies
   E) Transplant rejections

Answer: E
Skill: Recall

37) All of the following lead to drug–induced thrombocytopenic purpura.Which occurs first?
   A) Antibodies are made against the drug.
   B) Complement is fixed.
   C) Drug binds to platelets.
   D) Platelets are destroyed.

Answer: C
Skill: Analysis

38) Immunodeficiencies are caused by all of the following. Which one does *NOT* cause an acquired immunodeficiency?
    A) Chromosomal–linked B–cell deficiency
    B) Cyclosporine to inhibit IL–2 secretion
    C) HIV infection
    D) Rapamycin to inhibit IL–2 action
    E) All of the above cause an acquired immunodeficiency.

Answer: A
Skill: Analysis

39) Which of the following describes a cytotoxic autoimmune reaction?
    A) Antibodies react to cell–surface antigens.
    B) Antibodies are not made.
    C) Cells are killed.
    D) Immune complexes form.
    E) Mediate by T cells.

Answer: A
Skill: Recall

40) Symptoms of delayed cell–mediated reactions are due to
    A) IgE antibodies.
    B) Cytotoxic T cells.
    C) Cytokines.
    D) IgG antibodies.
    E) Antigens.

Answer: C
Skill: Analysis

41) Desensitization involves injection of
    A) Antigens.
    B) IgG antibodies.
    C) IgE antibodies.
    D) Antihistamine.
    E) Histamine.

Answer: A
Skill: Analysis

42) The following events occur if human cells expressing HLA–I are mixed with anti–HLA–I, complement, and trypan blue. What step indicates the cells are HLA–I?
    A) The MAC makes a pore in the plasma membrane.
    B) Complement is fixed.
    C) Trypan blue enters the cells.
    D) Antibody binds to the cells.
    E) None of the above; the T cells are missing.

Answer: C
Skill: Analysis

43) In rheumatoid arthritis, IgM, IgG, and complement deposit in joints. This is an example of
    A) Cytotoxic autoimmunity.
    B) Immune complex autoimmunity.
    C) Cell–mediated autoimmunity.
    D) Immunosuppression.
    E) Acquired immunodeficiency.

Answer: B
Skill: Recall

44) MMR vaccine contains hydrolyzed gelatin. A person receiving this vaccine could develop an anaphylactic reaction if the person has
    A) An immunodeficiency.
    B) Antibodies against eggs.
    C) Antibodies against gelatin.
    D) Received the influenza vaccine.
    E) Antibodies against measles.

Answer: C
Skill: Analysis

45) Delayed hypersensitivities are due to
    A) IgE antibodies.
    B) T cells.
    C) IgG antibodies.
    D) Platelets.
    E) Antibodies against self.

Answer: B
Skill: Recall

Essay Questions

1) Differentiate type II from type III hypersensitivity reactions.

2) Simian immune deficiency disease is caused by a virus that is closely related to HIV. This disease occurs naturally in African monkeys only. A primate center that raises Rhesus monkeys found an immunodeficiency disease in its Indian Rhesus monkeys. Provide a hypothesis to explain how the Rhesus monkeys acquired this disease.

3) What is desensitization? Explain how this treatment can induce systemic anaphylaxis. How is systemic anaphylaxis treated?

4) The ratio of CD4:CD8 is 2.0 in normal individuals. What can you conclude if a patient has a CD4:CD8 ratio of 0.5?

Chapter 20 Antimicrobial Drugs

Objective Questions

1) Penicillin was considered a "miracle drug" for all of the following reasons *EXCEPT*
    A) It was the first antibiotic.
    B) It doesn't affect eukaryotic cells.
    C) It inhibits gram–positive cell wall synthesis.
    D) It has selective toxicity.
    E) It kills bacteria.

Answer: A
Skill: Analysis

2) A drug that inhibits mitosis, such as griseofulvin, would be more effective against
    A) Gram–positive bacteria.
    B) Gram–negative bacteria.
    C) Fungi.
    D) Wall–less bacteria.
    E) Mycobacteria.

Answer: C
Skill: Analysis

3) Most of the available antimicrobial agents are effective against
    A) Viruses.
    B) Bacteria.
    C) Fungi.
    D) Protozoa.
    E) All of the above.

Answer: B
Skill: Recall

4) Antimicrobial peptides work by
    A) Inhibiting protein synthesis.
    B) Disrupting the plasma membrane.
    C) Complementary base pairing with DNA.
    D) Inhibiting cell–wall synthesis.
    E) Hydrolyzing peptidoglycan.

Answer: B
Skill: Recall

5) In what way are semisynthetic penicillins and natural penicillins alike?
    A) Both are broad spectrum.
    B) Both are resistant to penicillinase.
    C) Both are resistant to stomach acids.
    D) Both are bactericidal.
    E) Both are based on β–lactam.

Answer: E
Skill: Recall

6) Which of the following antibiotics is *NOT* bactericidal?
    A) Aminoglycosides
    B) Cephalosporins
    C) Polyenes
    D) Rifampins
    E) Penicillin

Answer: C
Skill: Analysis

7) Which one of the following does *NOT* belong with the others?
    A) Bacitracin
    B) Cephalosporin
    C) Monobactam
    D) Penicillin
    E) Streptomycin

Answer: E
Skill: Analysis

Figure 20.1

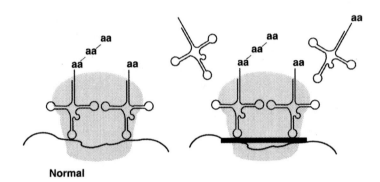

8) The antibiotic tetracycline binds to the 30S subunit of the ribosome as shown in Figure 20.1.
   The effect is to
    A) Prevent attachment of tRNA.
    B) Prevent peptide bond formation.
    C) Prevent transcription.
    D) Stop the ribosome from moving along the mRNA.
    E) Prevent attachment of tRNA and mRNA.

Answer: B
Skill: Understanding

Figure 20.2

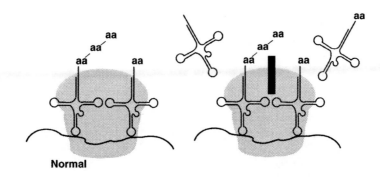

Normal

9) The antibiotic cycloheximide binds to the 60S subunit of the ribosome as shown in Figure 20.2.
   The effect is to
   A) Prevent mRNA—ribosome binding in eukaryotes.
   B) Prevent peptide bond formation in prokaryotes.
   C) Prevent polypeptide elongation in eukaryotes.
   D) Prevent transcription in prokaryotes.
   E) Prevent ribosome formation in bacteria.

   Answer: C
   Skill: Understanding

10) Which of these antimicrobial agents has the fewest side effects?
    A) Streptomycin
    B) Tetracycline
    C) Penicillin
    D) Erythromycin
    E) Chloramphenicol

    Answer: C
    Skill: Recall

11) Which of the following drugs does *NOT* act by competitive inhibition?
    A) Ethambutol
    B) Isoniazid
    C) Streptomycin
    D) Sulfonamide
    E) Tetracycline

    Answer: C
    Skill: Analysis

12) Which of the following methods of action would be bacteriostatic?
    A) Competitive inhibition with folic acid synthesis
    B) Inhibition of RNA synthesis
    C) Injury to plasma membrane
    D) Inhibition of cell wall synthesis
    E) Competitive inhibition with DNA gyrase

    Answer: B
    Skill: Understanding

13) Which of the following antibiotics is recommended for use against gram–negative bacteria?
    A) Polyenes
    B) Bacitracin
    C) Cephalosporin
    D) Penicillin
    E) Polymyxin

Answer: E
Skill: Recall

14) Which of the following antimicrobial agents is recommended for use against fungal infections?
    A) Amphotericin B
    B) Bacitracin
    C) Cephalosporin
    D) Penicillin
    E) Polymyxin

Answer: A
Skill: Recall

Table 20.1
The following data were obtained from a broth dilution test.

Concentration of Antibiotic X	Growth	Growth in Subculture
2 µg/ml	+	+
10 µg/ml	–	+
15 µg/ml	–	–
25 µg/ml	–	–

15) In Table 20.1, the minimal bactericidal concentration of antibiotic X is
    A) 2 µg/ml.
    B) 10 µg/ml.
    C) 15 µg/ml.
    D) 25 µg/ml.
    E) Can't tell.

Answer: C
Skill: Understanding

16) In Table 20.1, the minimal inhibitory concentration of antibiotic X is
    A) 2 µg/ml.
    B) 10 µg/ml.
    C) 15 µg/ml.
    D) 25 µg/ml.
    E) Can't tell.

Answer: B
Skill: Understanding

17) More than half of our antibiotics are
    A) Produced by fungi.
    B) Produced by bacteria.
    C) Synthesized in laboratories.
    D) Produced by Fleming.
    E) Produced by eukaryotic organisms.

Answer: B
Skill: Understanding

Figure 20.3

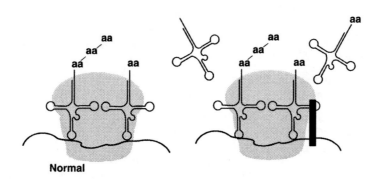

Normal

18) The antibiotic chloramphenicol binds to the 50S subunit of the ribosome as shown in Figure
    20.3. The effect is to
    A) Prevent attachment of tRNA.
    B) Prevent peptide bond formation.
    C) Prevent transcription.
    D) Stop the ribosome from moving along the mRNA.
    E) Prevent polypeptide formation in eukaryotes.

Answer: A
Skill: Understanding

Figure 20.4

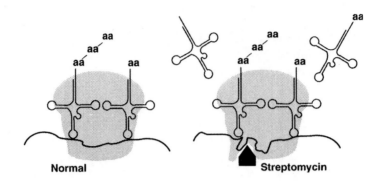

19) The antibiotic streptomycin binds to the 30S subunit of the ribosome as shown in Figure 20.4. The effect is to
A) Cause misreading of mRNA in 70S ribosomes.
B) Prevent binding of tRNA in eukaryotes.
C) Prevent polypeptide elongation in eukaryotes.
D) Prevent peptide bond formation in prokaryotes.
E) Prevent binding of tRNA in eukaryotes.

Answer: A
Skill: Understanding

20) Which compound would be the most useful to treat candidiasis?
A) Uracil
B) Thymine
C) Flucytosine
D) Guanine
E) Penicillin

Answer: C
Skill: Recall

21) Which of the following antibiotics are used to treat fungal infections?

1. Aminoglycosides
2. Cephalosporins
3. Griseofulvin
4. Polyenes
5. Bacitracin

A) 1, 2, and 3
B) 3 and 4
C) 3, 4, and 5
D) 4 and 5
E) All of the antibiotics

Answer: B
Skill: Recall

22) Which of the following antibiotics does *NOT* interfere with cell wall synthesis?
    A) Cephalosporins
    B) Macrolides
    C) Natural penicillins
    D) Semisynthetic penicillins
    E) Vancomycin

Answer: B
Skill: Recall

23) The antimicrobial drugs with the broadest spectrum of activity are
    A) Aminoglycosides.
    B) Chloramphenicol.
    C) Lincomycin.
    D) Macrolides.
    E) Tetracyclines.

Answer: E
Skill: Recall

24) Which of the following statements is false?
    A) Fluoroquinolone inhibits DNA synthesis.
    B) Acyclovir inhibits DNA synthesis.
    C) Amantadine inhibits release of viral nucleic acid.
    D) Interferon inhibits glycolysis.
    E) Azoles inhibit plasma membrane synthesis.

Answer: D
Skill: Analysis

25) Protozoan and helminthic diseases are difficult to treat because
    A) Their cells are structurally and functionally similar to human cells.
    B) They replicate inside human cells.
    C) They don't have ribosomes.
    D) They don't reproduce.
    E) They have more genes than bacteria.

Answer: A
Skill: Understanding

26) Which of the following organisms would most likely be sensitive to natural penicillin?
    A) L forms
    B) *Streptococcus pyogenes*
    C) Penicillinase–producing *Neisseria gonorrhoeae*
    D) *Penicillium*
    E) *Mycoplasma*

Answer: B
Skill: Understanding

27) Which of the following statements about drug resistance is false?
    A) It may be carried on a plasmid.
    B) It may be transferred from one bacterium to another during conjugation.
    C) It may be due to enzymes that degrade some antibiotics.
    D) It is found only in gram–negative bacteria.
    E) It may be due to increased uptake of a drug.

Answer: D
Skill: Recall

28) Which of the following does *NOT* constitute an advantage of using two antibiotics together?
    A) It can prevent drug resistance.
    B) It lessens the toxicity of individual drugs.
    C) Two are always twice as effective as one.
    D) It allows treatment to be provided prior to diagnosis.
    E) All of the above are advantages.

Answer: C
Skill: Analysis

29) Drug resistance occurs
    A) Because bacteria are normal microbiota.
    B) When antibiotics are used indiscriminately.
    C) Against antibiotics and not against synthetic chemotherapeutic agents.
    D) When antibiotics are taken after the symptoms disappear.
    E) All of the above.

Answer: B
Skill: Analysis

Table 20.2
The following results were obtained from a disk–diffusion test for microbial susceptibility to antibiotics. *Staphylococcus aureus* was the test organism.

Antibiotic	Zone of Inhibition
A	3 mm
B	7 mm
C	0 mm
D	10 mm

30) In Table 20.2, the most effective antibiotic tested was
    A) A.
    B) B.
    C) C.
    D) D.
    E) Can't tell.

Answer: D
Skill: Understanding

31) In Table 20.2, the antibiotic that exhibited bactericidal action was
   A) A.
   B) B.
   C) C.
   D) D.
   E) Can't tell.

Answer: E
Skill: Understanding

32) In Table 20.2, which antibiotic would be most useful for treating a *Salmonella* infection?
   A) A
   B) B
   C) C
   D) D
   E) Can't tell.

Answer: E
Skill: Understanding

33) Which of the following would be selective against the tubercle bacillus?
   A) Bacitracin — inhibits peptidoglycan synthesis
   B) Ethambutol — inhibits mycolic acid synthesis
   C) Streptogramin — inhibits protein synthesis
   D) Streptomycin — inhibits protein synthesis
   E) Vancomycin — inhibits peptidoglycan synthesis

Answer: B
Skill: Understanding

34) In the presence of penicillin, a cell dies because
   A) It lacks a cell wall.
   B) It plasmolyzes.
   C) It undergoes osmotic lysis.
   D) It lacks a cell membrane.
   E) Its contents leak out.

Answer: C
Skill: Understanding

35) Lamisil is an allylamine used to treat dermatomycoses. Lamisil's method of action is similar to that of
   A) Polymyxin B.
   B) Azole antibiotics.
   C) Echinocandins.
   D) Griseofulvin.
   E) Bacitracin.

Answer: B
Skill: Analysis

36) Niclosamide prevents ATP generation in mitochondria. You would expect this drug to be effective against
    A) Gram–negative bacteria.
    B) Gram–positive bacteria.
    C) Helminths.
    D) *Mycobacterium tuberculosis.*
    E) Viruses.

Answer: C
Skill: Understanding

Table 20.3
The following data were obtained from a broth dilution test:

Concentration of Antibiotic X	Growth
2.0 µg/ml	–
1.0 µg/ml	–
0.5 µg/ml	–
0.25 µg/ml	+
0.125 µg/ml	+
0	+

Bacteria from the 0.25 µg/ml tube were transferred to new growth media containing antibiotic X with the following results:

Concentration of Antibiotic X	Growth
2.0 µg/ml	–
1.0 µg/ml	+
0.5 µg/ml	+
0.25 µg/ml	+

37) The data in Table 20.3 show that these bacteria
    A) Can be subcultured.
    B) Developed resistance to antibiotics.
    C) Were killed by 0.125 µg/ml of antibiotic X.
    D) Were killed by 0.5 µg/ml of antibiotic X.
    E) Were resistant to 1.0 µg/ml at the start of the experiment.

Answer: B
Skill: Analysis

38) Which of the following statements about drugs that competitively inhibit DNA polymerase or RNA polymerase is false?
    A) They cause mutations.
    B) They are used against viral infections.
    C) They can affect host cell DNA.
    D) They are too dangerous to use.
    E) They interfere with protein synthesis.

Answer: D
Skill: Understanding

Figure 20.5

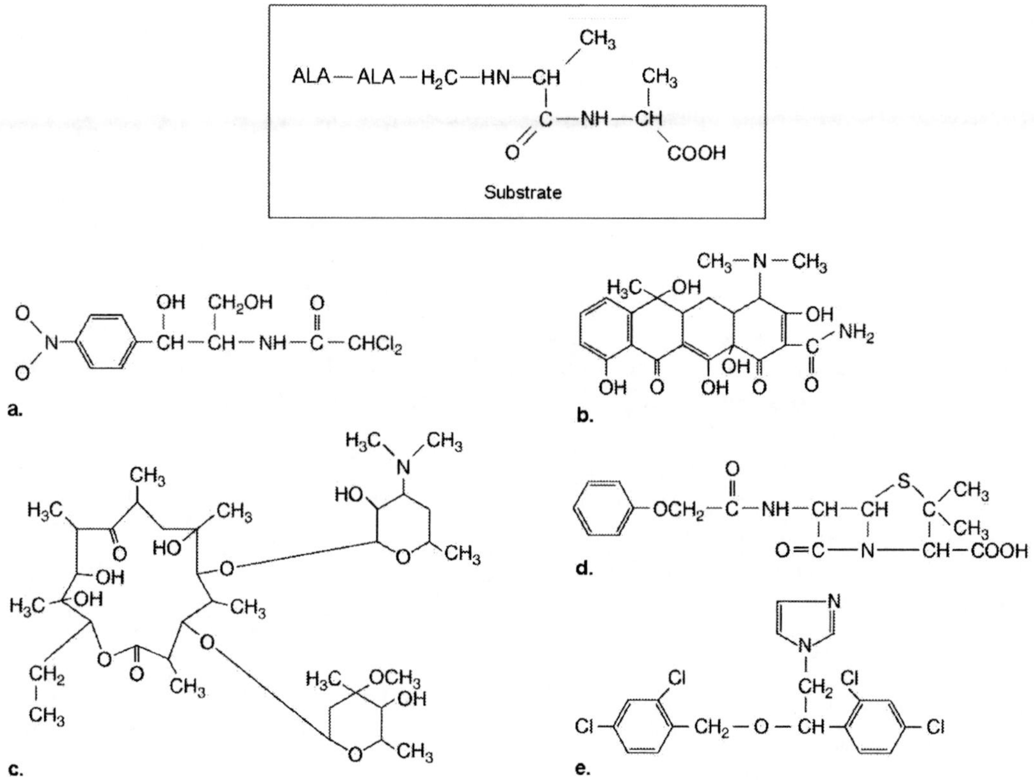

Substrate

a.

b.

c.

d.

e.

39) The substrate for transpeptidase used to synthesize peptidoglycan is shown in Figure 20.5. Which of the drugs shown would inhibit peptidoglycan synthesis?
    A) a
    B) b
    C) c
    D) d
    E) e

Answer: D
Skill: Analysis

Figure 20.6

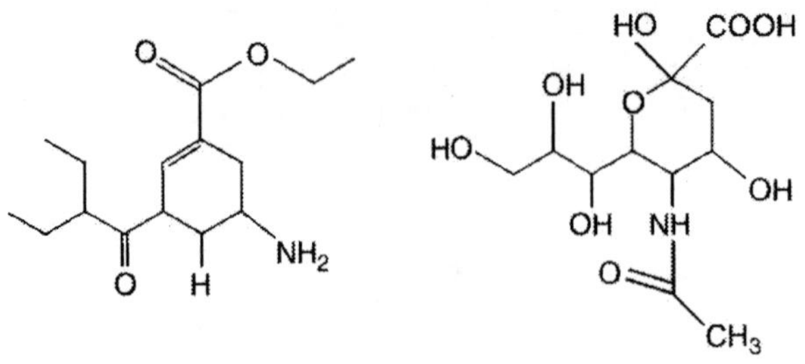

Tamiflu   Sialic acid

40) The structures of the influenza drug Tamiflu and sialic acid, the substrate for influenza virus's
neuramidase, are shown in Figure 20.6. What is the method of action of Tamiflu?
   A) Inhibits cell wall synthesis
   B) Inhibits plasma membrane synthesis
   C) Inhibits synthesis of neuramidase
   D) Competitive inhibition
   E) Prevents synthesis of virus spikes

Answer: D
Skill: Understanding

41) Which of the following does *NOT* affect eukaryotic cells?
   A) Antiprotozoan drugs
   B) Antihelminthic drugs
   C) Antifungal drugs
   D) Nucleotide analogs
   E) Semisynthetic penicillins

Answer: E
Skill: Analysis

42) Mebendazole is used to treat cestode infections. It interferes with microtubule formation;
therefore, it would *NOT* affect
   A) Bacteria.
   B) Fungi.
   C) Helminths.
   D) Human cells.
   E) Protozoa.

Answer: A
Skill: Understanding

43) Which of the following antibiotics causes misreading of mRNA?
   A) Aminoglycoside — changes shape of 30S units
   B) Chloramphenicol — inhibits peptide bonds at 50S subunit
   C) Oxazolidinone — prevents formation of 70S ribosome
   D) Streptogamin — prevents release of peptide from 70S ribosome
   E) Tetracyclines — bind with 30S subunit

Answer: A
Skill: Understanding

44) The antibiotic actinomycin D binds between adjacent G–C pairs, thus interfering with
   A) Transcription.
   B) Translation.
   C) Cellular respiration.
   D) Plasma membrane function.
   E) Peptide bond formation.

Answer: A
Skill: Understanding

45) Use of antibiotics in animal feed leads to antibiotic–resistant bacteria because
   A) Bacteria from other animals replace those killed by the antibiotics.
   B) The few surviving bacteria that are affected by the antibiotics develop immunity to the antibiotics, which they pass on to their progeny.
   C) The antibiotics cause new mutations to occur in the surviving bacteria, which results in resistance to antibiotics.
   D) The antibiotics kill susceptible bacteria, but the few that are naturally resistant live and reproduce, and their progeny repopulate the host animal.
   E) The antibiotics persist in soil and water.

Answer: D
Skill: Understanding

Essay Questions

1) Discuss why penicillin was called the "miracle drug" when it was first used in the 1940s.

2) Penicillin does not directly kill bacteria. Why do cells usually die in the presence of penicillin?

Chapter 21   Microbial Diseases of the Skin and Eyes

Objective Questions

1) Which of the following is *NOT* normal microbiota of the skin?
   A) *Streptococcus*
   B) *Pityrosporum*
   C) *Staphylococcus*
   D) *Propionibacterium*
   E) *Corynebacterium*

   Answer: A
   Skill: Recall

2) An 8-year-old girl has scabs and pus-filled vesicles on her face and throat. Three weeks earlier she had visited her grandmother, who had shingles. What infection does the 8-year-old have?
   A) Chickenpox
   B) Measles
   C) Fever blisters
   D) Scabies
   E) Rubella

   Answer: A
   Skill: Analysis

3) Which of the following pairs is mismatched?
   A) *Staphylococcus aureus* — impetigo
   B) *Streptococcus pyogenes* — erysipelas
   C) *Propionibacterium acnes* — pimples
   D) *Pseudomonas aeruginosa* — otitis externa
   E) *Str. pyogenes* — toxic shock syndrome

   Answer: C
   Skill: Analysis

4) The etiologic agent of warts is
   A) Papovavirus.
   B) Poxvirus.
   C) Herpesvirus.
   D) Parvovirus.
   E) *Staphylococcus aureus* .

   Answer: A
   Skill: Recall

5) Which of the following is *NOT* a characteristic of *Pseudomonas aeruginosa*?
    A) Gram–positive cell wall
    B) Oxidative metabolism
    C) Oxidase–positive
    D) Produce pyocyanin
    E) Rod shaped

Answer: A
Skill: Recall

6) Which of the following pairs is mismatched?
    A) Pustular rash — smallpox
    B) Koplik spots — rubella
    C) Papular rash — measles
    D) Vesicular rash — chickenpox
    E) Macular rash — fifth disease

Answer: B
Skill: Recall

7) Which of the following is *NOT* transmitted by the respiratory route?
    A) Smallpox
    B) Chickenpox
    C) Rubella
    D) *Trichophyton*
    E) Measles

Answer: D
Skill: Analysis

8) Which of these is *NOT* caused by herpesvirus?
    A) Chickenpox
    B) Shingles
    C) Keratitis
    D) Smallpox
    E) Roseola

Answer: D
Skill: Recall

9) Thrush and vaginitis are caused by
    A) Herpesvirus.
    B) *Chlamydia trachomatis.*
    C) *Candida albicans.*
    D) *Staphylococcus aureus.*
    E) *Streptococcus pyogenes.*

Answer: C
Skill: Recall

10) The greatest single cause of blindness in the world is
   A) Neonatal gonorrheal ophthalmia.
   B) Keratoconjunctivitis.
   C) Trachoma.
   D) Inclusion conjunctivitis.
   E) Pinkeye.

   Answer: C
   Skill: Recall

11) Which of the following can be treated with topical chemotherapeutic agents?
   A) Herpes gladiatorium
   B) Sporotrichosis
   C) Dermatomycosis
   D) Rubella
   E) Shingles

   Answer: C
   Skill: Analysis

12) Which of the following is *NOT* a cause of ringworm?
   A) *Microsporum*
   B) *Trichophyton*
   C) Tinea capitis
   D) *Epidermophyton*
   E) All of the above may cause ringworm.

   Answer: C
   Skill: Analysis

13) Newborns' eyes are treated with an antibiotic
   A) When *Neisseria gonorrhoeae* is isolated from the eyes.
   B) When the mother is blind.
   C) When the mother has genital herpes.
   D) When the mother has gonorrhea.
   E) Always.

   Answer: E
   Skill: Recall

14) A possible complication of herpetic keratitis is
   A) Encephalitis.
   B) Fever blisters.
   C) Subacute sclerosing panencephalitis.
   D) Congenital rubella syndrome.
   E) Macular rash.

   Answer: A
   Skill: Recall

15) Which of the following is sensitive to penicillin?
    A) *Chlamydia*
    B) Herpesvirus
    C) *Candida*
    D) *Streptococcus*
    E) *Pseudomonas*

Answer: D
Skill: Understanding

16) Which region of the skin supports the largest bacterial population?
    A) Axilla
    B) Scalp
    C) Forearms
    D) Legs
    E) All are equal.

Answer: A
Skill: Recall

17) Which infection is *NOT* caused by *Staphylococcus aureus*?
    A) Pimples
    B) Sty
    C) Furuncle
    D) Carbuncle
    E) Acne

Answer: E
Skill: Recall

18) Which of the following is *NOT* a characteristic used to identify *Streptococcus pyogenes*?
    A) Coagulase–positive
    B) Group A cell wall antigen
    C) Group M proteins
    D) Beta–hemolytic
    E) Cocci

Answer: A
Skill: Recall

19) Which of the following is *NOT* a causative agent of conjunctivitis?
    A) *Chlamydia trachomatis*
    B) Herpes simplex
    C) Adenovirus
    D) *Neisseria gonorrhoeae*
    E) *Haemophilus influenzae*

Answer: D
Skill: Recall

20) In which of the following respects is measles similar to German measles (rubella)?
    A) Rash
    B) Etiologic agent
    C) Encephalitis as a complication
    D) Congenital complications
    E) In name only

Answer: E
Skill: Analysis

21) Vaccination for rubella
    A) Is not necessary because the disease is mild.
    B) Is not necessary if a person has had an infection.
    C) Is recommended only for pregnant women.
    D) Is recommended for newborns to prevent congenital disease.
    E) Has reduced incidence of rubella.

Answer: E
Skill: Analysis

22) Which of the following statements about congenital rubella syndrome is false?
    A) It is contracted in utero.
    B) It may be fatal.
    C) It may result in deafness, blindness, and mental retardation.
    D) It doesn't occur with subclinical infections.
    E) All of the above are true.

Answer: D
Skill: Recall

23) The etiologic agent of chickenpox is
    A) Herpes simplex.
    B) Herpes zoster.
    C) HHV-6.
    D) Parvovirus.
    E) Poxvirus.

Answer: B
Skill: Recall

24) The etiologic agent of fifth disease is
    A) Herpes simplex.
    B) Herpes zoster.
    C) HHV-6.
    D) Parvovirus.
    E) Poxvirus.

Answer: D
Skill: Recall

25) The etiologic agent of roseola is
    A) Herpes simplex.
    B) Herpes zoster.
    C) HHV–6.
    D) Parvovirus.
    E) Poxvirus.

Answer: C
Skill: Recall

26) The etiologic agent of fever blisters is
    A) Herpes simplex.
    B) Herpes zoster.
    C) HHV–6.
    D) Parvovirus.
    E) Poxvirus.

Answer: A
Skill: Recall

27) Which of the following is used to treat epidemic herpetic keratitis?
    A) Penicillin
    B) Sulfonamide
    C) Trifluridine
    D) Fungicide
    E) None of the above

Answer: C
Skill: Understanding

28) Which of the following is used to treat smallpox?
    A) Penicillin
    B) Sulfonamide
    C) Trifluridine
    D) Fungicide
    E) None of the above

Answer: E
Skill: Understanding

29) Which of the following is used to treat sporotrichosis?
    A) Penicillin
    B) Sulfonamide
    C) Trifluridine
    D) Fungicide
    E) None of the above

Answer: D
Skill: Understanding

30) Which of the following is used to treat candidiasis?
   A) Penicillin
   B) Sulfonamide
   C) Trifluridine
   D) Fungicide
   E) None of the above

   Answer: D
   Skill: Understanding

31) Scabies is a skin disease caused by
   A) A slow virus.
   B) A protozoan.
   C) A mite.
   D) A bacterium.
   E) A prion.

   Answer: C
   Skill: Recall

32) Scabies is transmitted by
   A) Fomites.
   B) Food.
   C) Water.
   D) Soil.
   E) B and C.

   Answer: A
   Skill: Recall

33) A patient has pus–filled vesicles and scabs on her face, throat, and lower back. She most likely has
   A) Measles.
   B) Mumps.
   C) Chickenpox.
   D) Rubella.
   E) Smallpox.

   Answer: C
   Skill: Recall

34) Which of the following leads to all the others?
   A) Toxemia
   B) Scalded skin syndrome
   C) Staphylococcal infection
   D) TSST–1
   E) Sudden drop in blood pressure

   Answer: C
   Skill: Understanding

35) Buruli ulcer is caused by
    A) Direct contact.
    B) Acid-fast bacteria.
    C) A fungus.
    D) A virus.
    E) A mite.

Answer: B
Skill: Recall

36) The patient has a papular rash. Microscopic examination of skin scrapings reveals small 8-legged animals. The etiology is
    A) *Candida*
    B) *Microsporum*
    C) *Pseudomonas aeruginosa*
    D) *Staphylococcus aureus*
    E) *Sarcoptes*

Answer: E
Skill: Analysis

37) The patient has vesicles and scabs over her forehead. Microscopic examination of skin scrapings shows gram-positive cocci in clusters. The etiology is
    A) *Candida*
    B) *Microsporum*
    C) *Pseudomonas aeruginosa*
    D) *Staphylococcus aureus*
    E) *Sarcoptes*

Answer: D
Skill: Analysis

38) The patient has scaling skin on his fingers. Conidiospores are seen in microscopic examination of skin scrapings. The etiology is
    A) *Candida*
    B) *Microsporum*
    C) *Pseudomonas aeruginosa*
    D) *Staphylococcus aureus*
    E) *Mycobacterium ulcerans*

Answer: B
Skill: Analysis

39) A 45-year-old man has pus-filled vesicles distributed over his back in the upper right quadrant, over his right shoulder, and upper right quadrant of his chest. His symptoms are most likely due to
    A) *Candida albicans.*
    B) Herpes simplex virus.
    C) *Staphylococcus aureus.*
    D) *Streptococcus pyogenes.*
    E) Varicella-zoster virus.

Answer: E
Skill: Analysis

40) A 35-year-old woman has a red, raised rash on the inside of her thighs. Gram-stained skin scrapings show large budding cells with pseudohyphae. The infection is caused by
    A) *Candida albicans.*
    B) Herpes simplex virus.
    C) *Staphylococcus aureus.*
    D) *Streptococcus pyogenes.*
    E) Varicella-zoster virus.

Answer: A
Skill: Analysis

41) Cytoplasmic inclusions were observed in a fetus that died in utero after 6 months' gestation. The probable cause of the fetus's death was
    A) Fifth disease.
    B) Herpes simplex.
    C) Measles.
    D) *Staphylococcus aureus.*
    E) *Streptococcus pyogenes.*

Answer: A
Skill: Analysis

42) Assume that your lab partner swabs the side of his face and used the swab to inoculate a nutrient agar plate. The next day, he performs a Gram stain on the colonies. They are gram-positive cocci. You advise him that he should next look for
    A) An acid-fast reaction.
    B) A coagulase reaction.
    C) Conidiospores.
    D) Pseudohyphae.
    E) Pseudopods.

Answer: B
Skill: Understanding

43) Which of the following pairs is mismatched?
    A) Chickenpox — Poxvirus
    B) Conjunctivitis — *Chlamydia trachomatis*
    C) Keratitis — *Acanthamoeba*
    D) Infected tissue fluoresces — Dermatomycosis
    E) Buruli ulcer — *Mycobacterium*

Answer: A
Skill: Recall

44) A 17-year-old boy has pus-filled cysts on his face and upper back. Microscopic examination reveals gram-positive rods. This infection is caused by
    A) *Acanthamoeba.*
    B) Herpes simplex virus.
    C) *Propionibacterium acnes.*
    D) *Staphylococcus aureus.*
    E) *Streptococcus pyogenes.*

Answer: C
Skill: Analysis

45) Which of the following is *NOT* likely to spread MRSA among athletes?
    A) Physical contact
    B) Whirlpool baths
    C) Taping gels
    D) Antibiotic resistance
    E) Shared equipment
Answer: D
Skill: Analysis

Essay Questions

1) A teenaged boy knew an over-the-counter cortisone preparation would decrease the swelling and redness of insect bites and poison ivy, so he used it to decrease the swelling and redness of pimples. Why, in 24 hours, were his pimples more inflamed?

2) A 56-year-old Army officer received a smallpox vaccination at a military vaccination clinic. Within 2 weeks, a painful ulcer was noted at the vaccination site. Because of the appearance of an increasing number of peripheral lesions and because of continued enlargement of the initial ulcer, he was treated. Eventual recovery was complicated by *Pseudomonas* sepsis and the need for a skin graft at the vaccination site. What was the cause of the ulcer and lesions, and what were the treatments? What caused the *Pseudomonas* infection?

Chapter 22 Microbial Diseases of the Nervous System

Objective Questions

1) Which of the following is true about the normal microbiota of the nervous system?
    A) Only transient microbiota are present.
    B) There are no normal microbiota.
    C) Normal microbiota are present in the central nervous system only.
    D) Normal microbiota are present in the peripheral nervous system only.
    E) Only micrococci are present.

Answer: B
Skill: Recall

2) Encephalitis and meningitis are difficult to treat because
    A) They are not caused by bacteria.
    B) Antibiotics damage tissues.
    C) Antibiotics cannot penetrate the blood—brain barrier.
    D) The infections move along peripheral nerves.
    E) They are caused by viruses.

Answer: C
Skill: Recall

3) Which of the following organisms does *NOT* cause meningitis?
    A) *Neisseria meningitidis*
    B) *Haemophilus influenzae*
    C) *Cryptococcus neoformans*
    D) *Streptococcus pneumoniae*
    E) *Mycobacterium leprae*

Answer: E
Skill: Recall

4) Which of the following statements about *Haemophilus influenzae* is false?
    A) A healthy carrier state can exist.
    B) It is encapsulated.
    C) It requires a blood supplement in media.
    D) It usually infects children.
    E) It is used in a whole bacterial vaccine.

Answer: E
Skill: Analysis

5) Which of the following pairs is mismatched?
    A) *Neisseria meningitidis* — cultured in a candle jar
    B) *Haemophilus influenzae* — virulence due to capsule
    C) *Mycobacterium leprae* — cultured in armadillos
    D) *Cryptococcus neoformans* — acid-fast rod
    E) *Naegleria fowleri* — causes amoebic encephalitis

Answer: D
Skill: Recall

6) Which of the following organisms is *NOT* correctly matched to the recommended treatment?
   A) *Neisseria meningitidis* — cephalosporins
   B) *Haemophilus influenzae* — cephalosporins
   C) *Cryptococcus neoformans* — amphotericin B
   D) *Mycobacterium leprae* — dapsone
   E) Poliovirus — Salk vaccine

Answer: E
Skill: Understanding

7) Which of the following statements about leprosy is false?
   A) It is rarely fatal.
   B) Patients with leprosy must be isolated.
   C) It is transmitted by direct contact.
   D) Diagnosis is based on skin biopsy.
   E) The etiologic agent is acid–fast.

Answer: B
Skill: Analysis

8) Which of the following is *NOT* transmitted by the respiratory route?
   A) *Neisseria meningitidis*
   B) *Haemophilus influenzae*
   C) *Listeria monocytogenes*
   D) *Cryptococcus neoformans*
   E) All of the above are transmitted by the respiratory route.

Answer: C
Skill: Recall

9) Which of the following statements about rabies is false?
   A) It is caused by Rhabdovirus.
   B) Hydrophobia is an early symptom.
   C) The reservoir is mainly rodents.
   D) Diagnosis is based on immunofluorescent techniques.
   E) It is not fatal in bats.

Answer: C
Skill: Recall

10) The symptoms of tetanus are due to
   A) Deep puncture wounds.
   B) Hemolysins.
   C) Lack of oxygen.
   D) Clostridial neurotoxin.
   E) All of the above.

Answer: D
Skill: Recall

11) The treatment for tetanus is
    A) Penicillin.
    B) Antibodies.
    C) Toxoid.
    D) Cleansing the wound.
    E) There is no treatment.

Answer: B
Skill: Analysis

12) A 30-year-old woman was hospitalized after she experienced convulsions. On examination, she was alert and oriented and complained of a fever, headache, and stiff neck. Which of the following organisms could *NOT* be responsible for her symptoms?
    A) *Clostridium botulinum*
    B) *Listeria monocytogenes*
    C) *Naegleria fowleri*
    D) *Streptococcus pneumoniae*
    E) Any of the above could be the causative agent.

Answer: A
Skill: Analysis

13) The most effective control of a vector-borne disease is
    A) Treatment of infected humans.
    B) Treatment of infected wild animals.
    C) Elimination of the vector.
    D) Avoidance of endemic areas.
    E) Treatment of uninfected humans.

Answer: C
Skill: Understanding

14) Treatment for tetanus in an unimmunized person with a puncture wound is
    A) Tetanus toxoid.
    B) Tetanus immune globulin.
    C) Penicillin.
    D) DTaP.
    E) Debridement.

Answer: B
Skill: Analysis

15) Treatment for tetanus in an immunized person with a puncture wound is
    A) Tetanus toxoid.
    B) Tetanus immune globulin.
    C) Penicillin.
    D) DTaP.
    E) Debridement.

Answer: A
Skill: Analysis

16) The most common route of central nervous system invasion by pathogens is through
    A) The skin.
    B) The circulatory system.
    C) The gastrointestinal system.
    D) The parenteral route.
    E) Direct penetration into nerves.

Answer: B
Skill: Recall

17) The prodromal symptom(s) of meningitis is (are)
    A) Like a mild cold.
    B) Fever and headache.
    C) Stiff neck and back pains.
    D) Convulsions.
    E) Paralysis.

Answer: A
Skill: Understanding

18) Which of the following *CANNOT* lead to an outbreak of botulism?
    A) Killing bacteria that compete with *Clostridium*
    B) An anaerobic environment
    C) An incubation period
    D) A nutrient medium with a pH below 4.5
    E) Eating food from dented cans

Answer: D
Skill: Understanding

19) The most common cause of meningitis in children is
    A) *Mycobacterium tuberculosis.*
    B) *Streptococcus pneumoniae.*
    C) *Cryptococcus neoformans.*
    D) *Haemophilus influenzae.*
    E) *Neisseria meningitidis.*

Answer: B
Skill: Understanding

20) Meningitis that begins as an infection of the lungs is caused by
    A) *Flavobacterium meningosepticum.*
    B) *Streptococcus pneumoniae.*
    C) *Cryptococcus neoformans.*
    D) *Haemophilus influenzae.*
    E) *Neisseria meningitidis.*

Answer: C
Skill: Recall

21) Which of the following pairs is mismatched?
    A) Leprosy — direct contact
    B) Poliomyelitis — respiratory route
    C) Meningococcal meningitis — respiratory route
    D) Rabies — direct contact
    E) Listeriosis — ingestion

Answer: B
Skill: Analysis

22) A 30-year-old woman was hospitalized after she experienced convulsions. On examination, she was alert and oriented and complained of a fever, headache, and stiff neck. Which of the following is most likely to provide rapid identification of the cause of her symptoms?
    A) Gram stain of cerebrospinal fluid
    B) Gram stain of throat culture
    C) Biopsy of brain tissue
    D) Check serum antibodies
    E) None of the above; it can't be diagnosed.

Answer: A
Skill: Analysis

23) Which of the following is *NOT* caused by prions?
    A) Sheep scrapie
    B) Kuru
    C) Creutzfeldt–Jakob disease
    D) Elk chronic wasting disease
    E) Rabies

Answer: E
Skill: Analysis

24) Which of the following is (are) mismatched?

Salk Vaccine	Sabin Vaccine
1. Consists of a formalin–inactivated virus	4. Consists of a live, attenuated polio virus
2. Administered orally	5. Administered orally
3. Requires booster doses	6. May cause polio

    A) 1, 2, and 3
    B) 4, 5, and 6
    C) 1 and 3
    D) 2
    E) All are correctly matched.

Answer: C
Skill: Analysis

25) An 8-year-old girl in rural Wisconsin has chills, headache, and fever and reports having been bitten by mosquitoes. How would you confirm your diagnosis?
    A) ELISA test for IgM antibodies
    B) Brain biopsy for inclusions
    C) Gram stain of cerebrospinal fluid
    D) Examination of local mosquitoes
    E) Complement fixation test for IgG antibodies

Answer: A
Skill: Analysis

26) A red rash that does *NOT* blanch (whiten) when pressed is characteristic of an infection by
    A) *Cryptococcus neoformans.*
    B) *Haemophilus influenzae.*
    C) *Neisseria meningitidis.*
    D) *Streptococcus pneumoniae.*
    E) *Mycobacterium leprae.*

Answer: C
Skill: Recall

27) A 15-year-old girl was hospitalized with fever, lethargy, and rash. Gram–negative, oxidase–positive cocci were cultured from her cerebrospinal fluid. Her symptoms were caused by
    A) A prion.
    B) *Clostridium tetani.*
    C) *Mycobacterium leprae.*
    D) *Neisseria meningitidis.*
    E) *Lyssavirus.*

Answer: D
Skill: Analysis

28) A 15-year-old girl was hospitalized with fever, lethargy, and rash. Gram–negative, oxidase–positive cocci were cultured from her cerebrospinal fluid. Which of the following statements about the microbe responsible for her symptoms is false?
    A) It may be normal in the cerebrospinal fluid.
    B) It may be normal in the throat.
    C) It may be treated with antibiotics.
    D) It may cause epidemics.
    E) It may be prevented with a vaccine.

Answer: A
Skill: Analysis

29) On June 30, a 47–year–old man was hospitalized with dizziness, blurred vision, slurred speech, difficulty swallowing, and nausea. Examination revealed facial paralysis. The patient had partially healed superficial knee wounds incurred while laying cement. Cultures taken from the knee wounds should be incubated
   A) Aerobically.
   B) Anaerobically.
   C) In 5—10% CO_2.
   D) In animal cell culture.
   E) Any of the above will work.

Answer: B
Skill: Analysis

30) A diagnosis of rabies is confirmed by
   A) Gram stain.
   B) Direct fluorescent–antibody test.
   C) Patient's symptoms.
   D) Passive agglutination.
   E) Patient's death.

Answer: B
Skill: Recall

31) Which of the following is treated with antibiotics?
   A) Botulism
   B) Tetanus
   C) Streptococcal pneumonia
   D) Polio
   E) All of the above

Answer: C
Skill: Analysis

32) Which one of the following causes the most severe illness in humans, with a mortality rate of 30%?
   A) Western equine encephalitis
   B) Eastern equine encephalitis
   C) St. Louis encephalitis
   D) California encephalitis
   E) West Nile encephalitis

Answer: B
Skill: Recall

33) Which of the following is *NOT* a free-living amoeba that can cause encephalitis?
   A) *Acanthamoeba*
   B) *Balamuthia*
   C) *Entamoeba*
   D) *Naegleria*
   E) None of the above; free–living amoebas don't cause disease.

Answer: C
Skill: Analysis

34) Microscopic examination of cerebrospinal fluid reveals gram–positive rods. What is the organism?
   A) *Haemophilus*
   B) *Listeria*
   C) *Naegleria*
   D) *Neisseria*
   E) *Streptococcus*

Answer: B
Skill: Analysis

35) On June 30, a 47–year–old man was hospitalized with dizziness, blurred vision, slurred speech, difficulty swallowing, and nausea. Examination revealed facial paralysis. The patient had partially healed superficial knee wounds incurred while laying cement. He reported eating home–canned green beans and stew containing roast beef and potatoes 24 hours before onset of symptoms. The patient should be treated with
   A) Antibiotics.
   B) Antitoxin.
   C) Surgery.
   D) Vaccination.

Answer: C
Skill: Understanding

36) On October 5, a pet store sold a kitten that subsequently died. On October 22, rabies was diagnosed in the kitten. Between September 19 and October 23, the pet store had sold 34 kittens. Approximately 1000 people responded to health care providers following local media alerts. These people were given
   A) Antibiotics.
   B) Antirabies immunoglobulin.
   C) Rabies vaccination.
   D) Serological tests for rabies.
   E) Treatment if they tested positive.

Answer: B
Skill: Understanding

37) For which of the following is a vaccine *NOT* available?
   A) *Haemophilus* meningitis
   B) *Neisseria* meningitis
   C) Tetanus
   D) Rabies
   E) Botulism

Answer: E
Skill: Recall

38) Patients with leprosy usually die from
    A) Brain damage.
    B) Loss of nerve function.
    C) Tuberculosis.
    D) Influenza.
    E) Leprosy.

Answer: C
Skill: Recall

39) Which of the following is *NOT* acquired by ingestion?
    A) Botulism
    B) Cryptococcosis
    C) Listeriosis
    D) Poliomyelitis
    E) Creutzfeldt–Jakob disease

Answer: B
Skill: Recall

40) A 1–year–old boy was listless, irritable, and sleepy. Capsulated gram–negative rods were cultured from his cerebrospinal fluid. His symptoms were caused by
    A) *Neisseria meningitidis.*
    B) Rabies.
    C) *Clostridium tetani.*
    D) *Haemophilus influenzae.*
    E) A prion.

Answer: D
Skill: Analysis

41) Which of the following pairs is mismatched?
    A) Tetanus — blocks relaxation nerve impulse
    B) Botulism — stimulates transmission of nerve impulse
    C) Poliomyelitis — kills CNS cells
    D) Rabies virus — grows in brain cells
    E) All of the above are correctly matched.

Answer: B
Skill: Recall

42) Which of the following is *NOT* transmitted by ingestion?
    A) Poliomyelitis
    B) Listeriosis
    C) Botulism
    D) Meningococcal meningitis
    E) Creutzfeldt–Jakob disease

Answer: A
Skill: Recall

43) Which of the following vaccines can cause the disease it is designed to prevent?
    A) Tetanus toxoid vaccine
    B) Oral polio vaccine
    C) Inactivated polio vaccine
    D) *Haemophilus influenzae* capsule vaccine
    E) Meningococcal capsule vaccine

Answer: B
Skill: Recall

Situation 22.1
On July 5, an 11–year–old girl complained of pain in the knuckles of her left hand. During July 6—7, she had increasing pain that extended up to the left shoulder. A throat culture was obtained, and amoxicillin was prescribed. On July 9, she had difficulty walking and hallucinations. The throat culture was positive for *Streptococcus pyogenes.* She was treated with ceftriaxone. On July 11, she was hospitalized with a temperature of 40.7°C, and she could not drink. She developed respiratory distress and tachycardia; she died from cardiac arrest. Fluorescent–antibody testing of brain tissue revealed inclusions in the brain stem.

44) In Situation 22.1, the antibiotics did not cure her disease because the pathogen was
    A) A virus.
    B) Already growing in her brain.
    C) Part of her normal microbiota.
    D) Protected by the blood—brain barrier.
    E) Resistant to antibiotics.

Answer: A
Skill: Analysis

45) The disease described in Situation 22.1 is
    A) Botulism.
    B) Meningitis.
    C) Rabies.
    D) Streptococcal sore throat.
    E) Tetanus.

Answer: C
Skill: Analysis

Essay Questions

1) There is an antitoxin for botulism. Why, then, is the outcome of botulism often fatal?

2) On August 20, a man died of presumed Guillain–Barré syndrome. Within 90 minutes of his death, his eyes were removed and refrigerated. The following day, a cornea from one eye was transplanted into the right eye of a woman. The woman's postoperative course was uneventful until 30 days after the transplant, when she developed right retroorbital headache. Over the next few days her headache worsened, and she developed neurologic symptoms on the right side of her face and difficulty walking. She was hospitalized on September 27. Thereafter she developed flaccid paralysis, had loss of mental acuity, and died on October 10. Serum collected on October 2 was negative for rabies antibody, but serum collected on October 5 had a 23 titer.

What is the etiology of this disease? Identify the periods of incubation, prodromal, illness, and decline. What is the mode of transmission?

Chapter 23   Microbial Diseases of the Cardiovascular and Lymphatic Systems

Objective Questions

1) Which of the following statements about sepsis is false?
    A) Symptoms include fever and decreased blood pressure.
    B) Lymphangitis may occur.
    C) Symptoms are due to bacterial endotoxin.
    D) It usually is caused by gram–positive bacteria.
    E) It may be aggravated by antibiotics.

   Answer: D
   Skill: Recall

2) Which of the following pairs is mismatched?
    A) Subacute bacterial endocarditis — alpha–hemolytic streptococci
    B) Acute bacterial endocarditis — *Staphylococcus aureus*
    C) Pericarditis — *Streptococcus pneumoniae*
    D) Puerperal sepsis — *Staphylococcus aureus*
    E) Burkitt's lymphoma — EB virus

   Answer: D
   Skill: Recall

3) Which of the following grows outside host cells?
    A) *Ehrlichia*
    B) *Brucella*
    C) *Rickettsia*
    D) *Bartonella*
    E) *Streptobacillus*

   Answer: E
   Skill: Understanding

4) Which of the following is *NOT* treated with penicillin?
    A) Pericarditis
    B) Tularemia
    C) Anthrax
    D) Listeriosis
    E) Rat–bite fever

   Answer: B
   Skill: Analysis

5) Which of the following statements about tularemia is false?
    A) It is caused by *Francisella tularensis*.
    B) The reservoir is rabbits.
    C) It may be transmitted by arthropods.
    D) It may be transmitted by direct contact.
    E) It occurs only in California.

   Answer: E
   Skill: Recall

6) Which of the following is a symptom of brucellosis?
    A) A local infection
    B) Relapsing fever
    C) Undulant fever
    D) Pneumonia
    E) Jaundice

Answer: C
Skill: Recall

7) Which of the following is *NOT* transmitted in raw milk?
    A) Toxoplasmosis
    B) Anthrax
    C) Brucellosis
    D) Listeriosis
    E) All of the above can be transmitted in raw milk.

Answer: A
Skill: Recall

8) Which of the following is *NOT* a characteristic of *Bacillus anthracis*?
    A) Aerobic
    B) Gram–positive
    C) Forms endospores
    D) Found in soil
    E) Produces endotoxins

Answer: E
Skill: Understanding

9) The symptoms of gas gangrene are due to all of the following *EXCEPT*
    A) Microbial fermentation.
    B) Necrotizing exotoxins.
    C) Proteolytic enzymes.
    D) Hyaluronidase.
    E) Anaerobic environment.

Answer: E
Skill: Analysis

10) Which of the following bacterial infections *CANNOT* be transmitted by dog or cat bites?
    A) *Pasteurella multocida*
    B) *Streptobacillus*
    C) *Bacteroides*
    D) *Fusobacterium*
    E) All of the above can be transmitted by dog or cat bites.

Answer: B
Skill: Recall

11) Which of the following pairs is mismatched?
    A) Malaria — *Anopheles* (mosquito)
    B) Dengue — *Aedes* (mosquito)
    C) Epidemic typhus — *Pediculus* (louse)
    D) Rocky Mountain spotted fever — *Dermacentor* (tick)
    E) Encephalitis — *Ixodes* (tick)

Answer: E
Skill: Recall

12) Unsanitary and crowded conditions increase the incidence of all of the following diseases *EXCEPT*
    A) Plague.
    B) Epidemic typhus.
    C) Endemic murine typhus.
    D) Rocky Mountain spotted fever.
    E) Relapsing fever.

Answer: D
Skill: Analysis

13) Which of the following statements about toxoplasmosis is false?
    A) It is caused by a protozoan.
    B) The reservoir is cats.
    C) It is transmitted by the gastrointestinal route.
    D) It is a severe illness in adults.
    E) It can be congenital.

Answer: D
Skill: Recall

14) Which of the following pairs does *NOT* apply to Chagas' disease?
    A) Causative agent — *T. cruzi*
    B) Vector — kissing bug
    C) Reservoir — rodents
    D) Diagnosis — serological tests for antibodies
    E) Treatment — Nifurtimox

Answer: D
Skill: Recall

15) Which of the following is *NOT* caused by a bacterium?
    A) Epidemic typhus
    B) Tickborne typhus
    C) Malaria
    D) Plague
    E) Relapsing fever

Answer: C
Skill: Recall

16) A patient presents with inflammation of the heart valves, fever, malaise, and subcutaneous nodules at joints. The recommended treatment is
   A) Anti–inflammatory drugs.
   B) Streptomycin.
   C) Chloroquine.
   D) Hyperbaric chamber.
   E) Praziquantel.

Answer: A
Skill: Understanding

17) Which of the following statements about puerperal sepsis is false?
   A) It is transmitted from mother to fetus.
   B) It is caused by health care personnel.
   C) It begins as a focal infection.
   D) It is a complication of abortion or childbirth.
   E) It doesn't occur anymore because of antibiotics and aseptic techniques.

Answer: A
Skill: Recall

18) Which of the following statements about schistosomiasis is false?
   A) The cercariae penetrate human skin.
   B) A parasite of birds causes swimmer's itch in humans.
   C) The intermediate host is an aquatic snail.
   D) It is caused by a roundworm.
   E) The female worm is attached to the male.

Answer: D
Skill: Recall

19) Which of the following statements about rheumatic fever is false?
   A) It is a complication of a group A beta–hemolytic streptococcal infection.
   B) It is an inflammation of the heart.
   C) It is an inflammation of the joints.
   D) It is cured with penicillin.
   E) The incidence has declined in the last 10 years.

Answer: D
Skill: Recall

20) Which of the following pairs is mismatched?
   A) *Rickettsia* — intracellular parasite
   B) *Brucella* — gram–negative aerobic rods
   C) *Francisella* — gram–positive facultatively anaerobic pleomorphic rods
   D) *Bacillus* — gram–positive endospore–forming rods
   E) None of the above

Answer: C
Skill: Recall

21) Which of the following can be transmitted from an infected mother to her fetus across the placenta?
    A) *Borrelia*
    B) Cytomegalovirus
    C) *Spirillum*
    D) *Toxoplasma*
    E) *Yersinia*

Answer: B
Skill: Recall

22) Which of the following pairs is mismatched?
    A) *Borrelia* — relapsing fever
    B) *Yersinia* — plague
    C) *Streptobacillus* — rat–bite fever
    D) *Pasteurella* — cat–scratch disease
    E) *Spirillum* — rat–bite fever

Answer: D
Skill: Recall

23) A patient has the following symptoms: a papule, enlarged lymph nodes. Microscopic examination of the papule reveals nucleated cells in white blood cells. The patient most likely has
    A) Anthrax.
    B) Brucellosis.
    C) Leishmaniasis.
    D) Malaria.
    E) Schistosomiasis.

Answer: C
Skill: Analysis

24) Human–to–human transmission of plague is usually by
    A) Rat flea.
    B) Dog flea.
    C) The respiratory route.
    D) Wounds.
    E) Unsanitary conditions.

Answer: C
Skill: Analysis

25) A characteristic symptom of plague is
    A) Small red spots on the skin.
    B) Bruises on the skin.
    C) Rose–colored spots.
    D) Recurrent fever.
    E) Nausea and vomiting.

Answer: B
Skill: Recall

26) Which of the following pairs regarding the epidemiology of malaria is mismatched?
    A) Vector — *Anopheles*
    B) Etiology — *Plasmodium*
    C) Found in liver — sporozoites
    D) Diagnosis — presence of merozoites
    E) Treatment — antibiotics

Answer: E
Skill: Understanding

27) A predisposing factor for infection by *Clostridium perfringens* is
    A) Gangrene.
    B) Burns.
    C) Debridement.
    D) Hyperbaric treatment.
    E) An infected finger.

Answer: A
Skill: Analysis

28) Which of the following is *NOT* a zoonosis?
    A) Puerperal sepsis
    B) *Hantavirus* infection
    C) Anthrax
    D) Brucellosis
    E) Tularemia

Answer: A
Skill: Recall

29) Arthropods can serve as a reservoir for which of the following diseases?
    A) Plague
    B) Brucellosis
    C) Epidemic typhus
    D) Yellow fever
    E) Malaria

Answer: B
Skill: Recall

30) Which of the following pairs is mismatched?
    A) Cat–scratch disease — malignant pustule developing into septicemia
    B) Brucellosis — a temperature of 40°C each evening
    C) Tularemia — a localized infection appearing as a small ulcer
    D) *Borrelia* — rash and flulike
    E) Toxoplasmosis — congenital brain damage

Answer: A
Skill: Recall

31) Which of the following *CANNOT* be transmitted to humans from domestic cats?
    A) Toxoplasmosis
    B) Plague
    C) Chagas' disease
    D) *Bartonella*
    E) None of these diseases is transmitted by cats.

Answer: C
Skill: Analysis

32) Which of the following is the same for both relapsing fever and undulant fever?
    A) Vector
    B) Mode of transmission
    C) Presence of rash
    D) Reservoir
    E) Etiology

Answer: A
Skill: Analysis

33) Which of the following is *NOT* treated with antibiotics?
    A) Plague
    B) Tularemia
    C) Lyme disease
    D) Yellow fever
    E) Anthrax

Answer: D
Skill: Understanding

34) Which of the following produces a permanent carrier state following infection?
    A) *Borrelia*
    B) Cytomegalovirus
    C) *Spirillum*
    D) *Toxoplasma*
    E) *Yersinia*

Answer: B
Skill: Recall

35) EB virus has been implicated in all of the following *EXCEPT*
    A) Endocarditis.
    B) Infectious mononucleosis.
    C) Burkitt's lymphoma.
    D) Nasopharyngeal carcinoma.
    E) Hodgkin's disease.

Answer: A
Skill: Recall

36) Which of the following leads to all the others?
    A) Subcutaneous hemorrhaging
    B) Presence of antirickettsial antibodies
    C) Blockage of capillaries
    D) Bacterial growth in endothelial cells
    E) Breakage of capillaries

Answer: D
Skill: Analysis

37) A patient complains of fever, severe muscle and joint pain, and a rash. The patient reports returning from a Caribbean vacation one week ago. Which one of the following do you suspect?
    A) Bolivian hemorrhagic fever
    B) Dengue
    C) *Hantavirus* hemorrhagic fever
    D) Typhus
    E) Yellow fever

Answer: B
Skill: Analysis

38) Which of the following pairs is *NOT* correctly matched for Gram reaction?
    A) Lyme disease — gram-negative
    B) Tularemia — gram-negative
    C) Anthrax — gram-positive
    D) Rocky Mountain spotted fever — gram-negative
    E) *Ehrlichia* — gram-positive

Answer: E
Skill: Recall

39) Scrapings from a patient's rash reveal cercariae. The disease is most likely
    A) Lyme disease.
    B) Rocky Mountain spotted fever.
    C) Relapsing fever.
    D) Swimmer's itch.
    E) Chagas' disease.

Answer: D
Skill: Analysis

40) You advise your pregnant friend to give her cat away because
    A) She could contract plague.
    B) She could give the cat tularemia.
    C) She could get toxoplasmosis.
    D) She could get listeriosis.
    E) You don't like cats and want to see your friend without one.

Answer: C
Skill: Analysis

41) Which of the following is evidence that the arthritis afflicting children in Lyme, Connecticut, was due to bacterial infection?
   A) Treatable with penicillin
   B) Not contagious
   C) Accompanied by a rash
   D) Affected mostly children
   E) Transmitted by ticks

Answer: A
Skill: Analysis

42) Which of the following is *NOT* controlled by a mosquito eradication program?
   A) Chikungunya fever
   B) Yellow fever
   C) Dengue
   D) Toxoplasmosis
   E) Malaria

Answer: D
Skill: Analysis

43) A 62-year-old man was hospitalized with an 8-day history of fever, chills, sweats, and vomiting. His temperature on admission was 40°C. A routine peripheral blood smear revealed ring-shaped bodies in the RBCs. What treatment would you prescribe?
   A) Hyperbaric oxygen
   B) Mefloquine
   C) No treatment
   D) Penicillin
   E) Streptomycin

Answer: B
Skill: Understanding

44) Which of the following statements about group B streptococci is false?
   A) They are present in healthy carriers.
   B) They cause gram-positive sepsis.
   C) They cause strep throat.
   D) They cause neonatal sepsis.
   E) They are classified as *Str. agalactiae*.

Answer: C
Skill: Recall

45) Bioweapons
   A) Are all respiratory pathogens.
   B) Are not susceptible to antibiotics.
   C) Are all viruses.
   D) Are impossible to detect.
   E) Have been used for centuries.

Answer: E
Skill: Analysis

Essay Questions

1) Humans are not the normal hosts for *Ixodes* and *Xenopsylla*. How then do humans contract Lyme disease and plague?

2) On June 1, a 32–year–old hiker was bitten by a tick. After 1 week, he noticed an erythrematous ring at the location of the bite. Four weeks later, a physician found a large, macular, centrifugally spreading ring. During the next month, it expanded to 35 cm and faded. Over the next 2.5 years, the man experienced recurrent inflammation of a knee.

   Identify the periods of incubation, prodromal, illness, and decline. What is the etiology? What caused the symptoms? What treatment should have been administered in July? What treatment should be administered 2 years later?

3) Worldwide, which disease is the most serious public health threat: malaria, Chagas' disease, or brucellosis? Explain why, and provide a plan to reduce the incidence of the disease.

Chapter 24 Microbial Diseases of the Respiratory System

Objective Questions

1) Which of the following statements about otitis media is false?
   A) It is caused by *Streptococcus pyogenes*.
   B) It is a complication of tonsillitis.
   C) It is transmitted by swimming pool water.
   D) It is caused by rhinovirus.
   E) It is caused by *Staphylococcus aureus*.

   Answer: D
   Skill: Recall

2) Which of the following does *NOT* confirm a diagnosis of strep throat?
   A) Hemolytic reaction
   B) Bacitracin inhibition
   C) Symptoms
   D) Serological tests
   E) Gram stain

   Answer: C
   Skill: Recall

3) Penicillin is used to treat all of the following *EXCEPT*
   A) Streptococcal sore throat.
   B) Diphtheria.
   C) Pneumococcal pneumonia.
   D) Mycoplasmal pneumonia.
   E) Scarlet fever.

   Answer: D
   Skill: Analysis

4) Mycoplasmal pneumonia differs from viral pneumonia in that
   A) Mycoplasmal pneumonia doesn't have any known etiologic agent.
   B) Mycoplasmal pneumonia is treated with tetracyclines.
   C) Viral pneumonia is treated with tetracyclines.
   D) The symptoms are distinctly different.
   E) *Mycoplasma* can't be cultured.

   Answer: B
   Skill: Analysis

5) Which of the following diseases is *NOT* correctly matched to a virulence factor?
   A) Diphtheria — exotoxin
   B) Scarlet fever — exotoxin
   C) Pneumococcal pneumonia — exotoxin
   D) *Haemophilus* pneumonia — endotoxin
   E) Whooping cough — endotoxin

   Answer: C
   Skill: Understanding

6) Which of the following pairs is mismatched?
   A) *Corynebacterium* — gram-positive rod
   B) *Mycobacterium* — acid-fast rod
   C) *Mycoplasma* — gram-positive pleomorphic rod
   D) *Bordetella* — gram-negative pleomorphic rod
   E) *Haemophilus* — gram-negative rod

Answer: C
Skill: Recall

7) Which of the following microorganisms causes symptoms most like tuberculosis?
   A) *Histoplasma*
   B) *Coccidioides*
   C) *Legionella*
   D) *Mycoplasma*
   E) Influenzavirus

Answer: A
Skill: Analysis

8) Which of the following *CANNOT* lead to a positive tuberculin skin test?
   A) Vaccination
   B) Current tuberculosis infection
   C) Previous tuberculosis infection
   D) Immunity to tuberculosis
   E) Being near someone with tuberculosis

Answer: E
Skill: Understanding

9) Which of the following diseases is *NOT* correctly matched to its vaccine?
   A) Tuberculosis — toxoid
   B) Whooping cough — heat-killed bacteria
   C) Diphtheria — toxoid
   D) Influenza — viruses grown in embryonated eggs
   E) Pneumococcal pneumonia — capsular polysaccharides

Answer: A
Skill: Recall

10) Which of the following diseases has a cutaneous form, especially in individuals over 30 years of age?
    A) Coccidioidomycosis
    B) Diphtheria
    C) Legionellosis
    D) Scarlet fever
    E) Psittacosis

Answer: B
Skill: Recall

11) Which of the following causes an infection of the respiratory system that is transmitted by the gastrointestinal route?
   A) *Streptococcus pyogenes*
   B) *Mycobacterium tuberculosis*
   C) *Mycoplasma pneumoniae*
   D) *Haemophilus influenzae*
   E) *Streptococcus pneumoniae*

Answer: B
Skill: Understanding

12) Which of the following pairs is mismatched?
   A) Epiglottitis — *Haemophilus*
   B) Q fever — *Rickettsia*
   C) Psittacosis — *Chlamydia*
   D) Whooping cough — *Bordetella*
   E) Melioidosis — *Burkholderia*

Answer: B
Skill: Recall

13) Which of the following does *NOT* cause pneumonia?
   A) *Legionella*
   B) *Haemophilus*
   C) *Mycoplasma*
   D) RSV
   E) *Histoplasma*

Answer: E
Skill: Recall

14) Which of the following causes opportunistic infections in AIDS patients?
   A) *Pneumocystis*
   B) *Aspergillus*
   C) *Rhizopus*
   D) *Mucor*
   E) All of the above

Answer: E
Skill: Understanding

15) Which of the following diseases is *NOT* correctly matched to its reservoir?
   A) Tuberculosis — cattle
   B) Histoplasmosis — soil
   C) Psittacosis — parakeets
   D) Coccidioidomycosis — air
   E) *Pneumocystis* — humans

Answer: D
Skill: Analysis

16) Which of the following does *NOT* produce an exotoxin?
    A) *Bordetella pertussis*
    B) *Corynebacterium diphtheriae*
    C) *Mycobacterium tuberculosis*
    D) *Streptococcus pygogenes*
    E) All of the above produce an exotoxin.

Answer: C
Skill: Recall

17) Which one of the following causes a disease characterized by the catarrhal, paroxysmal, and convalescent stages?
    A) *Bordetella pertussis*
    B) *Corynebacterium diphtheriae*
    C) *Mycobacterium tuberculosis*
    D) *Streptococcus pyogenes*
    E) Respiratory syncytial virus

Answer: A
Skill: Recall

18) Which one of the following is an irregular, gram–positive rod?
    A) *Bordetella pertussis*
    B) *Corynebacterium diphtheriae*
    C) *Myobacterium tuberculosis*
    D) *Streptococcus pyogenes*
    E) *Pneumocystis jirovecii*

Answer: B
Skill: Recall

19) Infection by which of the following results in the formation of Ghon complexes?
    A) *Bordetella pertussis*
    B) *Corynebacterium diphtheriae*
    C) *Mycobacterium tuberculosis*
    D) *Streptococcus pyogenes*
    E) *Blastomyces dermatidis*

Answer: C
Skill: Recall

20) Which one of the following produces the most potent exotoxin?
    A) *Bordetella pertussis*
    B) *Corynebacterium diphtheriae*
    C) *Mycobacterium tuberculosis*
    D) *Streptococcus pyogenes*
    E) *Streptococcus pneumoniae*

Answer: B
Skill: Recall

21) The recurrence of influenza epidemics is due to
    A) Lack of antiviral drugs.
    B) The Guillain–Barré syndrome.
    C) Antigenic shift.
    D) Lack of naturally acquired active immunity.
    E) HA spikes.

Answer: C
Skill: Recall

22) Which of the following is an opportunistic pathogen?
    A) *Pneumocystis*
    B) *Legionella*
    C) *Histoplasma*
    D) *Mycoplasma*
    E) Rhinovirus

Answer: A
Skill: Analysis

23) Which of the following etiologic agents results in the formation of abscesses?
    A) *Staphylococcus*
    B) *Mycoplasma*
    C) *Streptococcus*
    D) *Blastomyces*
    E) *Coccidioides immitis*

Answer: D
Skill: Recall

24) Which of the following is most susceptible to destruction by phagocytes?
    A) *Chlamydophila psittaci*
    B) *Streptococcus pneumoniae*
    C) *Streptococcus pyogenes*
    D) Influenza virus
    E) *Histoplasma capsulatum*

Answer: C
Skill: Understanding

25) A healthy carrier state exists for
    A) *Corynebacterium diphtheriae.*
    B) *Streptococcus pneumoniae.*
    C) Beta–hemolytic streptococci.
    D) *Haemophilus influenzae.*
    E) All of the above.

Answer: E
Skill: Understanding

26) Infection by which of the following is often confused with viral pneumonia?
    A) *Blastomyces*
    B) *Coccidioides*
    C) *Mycoplasma*
    D) *Streptococcus*
    E) None of the above
Answer: C
Skill: Analysis

27) Which one of the following causes a disease characterized by a red rash?
    A) *Blastomyces*
    B) *Coccidioides*
    C) *Mycoplasma*
    D) *Streptococcus*
    E) RSV
Answer: D
Skill: Analysis

28) Inhalation of arthroconidia is responsible for infection by which of the following organisms?
    A) *Blastomyces*
    B) *Coccidioides*
    C) *Mycoplasma*
    D) *Streptococcus*
    E) *Chlamydophila*
Answer: B
Skill: Analysis

29) Which of the following pairs is mismatched?
    A) Q fever — fleas
    B) *Psittacosis* — parrots
    C) *Pneumocystis* — nosocomial
    D) *Coccidioides* — soil
    E) *Blastomyces* — soil
Answer: E
Skill: Recall

30) A patient has pneumonia. Gram-negative rods are cultured on nutrient agar from a sputum sample. The etiology is
    A) *Burkholderia pseudomallei.*
    B) *Chlamydophila psittaci.*
    C) *Haemophilus influenzae.*
    D) *Legionella pneumophila.*
    E) *Streptococcus pneumonia.*
Answer: A
Skill: Analysis

31) The patient is suffocating because of an inflamed epiglottis. What is the etiology?
   A) *Corynebacterium*
   B) *Haemophilus*
   C) *Bordetella*
   D) *Mycobacterium*
   E) Can't tell

Answer: B
Skill: Analysis

32) The patient has a sore throat. What is the etiology?
   A) *Corynebacterium*
   B) *Haemophilus*
   C) *Bordetella*
   D) *Mycobacterium*
   E) Can't tell

Answer: E
Skill: Analysis

33) The patient is suffocating because of the accumulation of dead tissue and fibrin in her throat.
   What is the etiology?
   A) *Corynebacterium*
   B) *Haemophilus*
   C) *Bordetella*
   D) *Mycobacterium*
   E) Can't tell

Answer: A
Skill: Analysis

34) Infection by which of the following begins in lungs and spreads to skin?
   A) *Blastomyces*
   B) *Coccidioides*
   C) *Histoplasma*
   D) *Mycobacterium*
   E) *Pneumocystis*

Answer: A
Skill: Analysis

35) Which one of the following organisms does *NOT* belong with the others?
   A) *Blastomyces*
   B) *Coccidioides*
   C) *Histoplasma*
   D) *Mycobacterium*
   E) *Pneumocystis*

Answer: D
Skill: Analysis

36) Microscopic examination of a lung biopsy shows thick-walled cysts. What is the etiology?
 A) *Blastomyces*
 B) *Coccidioides*
 C) *Histoplasma*
 D) *Mycobacterium*
 E) *Pneumocystis*

Answer: E
Skill: Analysis

37) Microscopic examination of a lung biopsy shows spherules. What is the etiology?
 A) *Blastomyces*
 B) *Coccidioides*
 C) *Histoplasma*
 D) *Mycobacterium*
 E) *Pneumocystis*

Answer: B
Skill: Analysis

38) You are trying to identify the cause of a patient's middle ear infection. After 24 hours, there is no growth on blood agar incubated aerobically at 37°C. Your next step is to try again,
 A) Using nutrient agar.
 B) Incubating at 25°C.
 C) Incubating anaerobically.
 D) Incubating at 45°C.
 E) Then give up.

Answer: C
Skill: Understanding

39) A patient has a paroxysmal cough and mucus accumulation. What is the etiology of the symptoms?
 A) *Bordetella*
 B) *Corynebacterium*
 C) *Klebsiella*
 D) *Mycobacterium*
 E) *Mycoplasma*

Answer: A
Skill: Analysis

40) A patient who presents with red throat and tonsils can be diagnosed as having
 A) Streptococcal pharyngitis.
 B) Scarlet fever.
 C) Diphtheria.
 D) Common cold.
 E) There is insufficient information.

Answer: E
Skill: Analysis

41) A patient has fever, difficulty breathing, chest pains, fluid in the alveoli, and a positive tuberculin skin test. Gram-positive cocci are isolated from the sputum. The patient most likely has
    A) Tuberculosis.
    B) Influenza.
    C) Pneumococcal pneumonia.
    D) Mycoplasmal pneumonia.
    E) Common cold.

Answer: C
Skill: Understanding

42) Which of the following respiratory infections can be contracted by ingestion?
    A) Streptococcal pharyngitis
    B) Diphtheria
    C) Tuberculosis
    D) Mycoplasmal pneumonia
    E) *Haemophilus* pneumonia

Answer: C
Skill: Analysis

43) Which of the following is *NOT* an intracellular parasite?
    A) *Chlamydophila*
    B) *Coccidioides*
    C) *Coxiella*
    D) *Influenzavirus*
    E) RSV

Answer: B
Skill: Recall

44) Which one of the following produces small "fried-egg" colonies on medium containing horse serum and yeast extract?
    A) *Chlamydophila*
    B) *Legionella*
    C) *Mycobacterium*
    D) *Mycoplasma*
    E) *Streptococcus*

Answer: D
Skill: Recall

45) *Legionella* is transmitted by
    A) Airborne transmission.
    B) Foodborne transmission.
    C) Person-to-person contact.
    D) Fomites.
    E) Vectors.

Answer: A
Skill: Recall

Essay Questions

1) Provide reasons why influenza vaccination is not recommended for everyone.

2) Pneumonia is diagnosed by the presence of fluid (dark shadows in an X–ray image) in the alveoli. Given that pneumonia usually is caused by a microorganism, what causes the fluid accumulation? Name a bacterium, a virus, a fungus, a protozoan, and a helminth that can cause pneumonia.

Chapter 25 Microbial Diseases of the Digestive System

Objective Questions

1) Which one of the following is *NOT* required for tooth decay?
    A) Sucrose
    B) Glucose
    C) Capsule-forming bacteria
    D) Acid-producing bacteria
    E) All of the above are required for tooth decay.

Answer: B
Skill: Analysis

2) *Clostridium difficile*-associated diarrhea is usually preceded by
    A) Eating contaminated food.
    B) A blood transfusion.
    C) Use of broad-spectrum antibiotics.
    D) Improper food storage.
    E) Travel to an underdeveloped country.

Answer: C
Skill: Analysis

3) Which of the following statements about salmonellosis is false?
    A) It is a bacterial infection.
    B) It requires a large infective dose.
    C) A healthy carrier state exists.
    D) The mortality rate is high.
    E) It is often associated with poultry products.

Answer: D
Skill: Recall

4) Which of the following does *NOT* produce a gastrointestinal disease due to an exotoxin?
    A) *Clostridium perfringens*
    B) *Vibrio cholerae*
    C) *Shigella dysenteriae*
    D) *Staphylococcus aureus*
    E) *Clostridium botulinum*

Answer: C
Skill: Analysis

5) Which of the following diseases of the gastrointestinal system is transmitted by the respiratory route?
    A) Staphylococcal enterotoxicosis
    B) Mumps
    C) *Vibrio* gastroenteritis
    D) Bacillary dysentery
    E) Traveler's diarrhea

Answer: B
Skill: Recall

6) Amoebic dysentery and bacillary dysentery differ in the
  A) Mode of transmission.
  B) Appearance of the patient's stools.
  C) Etiologic agent.
  D) Presence of diarrhea.
  E) Abscess formation.

Answer: C
Skill: Analysis

7) The symptoms of trichinellosis are due to the
  A) Growth of larval *Trichinella* in the large intestine.
  B) Growth of adult *Trichinella* in the large intestine.
  C) Formation of cysticerci.
  D) Encystment of adult *Trichinella* in muscles.
  E) Encystment of larval *Trichinella* in muscles.

Answer: E
Skill: Analysis

8) Poultry products are a likely source of infection by
  A) *Staphylococcus aureus*.
  B) *Salmonella enterica*.
  C) *Vibrio cholerae*.
  D) *Shigella* spp.
  E) *Clostridium perfringens*.

Answer: B
Skill: Recall

9) Which of the following is diagnosed by the presence of flagellated protozoa in the patient's feces?
  A) *Cyclospora* infection
  B) Giardiasis
  C) Trichinellosis
  D) Cholera
  E) Cryptosporidiosis

Answer: B
Skill: Recall

10) Which of the following feeds on red blood cells?
  A) *Giardia lamblia*
  B) *Escherichia coli*
  C) *Taenia* spp.
  D) *Vibrio parahaemolyticus*
  E) *Entamoeba histolytica*

Answer: E
Skill: Recall

11) In humans, beef tapeworm infestations are acquired by
   A) Ingesting the eggs of *Taenia saginata*.
   B) Ingesting segments of adult tapeworms.
   C) Ingesting contaminated water.
   D) Ingesting cysticerci in the intermediate host.
   E) Ingesting contaminated definitive hosts.

Answer: D
Skill: Recall

12) Which of the following statements about staphylococcal food poisoning is false?
   A) Suspect foods are those not cooked before eating.
   B) It can be prevented by refrigeration.
   C) It can be prevented by boiling foods for 5 minutes before eating.
   D) It is treated by replacing water and electrolytes.
   E) It is characterized by rapid onset and short duration of symptoms.

Answer: C
Skill: Recall

13) The most common cause of traveler's diarrhea is probably
   A) *Shigella* spp.
   B) *Salmonella enterica*.
   C) *Giardia lamblia*.
   D) *Escherichia coli*.
   E) *Campylobacter jejuni*.

Answer: D
Skill: Recall

14) Acute gastroenteritis that occurs after an incubation period of 2 to 3 days is probably caused by
   A) *Giardia*.
   B) Rotavirus.
   C) *Salmonella*.
   D) *Staphylococcus aureus*.
   E) *Trichinella*.

Answer: B
Skill: Analysis

15) Which of the following pairs is mismatched?
   A) Hydatid disease — humans are the definitive host
   B) *Taenia* infestation — humans are the definitive host
   C) Trichinellosis — humans eat larva of parasite
   D) Pinworm infestation — humans ingest parasite's eggs
   E) Hookworm infestation — parasite bores through skin

Answer: A
Skill: Understanding

16) Thorough cooking of food will prevent all of the following *EXCEPT*
    A) Trichinellosis.
    B) Beef tapeworm.
    C) Staphylococcal food poisoning.
    D) Salmonellosis.
    E) Shigellosis.

Answer: C
Skill: Understanding

17) Most of the normal microbiota of the digestive system are found in the
    A) Mouth.
    B) Stomach.
    C) Small intestine.
    D) Large intestine.
    E) C and D.

Answer: D
Skill: Analysis

18) Which of the following organisms is most likely to be responsible for periodontal disease?
    A) Gram-positive cocci
    B) Gram-positive rods
    C) Gram-negative cocci
    D) Gram-negative rods
    E) Gingivirus

Answer: B
Skill: Recall

19) Typhoid fever differs from salmonellosis in that in typhoid fever
    A) The microorganisms become invasive.
    B) The symptoms are due to an exotoxin.
    C) The symptoms are due to infection of the gallbladder.
    D) The classic symptom is diarrhea.
    E) Chemotherapy is highly effective.

Answer: A
Skill: Analysis

20) Which of the following organisms is likely to be transmitted via contaminated shrimp?
    A) *Trichinella*
    B) *Vibrio*
    C) *Giardia*
    D) *Clostridium perfringens*
    E) *Staphylococcus aureus*

Answer: B
Skill: Analysis

21) Which of the following organisms is likely to be transmitted via undercooked pork and horse?
    A) *Salmonella*
    B) *Staphylococcus*
    C) *Trichinella*
    D) *Entamoeba*
    E) *Shigella*

Answer: C
Skill: Recall

22) A vaccine to provide active immunity to serum hepatitis is prepared from
    A) Viruses grown in tissue culture.
    B) Genetically modified yeast.
    C) Pooled gamma globulin.
    D) Viruses grown in embryonated eggs.
    E) Viral particles in patients.

Answer: B
Skill: Analysis

23) Which one of the following is *NOT* transmitted by water?
    A) *Salmonella*
    B) *Cyclospora*
    C) *Trichinella*
    D) *Cryptosporidium*
    E) Hepatitis A virus

Answer: C
Skill: Analysis

24) Which of the following causes an infection of the liver?
    A) *Salmonella*
    B) *Shigella*
    C) Hepatitis A virus
    D) *Vibrio*
    E) *Escherichia*

Answer: C
Skill: Analysis

25) "Rice water stools" are characteristic of
    A) Salmonellosis.
    B) Cholera.
    C) Bacillary dysentery.
    D) Amebic dysentery.
    E) Tapeworm infestation.

Answer: B
Skill: Analysis

26) Epidemics of bacterial infections of the digestive system are transmitted by
    A) Food.
    B) Water.
    C) Milk.
    D) The respiratory route.
    E) All of the above.

Answer: B
Skill: Understanding

27) Most gastrointestinal infections are treated with
    A) Antitoxin.
    B) Penicillin.
    C) Water and electrolytes.
    D) Quinacrine.
    E) Thorough cooking.

Answer: C
Skill: Understanding

28) Which of the following is treated with tetracycline?
    A) Staphylococcal food poisoning
    B) *Vibrio parahaemolyticus* gastroenteritis
    C) Infectious hepatitis
    D) *Escherichia coli* gastroenteritis
    E) Trichinellosis

Answer: B
Skill: Understanding

29) Which of the following pairs is mismatched?
    A) Ergot — gangrene
    B) *Salmonella* endotoxin — coagulates blood
    C) *Vibrio* enterotoxin — secretion of Cl^-, K^+, and H_2O
    D) Aflatoxin — liver cancer
    E) Shiga toxin — tissue destruction

Answer: B
Skill: Understanding

30) Bacterial intoxications differ from bacterial infections of the digestive system in that intoxications
    A) Are transmitted via water.
    B) Are more severe.
    C) Have shorter incubation times.
    D) Are treated with antibiotics.
    E) Are accompanied by fever.

Answer: C
Skill: Analysis

31) The most common mode of HAV transmission is
     A) Contamination of food during preparation.
     B) Contamination of food before it reaches a food service establishment.
     C) Blood transfusion.
     D) Contaminated hypodermic needles.
     E) Airborne.

Answer: A
Skill: Recall

32) With which of the following substrates can *Streptococcus mutans* make a capsule?
     A) Xylitol
     B) Glucose
     C) Mannitol
     D) Sucrose
     E) All of the above

Answer: D
Skill: Analysis

33) A 38-year-old man had onset of fever, chills, nausea, and myalgia. On April 29, he had eaten raw oysters. On May 2, he was admitted to a hospital because of a fever of 39 °C and two circular necrotic lesions on the left leg. He had alcoholic liver disease. He was transferred to the ICU; therapy with ciprofloxacin was initiated. On May 4, he died. Which of the following is the most likely etiology?
     A) *Bacillus cereus*
     B) *Cyclospora*
     C) *Salmonella*
     D) *Vibrio vulnificus*
     E) *Yersinia enterocolitica*

Answer: D
Skill: Analysis

34) The easiest way to prevent outbreaks of gram-negative gastroenteritis is to
     A) Cook foods thoroughly.
     B) Salt foods.
     C) Add vinegar and spices to foods.
     D) Refrigerate foods.
     E) Avoid eating meat.

Answer: A
Skill: Analysis

35) Microscopic examination of a patient's fecal culture shows spiral bacteria. The bacteria probably belong to the genus
     A) *Campylobacter*.
     B) *Escherichia*.
     C) *Salmonella*.
     D) *Shigella*.
     E) *Vibrio*.

Answer: A
Skill: Recall

36) Feces from a patient with diarrhea lasting for weeks with frequent, watery stools should be examined for
    A) *Bacillus cereus.*
    B) *Cyclospora.*
    C) *Salmonella.*
    D) *Vibrio vulnificus.*
    E) *Yersinia enterocolitica.*

Answer: B
Skill: Analysis

37) Which of the following is *NOT* a gram–negative rod that causes gastroenteritis?
    A) *Clostridium*
    B) *Escherichia*
    C) *Salmonella*
    D) *Shigella*
    E) *Yersinia*

Answer: A
Skill: Analysis

38) *Helicobacter* can grow in the stomach because it
    A) Hides in macrophages.
    B) Makes a capsule.
    C) Makes NH_3.
    D) Makes HCl.
    E) Invades epithelial cells.

Answer: C
Skill: Analysis

39) Which of the following is *NOT* a eukaryote that causes gastroenteritis?
    A) *Cryptosporidium*
    B) *Cyclospora*
    C) *Entamoeba*
    D) *Giardia*
    E) *Campylobacter*

Answer: E
Skill: Analysis

40) Acute gastroenteritis that occurs after an incubation period of 4 to 24 hours is probably caused by
    A) *Giardia*
    B) Rotavirus
    C) *Salmonella*
    D) *Staphylococcus aureus*
    E) *Trichinella*

Answer: D
Skill: Analysis

41) Which of the viruses listed meets these criteria? diagnosed by PCR; incubation of 4 to 22 weeks; transmitted by the parenteral route; is a flavivirus.
   A) Hepatitis A virus
   B) Hepatitis B virus
   C) Hepatitis C virus
   D) Hepatitis D virus
   E) Hepatitis E virus

Answer: C
Skill: Analysis

42) Which of the following pairs is mismatched?
   A) Beef — *E. coli* O157:H7
   B) Delicatessen meats — *Listeria*
   C) Eggs — *Trichinella*
   D) Milk — *Campylobacter*
   E) Oysters — *Vibrio*

Answer: C
Skill: Analysis

Situation 25.1

Following a county fair, 160 persons complained of gastrointestinal symptoms. Symptoms included diarrhea (84%), abdominal cramps (96%), nausea (84%), vomiting (82%), body aches (50%), fever (60%; median body temperature = 38.3°C); median duration of illness 6 days (range 10 hr to 13 days).

43) In Situation 25.1, fecal samples should be cultured for all of the following *EXCEPT*
   A) *Salmonella.*
   B) *Shigella.*
   C) *Campylobacter.*
   D) Enteropathogenic *Escherichia coli.*
   E) *Giardia.*

Answer: E
Skill: Understanding

44) In Situation 25.1, assume the samples were culture–negative. The next step is
   A) To begin antibiotic therapy.
   B) Blood cultures.
   C) Microscopic examination for oocysts.
   D) Microscopic examination for viruses.
   E) Muscle biopsy.

Answer: C
Skill: Understanding

Table 25.1

Food	Relative Risk
Black beans	0.58
Corn soup	0.75
Jalapeño peppers	34.13
Roma tomatoes	5.40

45) Use Table 25.1 to answer this question. The relative risks shown were calculated for foods suspected of transmitting *Salmonella*. Which food is the most likely source of infection?
    A) Black beans
    B) Corn soup
    C) Jalapeño peppers
    D) Roma tomatoes
Answer: C
Skill: Understanding

Essay Questions

1) *Escherichia coli* is normally in the large intestines of humans. How can this bacterium be the etiologic agent of most cases of traveler's diarrhea?

2) Discuss why cholera epidemics are often associated with floods.

3) How can you avoid contracting the following diseases?
    a.   Trichinellosis
    b.   Hydatidosis
    c.   Tapeworm infestations
    d.   Staphylococcal food poisoning
    e.   Traveler's diarrhea
    f.   Giardiasis

Chapter 26 Microbial Diseases of the Urinary and Reproductive Systems

Objective Questions

1) Normal microbiota of the adult vagina consist primarily of
   A) *Lactobacillus.*
   B) *Streptococcus.*
   C) *Mycobacterium.*
   D) *Neisseria.*
   E) *Candida.*

   Answer: A
   Skill: Recall

2) Cystitis is most often caused by
   A) *Escherichia coli.*
   B) *Leptospira interrogans.*
   C) *Candida albicans.*
   D) *Neisseria gonorrhoeae.*
   E) *Pseudomonas aeruginosa.*

   Answer: A
   Skill: Recall

3) Pyelonephritis may result from
   A) Urethritis.
   B) Cystitis.
   C) Ureteritis.
   D) Systemic infections.
   E) All of the above.

   Answer: E
   Skill: Recall

4) All of the following result from *N. gonorrhoeae* infection. Which one *leads* to the others?
   A) Antibody production is stopped
   B) CD4[+] T lymphocytes don't reproduce
   C) Increased risk of other STIs
   D) Opa attaches to CD4[+] T lymphocytes
   E) Reinfection by *N. gonorrhoeae*

   Answer: D
   Skill: Understanding

5) Pyelonephritis usually is caused by
   A) *Pseudomonas aeruginosa.*
   B) *Proteus* spp.
   C) *Escherichia coli.*
   D) *Enterobacter aerogenes.*
   E) *Streptococcus pyogenes.*

   Answer: C
   Skill: Recall

6) The reservoir for leptospirosis is
   A) Humans.
   B) Water.
   C) Domestic dogs.
   D) Domestic cats.
   E) Hospitals.

   Answer: C
   Skill: Recall

7) Which of the following is *NOT* primarily a sexually transmitted infection (STI)?
   A) Lymphogranuloma venereum
   B) Genital herpes
   C) Gonorrhea
   D) Chancroid
   E) Trichomoniasis

   Answer: E
   Skill: Analysis

8) Which of the following is treated with penicillin?
   A) Lymphogranuloma venereum
   B) Genital warts
   C) Candidiasis
   D) Syphilis
   E) Trichomoniasis

   Answer: D
   Skill: Analysis

9) Which of the following pairs is mismatched?
   A) Trichomoniasis — fungus
   B) Gonorrhea — gram-negative cocci
   C) Chancroid — gram-negative rod
   D) *Gardnerella* — clue cells
   E) Syphilis — gram-negative spirochete

   Answer: A
   Skill: Recall

10) One form of NGU is lymphogranuloma venereum caused by
    A) *Leptospira interrogans.*
    B) *Chlamydia trachomatis.*
    C) *Neisseria gonorrhoeae.*
    D) *Treponema pallidum.*
    E) *Candida albicans.*

Answer: B
Skill: Recall

11) All of the following can cause congenital infections or infections of the newborn *EXCEPT*
    A) Syphilis.
    B) Gonorrhea.
    C) Nongonococcal urethritis.
    D) Genital herpes.
    E) Lymphogranuloma venereum.

Answer: E
Skill: Recall

12) Which of the following recurs at the initial site of infection?
    A) Gonorrhea
    B) Syphilis
    C) Genital herpes
    D) Chancroid
    E) LGV

Answer: C
Skill: Analysis

13) Which of the following is diagnosed by detection of antibodies against the causative agent?
    A) Nongonococcal urethritis
    B) Gonorrhea
    C) Syphilis
    D) Lymphogranuloma venereum
    E) Candidiasis

Answer: C
Skill: Recall

14) Nongonococcal urethritis can be caused by all of the following *EXCEPT*
    A) *Mycoplasma homini.*
    B) *Candida albicans.*
    C) *Trichomonas vaginalis.*
    D) Streptococci.
    E) *Neisseria gonorrhoeae.*

Answer: E
Skill: Analysis

15) Which of the following is caused by an opportunistic pathogen?
   A) Trichomoniasis
   B) Genital herpes
   C) Candidiasis
   D) Gonorrhea
   E) Chancroid

Answer: C
Skill: Analysis

16) The pH of the adult vagina is acidic due to the conversion of _____ to _____ by bacteria.
   A) Glucose; ethanol
   B) Protein; acetic acid
   C) Glycogen; lactic acid
   D) Mucosal cells; lactic acid
   E) Urine; lactic acid

Answer: C
Skill: Analysis

17) A normal urine sample collected by urinating into a sterile collection cup
   A) Is sterile.
   B) Contains fewer than 100 pathogens/ml.
   C) Contains fewer than 10,000 pathogens/ml.
   D) Contains more than 100,000 pathogens/ml.
   E) Has leukocyte esterase.

Answer: C
Skill: Recall

18) Most nosocomial infections of the urinary tract are caused by
   A) *E. coli.*
   B) *Enterococcus.*
   C) *Proteus.*
   D) *Klebsiella.*
   E) *Pseudomonas.*

Answer: A
Skill: Recall

19) Glomerulonephritis is
   A) Caused by *Streptococcus pyogenes.*
   B) An immune complex disease.
   C) Treated with penicillin.
   D) Transmitted by contaminated water.
   E) A and C

Answer: B
Skill: Recall

20) Which of the following is *NOT* a predisposing factors to cystitis in females?
    A) The proximity of the anus to the urethra
    B) The length of the urethra
    C) Sexual intercourse
    D) Poor personal hygiene
    E) All of the above are predisposing factors.

Answer: E
Skill: Analysis

21) The most common reportable disease in the United States is
    A) Cystitis.
    B) Lymphogranuloma venereum.
    C) Gonorrhea.
    D) Syphilis.
    E) Candidiasis.

Answer: C
Skill: Recall

22) Which of the following is *NOT* a complication of gonorrhea?
    A) Arthritis
    B) Pelvic inflammatory disease
    C) Endocarditis
    D) Meningitis
    E) All of the above are potential complications of gonorrhea.

Answer: E
Skill: Analysis

23) Which of the following is the most difficult to treat with chemotherapeutic agents?
    A) Genital herpes
    B) Gonorrhea
    C) Syphilis
    D) Trichomoniasis
    E) Leptospirosis

Answer: A
Skill: Understanding

24) Itching and cheesy discharge are symptoms of
    A) *Gardnerella* vaginosis.
    B) Genital herpes.
    C) Candidiasis.
    D) Trichomoniasis.
    E) Lymphogranuloma venereum.

Answer: C
Skill: Recall

25) Recurring vesicles are symptoms of
    A) *Gardnerella* vaginosis.
    B) Genital herpes.
    C) Candidiasis.
    D) Trichomoniasis.
    E) Lymphogranuloma venereum.

Answer: B
Skill: Recall

26) Leukocytes at the infected site is a symptom of
    A) *Gardnerella* vaginosis.
    B) Genital herpes.
    C) Candidiasis.
    D) Trichomoniasis.
    E) Lymphogranuloma venereum.

Answer: D
Skill: Recall

27) Which of the following is caused by *Chlamydia*?
    A) *Gardnerella* vaginosis
    B) Genital herpes
    C) Candidiasis
    D) Trichomoniasis
    E) Lymphogranuloma venereum

Answer: E
Skill: Recall

28) A positive LE text and 10,000 CFU/ml in urine indicates
    A) Cystitis.
    B) Gonorrhea.
    C) Urethritis.
    D) Pyelonephritis.
    E) Genital herpes.

Answer: D
Skill: Recall

29) Which of the following diseases causes a skin rash, hair loss, malaise, and fever?
    A) Gonorrhea
    B) Syphilis
    C) NGU
    D) Trichomoniasis
    E) Genital herpes

Answer: B
Skill: Recall

30) *Staphylococcus saprophyticus* causes
   A) Cystitis.
   B) Pyelonephritis.
   C) Vaginitis.
   D) Gonorrhea.
   E) Syphilis.

Answer: A
Skill: Recall

31) Which one of the following statements about genital warts is false?
   A) It is transmitted by direct contact.
   B) It is caused by papillomaviruses.
   C) It is always precancerous.
   D) It is treated by removing them.
   E) All of the above.

Answer: C
Skill: Analysis

32) The most common NGU in the United States is treated with
   A) Penicillin.
   B) Cephalosporins.
   C) Acyclovir.
   D) AZT.
   E) Doxycycline.

Answer: B
Skill: Analysis

33) Which of the following statements about pelvic inflammatory disease is false?
   A) It can cause sterility and chronic pain.
   B) It can be caused by *N. gonorrhoeae*.
   C) It can be transmitted sexually.
   D) It can be caused by *C. trachomatis*.
   E) It affects men and women equally.

Answer: E
Skill: Analysis

34) Which one of the following does *NOT* cause nongonococcal urethritis?
   A) *Chlamydia*.
   B) *Mycoplasma*.
   C) *Neisseria*.
   D) *Ureaplasma*.
   E) All of the above cause NGU.

Answer: C
Skill: Analysis

35) Infants born to asymptomatic mothers with recurrent genital herpes are less likely to acquire herpesvirus at birth than infants born to newly infected mothers because
    A) Maternal antibodies offer protection.
    B) The disease cannot be transmitted to newborns.
    C) The disease is not communicable.
    D) Prophylactic antibiotics are administered to the newborn.
    E) The virus isn't growing.

Answer: A
Skill: Understanding

36) Which of the following is greater?
    A) The number of reported cases of gonorrhea last year
    B) The number of reported cases of AIDS last year
    C) They are equal.

Answer: A
Skill: Understanding

37) A patient presents with fever and extensive lesions of the labia minora. Her VDRL test was negative. What is the most likely treatment?
    A) Metronidazole
    B) Cephalosporins
    C) Acyclovir
    D) Miconazole
    E) No treatment is available.

Answer: C
Skill: Understanding

38) A patient is experiencing profuse greenish yellow, foul-smelling discharge from her vagina. She is complaining of itching and irritation. What is the most likely treatment?
    A) Metronidazole
    B) Cephalosporins
    C) Acyclovir
    D) Miconazole
    E) No treatment is available.

Answer: A
Skill: Understanding

39) A 25-year-old man presented with fever, malaise, and a rash on his chest, arms, and feet. The etiology could be any of the following *EXCEPT*
    A) *Borrelia.*
    B) Mumps virus.
    C) *Rickettsia.*
    D) *Streptococcus.*
    E) *Treponema.*

Answer: B
Skill: Analysis

40) A 25-year-old man presented with fever, malaise, and a rash on his chest, arms, and feet. Which of the following will be most useful for a rapid diagnosis?
    A) Bacterial culture
    B) Microscopic examination of blood
    C) Serological test for antibodies
    D) Serological test for antigen
    E) Viral culture

Answer: C
Skill: Understanding

41) A 25-year-old man presented with fever, malaise, and a rash on his chest, arms, and feet. Diagnosis was based on serological testing. The patient then reported that he had an ulcer on his penis 2 months earlier. What stage of disease is the patient in?
    A) NGU
    B) Primary
    C) Secondary
    D) Tertiary

Answer: C
Skill: Analysis

42) A 25-year-old male presented with fever, malaise, and a rash on his chest, arms, and feet. Diagnosis was based on serological testing. The patient then reported that he had an ulcer on his penis 2 months earlier. This disease can be treated with
    A) Acyclovir.
    B) Metronidazole.
    C) Miconazole.
    D) Penicillin.
    E) Surgery.

Answer: D
Skill: Analysis

43) A pelvic examination of a 23-year-old woman showed vesicles and ulcerated lesions on her labia. Cultures were negative for *Neisseria* and *Chlamydia*; the VDRL test was negative. Which treatment is appropriate?
    A) Acyclovir
    B) Metronidazole
    C) Miconazole
    D) Penicillin
    E) Surgery

Answer: A
Skill: Analysis

44) A pelvic examination of a 23–year–old woman showed vesicles and ulcerated lesions on her labia. Cultures were negative for *Neisseria* and *Chlamydia*; the VDRL test was negative. Which of the following is probable?
   A) Candidiasis
   B) Genital herpes
   C) Gonorrhea
   D) NGU
   E) Syphilis

Answer: B
Skill: Analysis

45) Which of the following is treated with cephalosporins because the organism is resistant to penicillin and fluoroquinolones?
   A) *Mycoplasma hominis*
   B) *Haemophilus ducreyi*
   C) *Neisseria gonorrhoeae*
   D) *Treponema pallidum*
   E) *Gardnerella vaginalis*

Answer: C
Skill: Recall

Essay Questions

1) Why are the unreported cases of STIs an important public health concern?

2) Nearly 70% of the patients seen in STI clinics are men.
   a.   Offer a reason men are more likely to seek treatment than women.
   b.   Why is it important that women seek treatment for STIs?

Chapter 27 Environmental Microbiology

Objective Questions

1) Which of the following is *NOT* a habitat for an extremophile?
   A) Acid mine wash
   B) The Atlantic Ocean
   C) Inside rock
   D) Salt–evaporating pond
   E) 100°C water

Answer: B
Skill: Recall

2) Which of the following organisms is using sulfur as a source of energy?
   A) *Thiobacillus*: $H_2S \rightarrow S^0$
   B) *Desulfovibrio*: $SO_4^{2-} \rightarrow H_2S$
   C) *Proteus*: Amino acids $\rightarrow H_2S$
   D) Redwood tree: $SO_4^{2-} \rightarrow$ Amino acids
   E) Photosynthetic bacteria: $H_2S \rightarrow S^0$

Answer: A
Skill: Understanding

3) Which of the following is *NOT* a symbiotic pair of organisms?
   A) Elk and rumen bacteria
   B) Orchid and mycorrhizae
   C) Onions and arbuscules
   D) Bean plant and *Rhizobium*
   E) Sulfur and *Thiobacillus*

Answer: E
Skill: Understanding

4) In which of the following animals would you expect to find a specialized organ that holds cellulose–degrading bacteria and fungi?
   A) Cat
   B) Dog
   C) Termite
   D) Human
   E) Wolf

Answer: C
Skill: Understanding

5) Which of the following pairs is mismatched?
   A) *Rhizobium* — legumes
   B) *Bacillus thuringiensis* — insect control
   C) *Thiobacillus ferrooxidans* — uranium mining
   D) *Frankia* — alders
   E) Lichen — an alga and a bacterium

Answer: E
Skill: Analysis

6) Adding untreated sewage to a freshwater lake would cause the biochemical oxygen demand
to
   A) Increase.
   B) Decrease.
   C) Stay the same.
   D) Can't tell.

Answer: A
Skill: Analysis

7) Coal formation
   A) Requires aerobic conditions.
   B) Requires anaerobic conditions.
   C) The amount of oxygen doesn't make any difference.

Answer: B
Skill: Understanding

8) A trickling filter
   A) Requires aerobic conditions.
   B) Requires anaerobic conditions.
   C) The amount of oxygen doesn't make any difference.

Answer: A
Skill: Understanding

9) $6H_2S + 6CO_2 \xrightarrow{\text{light}} 6S^0 + \text{glucose}$
   A) Takes place under aerobic conditions.
   B) Takes place under anaerobic conditions.
   C) The amount of oxygen doesn't make any difference.

Answer: B
Skill: Understanding

10) Nitrogen fixation
   A) Requires aerobic conditions.
   B) Requires anaerobic conditions.
   C) The amount of oxygen doesn't make any difference.

Answer: B
Skill: Understanding

11) Sludge digestion
    A) Takes place under aerobic conditions.
    B) Takes place under anaerobic conditions.
    C) The amount of oxygen doesn't make any difference.

Answer: B
Skill: Understanding

12) Primary sewage treatment
    A) Takes place under aerobic conditions.
    B) Takes place under anaerobic conditions.
    C) The amount of oxygen doesn't make any difference.

Answer: C
Skill: Understanding

13) $NH_3 \rightarrow NO_2^-$
    A) Takes place under aerobic conditions.
    B) Takes place under anaerobic conditions.
    C) The amount of oxygen doesn't make any difference.

Answer: A
Skill: Understanding

14) Bioremediation of petroleum
    A) Takes place under aerobic conditions.
    B) Takes place under anaerobic conditions.
    C) The amount of oxygen doesn't make any difference.

Answer: A
Skill: Understanding

15) Biochemical oxygen demand is a measure of
    A) The number of bacteria present in a water sample.
    B) The amount of oxygen present in a water sample.
    C) The amount of organic matter present in a water sample.
    D) The amount of undissolved solid matter present in a water sample.
    E) The amount of nitrogen in a water sample.

Answer: C
Skill: Analysis

16) Eighty-one percent of the microorganisms in the soil are
    A) Actinomycetes.
    B) Algae
    C) Bacteria.
    D) Fungi.
    E) Protozoa.

Answer: C
Skill: Recall

17) Most of the microorganisms in the soil are found at a depth
    A) Between 3 and 8 cm.
    B) Between 20 and 25 cm.
    C) Between 35 and 40 cm.
    D) Between 65 and 75 cm.
    E) Evenly distributed from the surface to 76 cm.

Answer: A
Skill: Recall

Figure 27.1

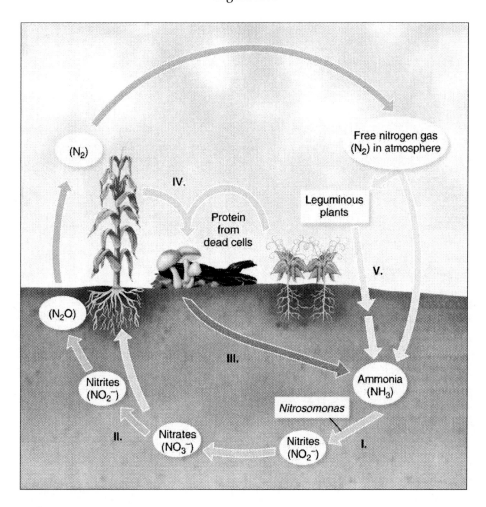

18) Which step in Figure 27.1 represents anaerobic respiration?
    A) I
    B) II
    C) III
    D) IV
    E) V

Answer: B
Skill: Understanding

19) Which term in Figure 27.1 describes step V?
   A) Ammonification
   B) Denitrification
   C) Dissimilation
   D) Nitrification
   E) Nitrogen fixation

Answer: E
Skill: Understanding

20) Which step in Figure 27.1 represents the following reaction: amino acid ($-NH_2$) → NH_3?
   A) I
   B) II
   C) III
   D) IV
   E) V

Answer: C
Skill: Understanding

21) Nitrification is beneficial to farmers. It is represented by which step in Figure 27.1?
   A) I
   B) II
   C) III
   D) IV
   E) V

Answer: A
Skill: Understanding

22) Which of the following terms describes step III in Figure 27.1?
   A) Ammonification
   B) Denitrification
   C) Nitrification
   D) Nitrogen fixation
   E) Assimilation

Answer: A
Skill: Understanding

23) Which of the following terms describes $NH_3 \rightarrow NO_2^- \rightarrow NO_3^-$?
   A) Ammonification
   B) Denitrification
   C) Nitrification
   D) Nitrogen fixation
   E) Anaerobic respiration

Answer: C
Skill: Understanding

24) Which of the following is an assimilation process?
   A) *Thiobacillus*: $H_2S \rightarrow S^0$
   B) *Desulfovibrio*: $SO_4^{2-} \rightarrow H_2S$
   C) *Proteus*: Amino acids $\rightarrow H_2S$
   D) Redwood tree: $SO_4^{2-} \rightarrow$ Amino acids
   E) Photosynthetic bacteria: $H_2S \rightarrow S^0$

Answer: D
Skill: Understanding

25) Which wastewater treatment process is responsible for removal of most of the BOD in sewage?
   A) Anaerobic sludge digestion
   B) Primary sewage treatment
   C) Secondary sewage treatment
   D) Tertiary sewage treatment
   E) Water treatment

Answer: C
Skill: Understanding

26) Which wastewater treatment process produces BOD–containing effluent used for irrigation?
   A) Anaerobic sludge digestion
   B) Primary sewage treatment
   C) Secondary sewage treatment
   D) Tertiary sewage treatment
   E) Water treatment

Answer: C
Skill: Understanding

27) Residual chlorine must be maintained in
   A) Anaerobic sludge digestion.
   B) Primary sewage treatment.
   C) Secondary sewage treatment.
   D) Tertiary sewage treatment.
   E) Water treatment.

Answer: E
Skill: Understanding

28) Sedimentation of sludge occurs in
   A) Anaerobic sludge digestion.
   B) Primary sewage treatment.
   C) Secondary sewage treatment.
   D) Tertiary sewage treatment.
   E) Water treatment.

Answer: B
Skill: Understanding

29) The product of which process contains the highest BOD?
   A) Anaerobic sludge digestion
   B) Primary sewage treatment
   C) Secondary sewage treatment
   D) Tertiary sewage treatment
   E) Water treatment

Answer: B
Skill: Understanding

30) *Zoogloea* form flocculent masses in
   A) Anaerobic sludge digestion.
   B) Primary sewage treatment.
   C) Secondary sewage treatment.
   D) Tertiary sewage treatment.
   E) Water treatment.

Answer: C
Skill: Understanding

31) Rotating biological contactors are used in
   A) Anaerobic sludge digestion.
   B) Primary sewage treatment.
   C) Secondary sewage treatment.
   D) Tertiary sewage treatment.
   E) Water treatment.

Answer: C
Skill: Understanding

32) Aerobic respiration occurs in
   A) Anaerobic sludge digestion.
   B) Primary sewage treatment.
   C) Secondary sewage treatment.
   D) Tertiary sewage treatment.
   E) Water treatment.

Answer: C
Skill: Understanding

33) Anaerobic respiration occurs in
   A) Anaerobic sludge digestion.
   B) Primary sewage treatment.
   C) Secondary sewage treatment.
   D) Tertiary sewage treatment.
   E) Water treatment.

Answer: A
Skill: Understanding

34) Filtration to remove protozoa occurs in
   A) Anaerobic sludge digestion.
   B) Primary sewage treatment.
   C) Secondary sewage treatment.
   D) Tertiary sewage treatment.
   E) Water treatment.

Answer: E
Skill: Understanding

35) Which of the following do *NOT* fix atmospheric nitrogen?
   A) Cyanobacteria
   B) Lichens
   C) Mycorrhizae
   D) *Frankia*
   E) *Azotobacter*

Answer: C
Skill: Recall

36) Which of the following pairs is mismatched?
   A) $CO_2 + 4H_2 \rightarrow CH_4 + 2H_2O$ — Methane–producing bacteria
   B) $Fe^{2+} \rightarrow Fe^{3+}$ — *Thiobacillus ferrooxidans*
   C) $6CO_2 + 6H_2O \rightarrow C_6H_{12}O_6 + 6O_2$ — *Clostridium*
   D) $N_2 + 6H^+ \rightarrow 2NH_3$ — *Beijerinckia*
   E) $SO_4{}^{2-} + 10H^+ \rightarrow H_2S + 4H_2O$ — *Desulfovibrio*

Answer: C
Skill: Understanding

37) Bacteria can increase the Earth's temperature by
   A) Generating a great deal of heat in metabolism.
   B) Producing CH_4, which is a greenhouse gas.
   C) Using the greenhouse gas CO_2.
   D) Providing nutrients for plant growth.
   E) Oxidizing CH_4.

Answer: B
Skill: Recall

38) The bacteria contributing most of the bacterial biomass to soil are
   A) Actinomycetes.
   B) Rhizobiaceae.
   C) Chemoautotrophs.
   D) Photoheterotrophs.
   E) Coliforms.

Answer: A
Skill: Analysis

39) Which one of the following processes in sewage treatment requires bacterial metabolism?
    A) Chlorination
    B) Primary treatment
    C) Removal of BOD
    D) Sedimentation
    E) None of the above

Answer: C
Skill: Understanding

Figure 27.2

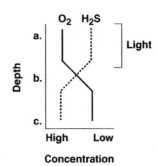

40) Where are photosynthetic bacteria most likely to be found in Figure 27.2?
    A) a
    B) b
    C) c
    D) a and b
    E) b and c

Answer: B
Skill: Understanding

41) Where are eukaryotic algae most likely to be found in Figure 27.2?
    A) a
    B) b
    C) c
    D) a and b
    E) b and c

Answer: A
Skill: Understanding

42) The bacteria that grow first in the microbial succession in a compost pile are
    A) Anaerobic mesophiles.
    B) Aerobic thermophiles.
    C) Anaerobic psychrophiles.
    D) Aerobic mesophiles.
    E) Anaerobic thermophiles.

Answer: A
Skill: Analysis

43) The release of phosphate–containing detergents into a river would
  A) Kill algae.
  B) Increase algal growth.
  C) Kill bacteria.
  D) Increase oxygen in the water.
  E) None of the above.

Answer: B
Skill: Analysis

44) Untreated sewage is released into a river. Which of the following statements is false?
  A) The untreated sewage is a health hazard.
  B) The untreated sewage increases the BOD.
  C) The untreated sewage decreases the dissolved oxygen.
  D) The untreated sewage kills bacteria.
  E) All of the above statements are true.

Answer: D
Skill: Understanding

45) Bacteria that emit light can be used as biosensors because
  A) They migrate to hazardous chemical.
  B) They don't emit light in the presence of a hazardous chemical.
  C) They degrade hazardous chemicals.
  D) They have FMN.
  E) They have the *lux* gene.

Answer: D
Skill: Understanding

Essay Questions

1) What is the effect of discharging primary–treated sewage on the BOD and dissolved O_2 (DO) of the receiving body of water? What is the effect of secondary–treated sewage on the BOD and DO?

2) A newspaper headline reported "Algal Bloom Kills Fish."
  a. What actually caused fish death, given that the algae were not toxic?
  b. What could have caused the algal bloom?

Table 27.1

These results were obtained from a bioremediation experiment:

Number of Colonies on				
Minimal Salts Agar Inoculated with Soil		Agar Inoculated with Soil		Uninoculated Minimal Salts Agar
Without Gasoline	With Gasoline	Without Gasoline	With Gasoline	Without Gasoline
3	33	0	0	0

3) Explain the data in Table 27.1.

Chapter 28 Applied and Industrial Microbiology

Objective Questions

1) Spoilage due to can leakage after processing is
  A) Thermophilic anaerobic spoilage.
  B) Flat sour spoilage.
  C) Spoilage by mesophilic bacteria.
  D) Caused by acid–tolerant fungi.
  E) Putrefactive anaerobic spoilage.

Answer: C
Skill: Recall

2) Spoilage of canned foods stored at high temperatures, accompanied by gas production, is
  A) Thermophilic anaerobic spoilage.
  B) Flat sour spoilage.
  C) Spoilage by mesophilic bacteria.
  D) Caused by acid–tolerant fungi.
  E) Putrefactive anaerobic spoilage.

Answer: A
Skill: Recall

3) Spoilage of canned foods due to inadequate processing, not accompanied by gas production, is
  A) Thermophilic anaerobic spoilage.
  B) Flat sour spoilage.
  C) Spoilage by mesophilic bacteria.
  D) Caused by acid–tolerant fungi.
  E) Putrefactive anaerobic spoilage.

Answer: B
Skill: Recall

4) Which of the following pairs is mismatched?
  A) *Propionibacterium* — Swiss cheese
  B) *Penicillium* — blue cheese
  C) *Streptococcus* — yogurt
  D) *Acetobacter* — vinegar
  E) *Bacillus* — hard cheese

Answer: E
Skill: Analysis

5) Which of the following is *NOT* an alternative fuel (energy source) produced by bacteria?
  A) Lactic acid
  B) Methanol
  C) Ethanol
  D) Hydrogen
  E) Methane

Answer: A
Skill: Understanding

6) Which one of the following is *NOT* a fuel produced by microorganisms?
   A) Cellulose
   B) Ethanol
   C) Hydrogen
   D) Methane
   E) Oil from algae

Answer: A
Skill: Analysis

7) Microorganisms themselves are industrial products. Which of the following pairs is mismatched?
   A) *Penicillium* — treatment of disease
   B) *Saccharomyces cerevisiae* — for fermentation
   C) *Rhizobium* — increases nitrogen in the soil
   D) *Bacillus thuringiensis* — insecticide
   E) Algae — citric acid

Answer: E
Skill: Understanding

8) Which of the following is an undesirable contaminant in wine-making?
   A) *Acetobacter*
   B) Lactic acid bacteria
   C) *Clostridium*
   D) *Bacillus*
   E) *Saccharomyces* (yeast)

Answer: A
Skill: Understanding

9) Commercial sterilization differs from true sterilization in that commercial sterilization
   A) Kills all microorganisms.
   B) Kills only bacteria.
   C) May result in the survival of thermophiles.
   D) Employs a higher temperature.
   E) May result in the survival of fungal spores.

Answer: C
Skill: Recall

Figure 28.1

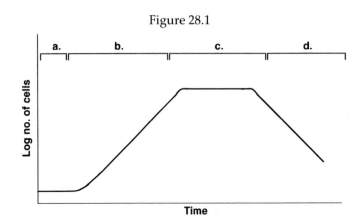

10) In Figure 28.1, assume that cells are your desired product. When would you harvest cells to maximize your yield?
  A) a
  B) b
  C) c
  D) d
  Answer: B
  Skill: Understanding

11) In Figure 28.1, assume that a secondary metabolite is your desired product. When would you be able to obtain it?
  A) a
  B) b
  C) c
  D) d
  Answer: C
  Skill: Understanding

12) In Figure 28.1, assume you want an enzyme that is not secreted. You would harvest at the end of what time?
  A) a
  B) b
  C) c
  D) d
  Answer: B
  Skill: Understanding

13) Which reaction is performed by yeast in wine–making?
    A) Sucrose → Ethanol
    B) Ethanol → Acetic acid
    C) Malic acid → Lactic acid
    D) Carbon dioxide → Sucrose
    E) Sucrose → CO_2 + H_2O

  Answer: A
  Skill: Recall

14) Which reaction makes wine less acidic?
    A) Sucrose → Ethanol
    B) Ethanol → Acetic acid
    C) Malic acid → Lactic acid
    D) Carbon dioxide → Sucrose
    E) Sucrose → $CO_2 + H_2O$

Answer: C
Skill: Analysis

15) If the *lac* operon is used as a receptor for the *lux* operon, the presence of lactose would cause the cell to
    A) Die.
    B) Emit light.
    C) Produce lactose.
    D) Grow better.
    E) Use light energy.

Answer: B
Skill: Understanding

16) Which of the following is *NOT* an advantage of a bioreactor over a flask culture?
    A) Larger culture volumes can be grown.
    B) Instrumentation for monitoring environmental conditions.
    C) Uniform aeration and mixing.
    D) Aseptic sampling.
    E) All of the above are advantages of using a bioreactor instead of a flask culture.

Answer: E
Skill: Recall

17) Microbial products can be improved by all of the following *EXCEPT*
    A) Isolating new strains.
    B) Mutating existing strains.
    C) Genetically modifying strains.
    D) Modifying culture conditions.
    E) Sterilization.

Answer: E
Skill: Understanding

18) Cellulase attached to a membrane filter will
    A) Degrade cellulose.
    B) Degrade the membrane.
    C) Do nothing; it requires a cell.
    D) Degrade lactose.
    E) Produce ethanol.

Answer: A
Skill: Analysis

Figure 28.2

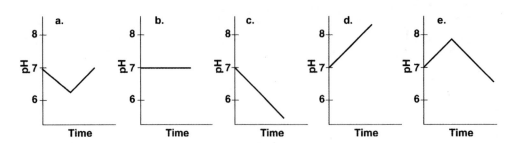

19) Which of the graphs in Figure 28.2 shows the pH in a culture flask as cells metabolize glucose and then protein?

    A) a
    B) b
    C) c
    D) d
    E) e

Answer: A
Skill: Understanding

20) Which of the following is *NOT* an industrial product produced by microbes?

    A) Amino acids in food supplements
    B) Antibiotics
    C) Industrial enzymes
    D) Uranium
    E) Vitamin B_{12} and riboflavin

Answer: D
Skill: Understanding

21) Which of the following is *NOT* produced using microbial fermentations?

    A) Aspartame
    B) Citric acid
    C) MSG
    D) Riboflavin
    E) Saccharin

Answer: E
Skill: Recall

22) Which of the following is *NOT* produced using microbial fermentations?

    A) Citric acid
    B) Ice cream
    C) Sour cream
    D) Yogurt
    E) Amino acids

Answer: B
Skill: Recall

23) Which of the following is an oxidation reaction that *Thiobacillus ferooxidans* might do?

A) $Fe^{3+} \to Fe^{2+}$

B) $U^{4+} \to U^{6+}$

C) $Cu^{2+} \to Cu^{+}$

D) $Cu^{+} \to Cu^{0}$

E) $Al^{3+} \to Al^{2+}$

Answer: B
Skill: Understanding

24) Methane made from biomass is produced by

A) Anaerobic respiration.

B) Fermentation.

C) The Krebs cycle.

D) Oxidation.

E) Photosynthetic algae.

Answer: A
Skill: Understanding

25) Which of the following is *NOT* an industrial enzyme made by microbial fermentations?

A) Glucose isomerase

B) Rennin

C) Proteases

D) Cellulases

E) Vitamin C

Answer: E
Skill: Recall

26) What process does yeast use to produce ethanol for automobile fuel from corn?

A) Anaerobic respiration

B) Fermentation

C) The Krebs cycle

D) Oxidation

E) Photosynthesis

Answer: B
Skill: Understanding

27) The following steps are required for making cheese. What is the second step?

A) Enzymatic coagulation of milk

B) Fermentation of curd

C) Inoculate with lactic acid bacteria

D) Inoculate with *Penicillium*

E) Separate curds and whey

Answer: C
Skill: Analysis

28) As cheese ages, it gets
    A) More acidic.
    B) More whey.
    C) More protein.
    D) Saltier.
    E) More alcoholic.

Answer: A
Skill: Recall

29) Assume that you bought a semisoft cheese, such as blue cheese, and put it in your refrigerator. Three weeks later, you slice the cheese and notice the center is now liquid because
    A) Lactic acid bacteria have grown in the center.
    B) Fungal enzymes have digested the curd.
    C) Fungal enzymes have made more curd.
    D) Fungi have accumulated in the center.
    E) The cheese melted.

Answer: B
Skill: Understanding

30) Your friend says he had stored a semisoft cheese (blue cheese) in his refrigerator for 3 weeks. He asks you why the outer "skin" of the cheese is so much thicker than it was when he originally purchased the cheese. You tell him that
    A) Lactic acid bacteria have grown on the outside.
    B) Fungal enzymes have digested the curd.
    C) Fungal enzymes have made more curd.
    D) Fungi have been growing.
    E) It dried out.

Answer: D
Skill: Understanding

31) You are growing *Bacillus subtilis* in a bioreactor and notice that the growth rate has slowed and the pH has decreased. You suspect the bacteria are
    A) Using the Krebs cycle.
    B) Fermenting.
    C) Photosynthesizing.
    D) Using proteins.
    E) Dead.

Answer: B
Skill: Understanding

32) You are growing *Bacillus subtilis* in a bioreactor and notice that the growth rate has slowed and the pH has decreased. What could you do?
    A) Add glucose.
    B) Add lactose.
    C) Add peptides.
    D) Add oxygen.
    E) Add lactic acid.

Answer: D
Skill: Understanding

33) Radiation and canning are used for all of the following reasons *EXCEPT* to
    A) Prevent diseases.
    B) Prolong the shelf life of foods.
    C) Prevent spoilage of foods.
    D) Sell more food.
    E) All of the above are reasons to use radiation and canning.

Answer: D
Skill: Analysis

34) Which of the following is *NOT* a use for radiation?
    A) Foods that cannot be heated
    B) Sterilizing food
    C) Killing *Trichinella*
    D) Killing insect eggs and larva
    E) Preventing sprouting

Answer: B
Skill: Analysis

35) Canning preserves food by
    A) Aseptic packaging.
    B) Chemicals.
    C) Heating.
    D) Radiation.
    E) All of the above.

Answer: C
Skill: Recall

36) Microorganisms themselves are commercial products. Which of the following microbes is available in retail stores?
    A) *Bacillus thuringiensis*
    B) *Lactobacillus*
    C) *Rhizobium*
    D) *Saccharomyces*
    E) All of the above

Answer: E
Skill: Understanding

Figure 28.3

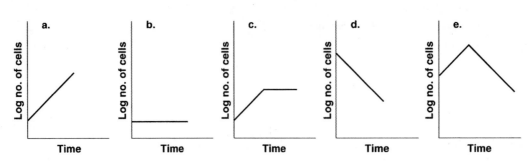

37) Figure 28.3 shows the growth curves of *Acetobacter* under different conditions. Which culture would have the highest amount of acetic acid?
   A) a
   B) b
   C) c
   D) d
   E) e
   Answer: A
   Skill: Analysis

38) Which of the growth curves in Figure 28.3 will give the highest yield of a secondary metabolite?
   A) a
   B) b
   C) c
   D) d
   E) e
   Answer: C
   Skill: Analysis

39) Canning works to preserve foods because of this:
   A) Anaerobic environment.
   B) Anaerobic environment and heat.
   C) Heat.
   D) Lethal mutations.
   E) pH.
   Answer: B
   Skill: Analysis

40) Aseptic packaging works to preserve foods because of this:
   A) Anaerobic environment.
   B) Anaerobic environment and heat.
   C) Heat.
   D) Lethal mutations.
   E) pH.
   Answer: C
   Skill: Analysis

41) Radiation works to preserve foods because of this:
   A) Anaerobic environment.
   B) Anaerobic environment and heat.
   C) Heat.
   D) Lethal mutations.
   E) pH.

Answer: D
Skill: Analysis

42) Fermentation works to preserve foods because of this:
   A) Anaerobic environment.
   B) Anaerobic environment and heat.
   C) Heat.
   D) Lethal mutations.
   E) Acids and alcohols.

Answer: E
Skill: Analysis

43) What will be produced if wine is aerated?
   A) Ethanol + CO_2
   B) CO_2 + H_2O
   C) CH_4
   D) Acetic acid
   E) None of the above

Answer: D
Skill: Understanding

44) Grape juice before fermentation is called must. What will be produced if must is aerated?
   A) Ethanol + CO_2
   B) CO_2 + H_2O
   C) CH_4
   D) Acetic acid
   E) None of the above

Answer: B
Skill: Understanding

45) Xanthan used in household products is produced by bacteria
   A) That were genetically modified.
   B) That were irradiated to mutate them.
   C) Selected for their ability to grow on lactose.
   D) That are plant pathogens.
   E) C and D

Answer: E
Skill: Recall

Essay Questions

1) Why does fermentation preserve foods?

2) Why would a farmer purchase *Rhizobium*? *Bacillus thuringiensis*?

3) Most of the world's population relies on wheat for food. Research is being conducted to produce wheat with a higher protein content. Design a biotechnological approach to improving the amino acid content of wheat.